The Mahabharata

The Mahabharata

Shanta Rameshwar Rao

Illustrations by
Badri Narayan

Orient Longman

ORIENT LONGMAN LIMITED

Registered Office

3-6-272 Himayatnagar, Hyderabad 500 029

Other Offices

Kamani Marg, Ballard Estate, Bombay 400 038

17 Chittaranjan Avenue, Calcutta 700 072

160 Anna Salai, Madras 600 002

1/24 Asaf Ali Road, New Delhi 110 002

80/1 Mahatma Gandhi Road, Bangalore 560 001

3-6-272 Himayatnagar, Hyderabad 500 029

Birla Mandir Road, Patna 800 004

Patiala House, 16-A Ashok Marg, Lucknow 226 001

S.C. Goswami Road, Panbazar, Guwahati 781 001

The text has been adapted from the original published by
Orient Longmans in 1968

Reprinted 1987, 1990

ISBN 0 86131 607 X

Book Design: Orient Longman

Phototypeset in Garamond by Phoenix Phototype Setters,
708, Dalamal Tower, Nariman Point, Bombay 400 021

Printed in India at Printwell,
Laxmi Mills Estate, Mahalaxmi, Bombay 400 011

Published by Orient Longman Limited
Kamani Marg, Ballard Estate, Bombay 400 038

Table of Contents

Colour Plates

THE FAMILIES OF THE RULING KINGS IN THE *MAHABHARATA*

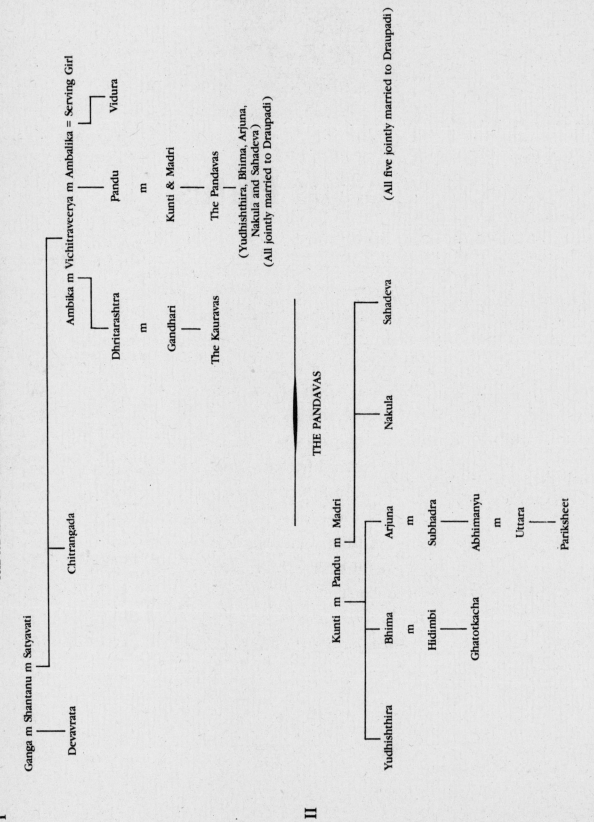

I

Ganga m Shantanu m Satyavati

Devavrata

Chitrangada

Ambika m Vichitraveerya m Ambalika = Serving Girl

Dhritarashtra   Pandu   Vidura

m   m

Gandhari   Kunti & Madri

The Kauravas   The Pandavas

(Yudhishthira, Bhima, Arjuna,
Nakula and Sahadeva)
(All jointly married to Draupadi)

II

THE PANDAVAS

Kunti m Pandu m Madri

Yudhishthira   Bhima   Arjuna   Nakula   Sahadeva

m   m

Hidimbi   Subhadra

Ghatotkacha   Abhimanyu

m

Uttara

Pariksheet

(All five jointly married to Draupadi)

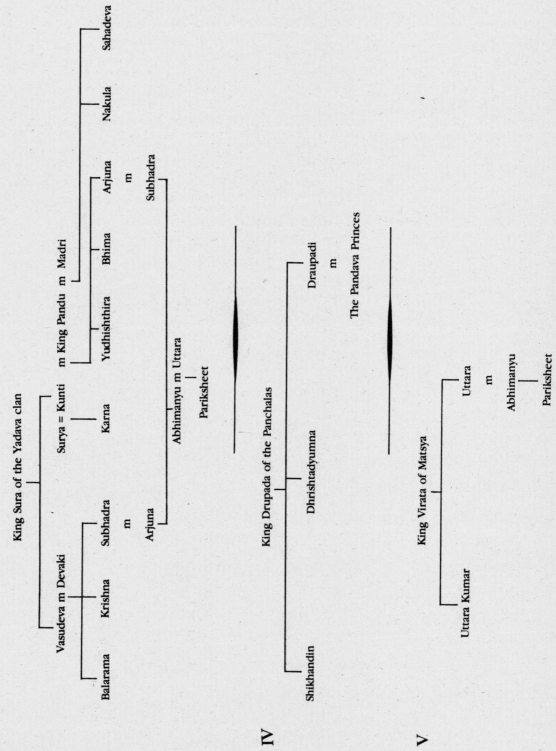

III

Balarama

Krishna

Vasudeva m Devaki

Subhadra
m
Arjuna

King Sura of the Yadava clan

Surya = Kunti

Karna

Abhimanyu m Uttara

Pariksheet

m King Pandu m Madri

Yudhishthira

Bhima

Arjuna
m
Subhadra

Nakula

Sahadeva

IV

Shikhandin

King Drupada of the Panchalas

Dhrishtadyumna

Draupadi
m

The Pandava Princes

V

Uttara Kumar

King Virata of Matsya

Uttara
m
Abhimanyu

Pariksheet

To My Mother

Introduction to the text

The Sanskrit epic poem called the *Mahabharata* tells the story of the warrior princes called the Kauravas and the Pandavas, two branches of the royal clan of Kurus who lived in northern India thousands of years ago. No one is quite certain when the epic was composed, but scholars, who give various estimates between 3000 and 1500 B.C., all agree that the *Mahabharata* is one of the oldest literary works known to mankind. In the form in which it survives today, it is the world's longest poem and indeed its longest literary work. It contains 100,000 stanzas, is several times the length of the Bible, and is about eight times longer than the *Iliad* and the *Odyssey* put together.

In India, the *Mahabharata* is often called "the fifth Veda", and in it may be found nearly every branch of knowledge. The poets who composed it—for it does not seem possible that this vast poem could be the work of one individual—have woven into it history and legend, myth and folklore, fable and parable, philosophy and religion, statecraft and the art of war, morality and romance.

For centuries it has been known throughout the length and breadth of India as an inexhaustible treasure-house of anecdotes, proverbs and sayings that have formed a continuous oral tradition. It has provided a powerful and universally identifiable source-work for themes in Indian literature, art, drama, dance and song. Most important of all, the section of it known as the *Bhagavad Gita* is one of Hinduism's central scriptures, on the one hand inspiring in each era philosophical search and questioning documented in commentaries in the many languages of India; on the other, providing a vital ethic that shapes the lives of hundreds of millions of Indians today as in centuries past.

The *Mahabharata* has not only spread to become part of the tradition of every corner of India, but has travelled (along with other ancient Indian literature) over the seas to other Asian countries such as Indonesia, Thailand and Cambodia. In each different setting, its characters have taken some of the flavour of the region, and so the separate versions of the epic differ from each other. However, the basic story remains the same.

It is this basic story—the strong central strand around which innumerable side stories and legends are interwoven in the vast epic—that is retold in this shortened version of the *Mahabharata*. At least once in a lifetime one should read the massive work in its entirety;

in this version, however, one finds a thread of the whole rich fabric that captures more than a little of its grandeur, beauty and colour.

The relevance of the central theme of the *Mahabharata* is undiminished; it is resonant with warnings for our future. It tells of a great war that destroyed almost an entire civilisation; of how it took place between two kingdoms linked by kinship, and how this happened in spite of a despairing awareness in both kingdoms that the war could lead only to universal destruction.

From small events, some comic, some sad, some beautiful, the story rises into a bitter and tragic dimension. No character, from the "heroes" Yudhishthira and Arjuna to the "villains" Duryodhana and Shakuni, is totally good or totally evil. Each has his or her own nobility or exculpating motive of injury; each has, equally, a moment in which he or she furthers the inexorable course of the tragedy. Blind King Dhritarashtra, loving but weak and wavering in the face of wrongdoing; his wife Gandhari, who understands, but blindfolds herself and refuses to see; gentle Yudhishthira, who hates war and violence, and in his excessive love of peace is open to manipulation by people less scrupulous than he.

Intensely human in their passionate loves and hates, happinesses and griefs, the characters of the story have their recognisable counterparts in all ages and civilisations.

Today the great clan of the Kurus is more a legend than a memory. A town called Kurukshetra in present-day Haryana State, on the traditional site of the battlefield, is one of the very few physical reminders of their kingdom that once spread over large tracts of northern India.

But the *Mahabharata* remains—a book for all times and all occasions, with a message for all people, young and old, man, woman and child. No two people who read the story will derive the same meaning from it. For each individual the *Mahabharata* has a separate message, according to how he looks for it. This is perhaps the secret of its power and popularity, and of its survival for nearly fifty centuries.

The Noble Prince

Long ago, there ruled over the kingdom of Hastinapura, in the ancient land of Bharata, a king named Shantanu. Head of the great Aryan clan of the Kurus, he was loved and honoured by his subjects. They trusted him completely, for they knew him to be wise and just. When therefore he called their representatives together to tell them of his intention to name his only son, the beloved prince Devavrata, heir to his throne, they were delighted beyond measure. They received his announcement with great joy and praised Shantanu for his foresight and good sense. Preparations were forthwith made for the joyful occasion. On the chosen day, amid great pomp and ceremony, the young prince was named heir to Hastinapura's throne.

The people had reason to be happy: Devavrata, though young in years, was famed for his goodness and wisdom. He was tall and handsome, and his eyes seemed to glow with a hidden light. It was said that his mother had been no ordinary mortal; she was the river Goddess Ganga. It was also said that Devavrata himself had been an immortal Prabhasa, who had been cursed by an angry sage to spend a lifetime on earth. It had happened this way.

Prabhasa was the youngest of the eight Vasu brothers. The Vasus were gods and had everything they could desire to make them happy. But they were not happy; for in their hearts they constantly craved for more possessions and they were never satisfied. One day their covetous eyes fell on a cow that belonged to Vasishtha. They schemed and plotted to find ways and means of acquiring the cow and eventually decided to steal her.

However, when the moment came, the seven older brothers suddenly grew afraid, knowing how angry Vasishtha would be when he found out. Prabhasa alone, spurred on by the taunts of his wife, was ready to do the deed. He stole the cow and brought her to his brothers and together they hid her away. The sage, wild with grief at his loss, searched everywhere, until he found the thieves crouching guilty-faced in heaven. He strode up to them and, as he took possession of his beloved cow, cursed them angrily for their covetousness and deceit: They would fall from their high estate, he said, and be born on earth as mortal men, for they did not deserve to be gods.

His words struck fear and sorrow into the hearts of the Vasus. They had no wish to be born as mortals, to suffer pain and sorrow and eventually death. It seemed to them that even one human lifetime was too long to spend away from heaven. They fell at the sage's feet and begged forgiveness, upon which Vasishtha's heart melted and he relented. "I cannot take away my curse," he said. "But I can soften it and make it easier for you to bear."

Then he told them that the seven older brothers who had only sinned in thought, desiring the cow and plotting how to get her, would have a short life on earth, the space of only a few hours. But Prabhasa, who had done the deed, must suffer the full consequences. He must spend one complete lifetime on earth as a mortal. Hearing this, Prabhasa wept bitterly, but the Rishi consoled him. He would be a mortal above all other mortals, said Vasishtha. All men would honour him and he would live a life of such wisdom and glory that his name would be known all over the earth and in heaven!

Vasishtha then advised the Vasus to seek help from the river Goddess Ganga. The Vasus hurried to the Goddess and, falling at her feet, told her their sad story.

"Help us," they prayed, "Help us, Goddess. Come down to the earth and be our mother and we shall take birth in your womb. And when we are born, in that same hour, take us away and put an end to our lives, so that our time on earth may end soon, and we may return to our heavenly home."

The Goddess Ganga took pity on them and agreed to do as they asked. Thus it came about that one day, in the years of King Shantanu's youth, he met a beautiful woman upon the bank of the river Ganga. Indeed, so beautiful was she that Shantanu was immediately struck with love for her. He went up to her and, though he did not know her, nor anything about her, he begged her to be his wife and queen. The woman did not seem surprised. She was willing enough to do as he said, but only if he agreed to certain conditions.

"If I am to marry you," said the woman to her royal suitor, "you must promise never to question me, neither about who I am, nor where I come from; and you must never cross me, whatever I do, good or evil! Can you agree to these conditions, King Shantanu? I warn you, you will not find them easy!" The conditions were very strange but so infatuated was Shantanu that he was ready to accept anything. "Anything, anything you say, dear one," he promised impetuously. The woman smiled and allowed him to lead her to the palace.

2

Shantanu and the strange woman were married, and lived happily together for a whole year. So good and dutiful a wife, so sweet-natured and gracious was she, that Shantanu thought himself the happiest man in the world. And then a son was born to the royal couple, and Shantanu was overjoyed to see him. But in the darkness of the same night, Shantanu awoke to see his wife leaving with the child. Filled with surprise, he followed her out of the palace gates and down the street until she came to the river-bank. There, in the pale moonlight, Shantanu saw her lift the baby and throw him into the swirling waters. Horrified, Shantanu opened his mouth to cry out.

But, as she turned, he caught the warning look in her eye and remembered the promise he had made—never to question her, whatever she did, good or evil. His heart wept and he wondered who or what she was, demon or human, but he remained silent, not daring to speak. The terrible act accomplished, the queen calmly returned to the palace, while Shantanu followed her, trembling in every limb, and pale and cold with fear.

Back in the palace, Shantanu found himself wondering if it had all been an evil dream, for his wife became once more the sweet and gentle woman he knew and loved. He saw nothing in her behaviour to support what he had seen until another year went by and a second child was born. Again, the mother who had borne him carried him away at dead of night and drowned him in the waters of the river. Once again, the grief-stricken Shantanu looked on in silence, not daring to speak because of his promise.

Another year went by. A third boy was born. He met the same cruel end. After him came four more. Each year Shantanu's wife gave birth to a son. Each year she killed the baby with her own hands within a few hours of its birth. Shantanu was mad with grief and fear. He did not know that his sons were the Vasus, being freed from their curse to return to the joys of heaven.

When the eighth child came, he followed her again to the river-bank as he had done seven times before. She carried the baby in her arms and this time Shantanu felt that he could bear it no longer. He was desperate, and made up his mind to save the child from death, no matter what might happen. And so, when his wife was about to cast the little child into the river, he rushed forward with drawn sword, crying out to her to stop. In a choking voice, he reproached her bitterly. "Who are you?" he cried. "Are you human? Or an evil demoness in human guise? Seven children born of your womb have you destroyed in cold blood. But this eighth one shall live. For I have come to save him."

At these words, the woman who was his wife smiled a strange smile.

"You have broken your promise to me, Shantanu!" she reminded him softly. "You have asked me who I am; you have crossed me. Now I can stay with you no longer."

Shantanu stared at her amazed. Her words struck cold fear into his heart. "Where?" he cried out. "Where will you go? What will become of me?"

But she only smiled her mysterious smile as he begged her not to leave him. For, in spite of all that had happened, he knew he loved her to distraction and could not bear the thought of losing her. "Let us forget what has happened," he said, "let us start a new life together."

Seeing his distress, the woman pitied him, and gently told him her story—explaining how she had come down to earth to free the Vasus from their curse. Now her work was done. She would return to the heavenly regions, taking the child with her for a while, since the baby was too young to be left without a mother. But one day, she assured Shantanu, when the boy was older, he would return to claim his rightful heritage in his father's kingdom.

·As Shantanu stood staring in astonishment, the Goddess Ganga vanished, merging into the waters of the river, leaving him alone on the

3

riverside. Slowly, sadly, he retraced his steps and returned to the palace.

Seven years went by. Then, one day the Goddess Ganga returned. Shantanu was walking on the river-bank one evening, when a fearful storm arose. The sky grew dark as the winds howled and screeched around him. He was about to take shelter, when he saw the child—a little boy, sitting on the river-bank all alone, laughing. The boy had a toy bow in his hand and on his back a quiver of little golden arrows. One by one he shot the arrows into the river so that they made a dam in the stormy water. Shantanu's heart went out to the child and he hurried to protect him from danger.

At that moment, the Goddess Ganga appeared and the child ran to her side. Shantanu recognised her at once. She smiled at him and held out the boy. "This is your son, Shantanu," she said. "This is Devavrata. I have brought him back to you as I promised. Take him. Love him and look after him well, for he is born to be great."

She handed the boy over to Shantanu and then once again she vanished into the river. The little boy looked up trustingly into Shantanu's eyes.

"Come, my son," said Shantanu to him. "Let us go home."

King Shantanu had grieved many years for his lost wife. But now his heart rejoiced. As the boy grew up in the palace, he was the light of his father's life, his pride and his joy. The king engaged many famous tutors for the boy, and they found him eager for knowledge and quick to learn. In a short while he had learnt all they had to teach him, and yet he was never satisfied with his knowledge. As he grew up, he mastered every science, every skill, and soon became learned in all the sacred writings. But, above all, he was a Kshatriya and a warrior. It was as a warrior that Devavrata was best known; for there was none in the world who could send a surer arrow than he and none who was so learned in the science of warfare. He was a true prince whose every thought and every action was worthy of his royal birth. He did nothing that was low or dishonest or cowardly. He was never mean or jealous. All men honoured him for his nobility of heart. When the king declared Devavrata his heir, it was no wonder, then, that the people of Hastinapura hailed Shantanu's choice with joy. They knew that the future of Hastinapura would be safe in the hands of one who was as noble and wise as Devavrata.

But one day, not long after Devavrata had been chosen heir-apparent, it happened that King Shantanu met a young and beautiful fisher-girl, with whom he fell instantly in love. When he sent messengers to her father asking for her hand in marriage, he found the shrewd old fisherman not at all easy to persuade. He received the king's offer coldly, with none of the enthusiasm Shantanu had expected. It was all very well, said the fisherman, to give her to the king in marriage; but Shantanu was not young any more; he did not have many years to live. What would happen to his daughter if Shantanu died and left her a widow? Who would care for her then?

Back went the messengers to the royal palace and related everything to Shantanu. Shantanu decided to go in person and speak to the

4

fisherman, for he was infatuated with the fisher-girl. But the old man remained obstinate. He declared that he would allow the marriage only if Shantanu promised to make his daughter the principal queen and the son born to her the only heir. Shantanu tried to persuade him with promises of much money and many rewards but the fisherman was adamant. "The throne for my daughter and her descendants," he said stubbornly. "I cannot give her away for less."

Shantanu was very troubled. He knew that he could not make the promise. He could not pass over Devavrata, his chosen heir, whom the people loved so dearly. There was no one in the world as good as Devavrata or as worthy to be king. So, greatly though Shantanu wanted to marry the fisher-girl, Satyavati, he returned to the palace alone.

But the king was sad. He could not forget Satyavati's beautiful face. He grew thin and pale as he pined for her. He began to neglect his royal duties and no longer took joy in the hunt. The palace minstrels and jesters could give him no pleasure.

Prince Devavrata watched his father anxiously. He loved him deeply and could not bear to see him suffer. He questioned the king's attendants and soon discovered the reason for his father's unhappiness.

Then Devavrata went down to the riverside and, sending for the fisherman, begged the hand of Satyavati for his royal father. The fisherman spoke frankly. "When your father dies, Devavrata," he said, "Satyavati will not be queen. Your father is old and does not have many years to live. What will become of Satyavati and her children after he dies? No, no, Devavrata; I cannot allow my daughter to be sacrificed in this manner. The king may have her only if he can promise that he will make her his first queen and that her children and her children's children will inherit the throne. Only then will I consent to this marriage."

Devavrata exclaimed, "But surely the king could easily have granted this request!" With keen eyes, the fisherman studied the prince. "How could the king promise this, Devavrata?" he asked. "The throne is yours by right. How can the king give it away without your consent?" Then, drawing closer to the young prince, the fisherman whispered, "Are you willing to agree to this, Devavrata? Will you give up your throne for your father's happiness?"

Devavrata answered scornfully, "Do you think I lay store by such things as a throne? If it will make my father happy, fisherman, I will gladly give it up." The fisherman looked doubtful. Devavrata then swore a solemn oath. "I, Prince Devavrata, give you my word of honour that Satyavati's children shall rule after Shantanu and that I shall give up my claim to the royal throne." But the fisherman was not satisfied.

"Prince Devavrata," he said, "this is indeed a great and noble thing you have done. But surely it is not enough. You are mortal, and one day you too will die. After you will come your sons and your sons' sons. Surely, Devavrata, they will not be bound by your word to me. Surely they will claim the throne which you have given up."

Devavrata looked away. For a while he stood silent, lost in deep thought. Then, with firm purpose, he turned back to the fisherman and

said, "I give you my word that I will never marry. Would this satisfy you?" His eyes were clear as he spoke, his voice was steady. "With me, my line shall end! You need have no fear. I shall have neither sons nor grandsons." As the young Devavrata, his eyes shining with a wonderful light, stood in front of the fisherman and made this great promise, it is said that the heavens opened and the gods cried out "Bhishma!" as they showered flowers upon him, to honour his sacrifice of his own happiness. And ever after that, Devavrata was known as Bhishma or "the one who makes and keeps a great oath."

The fisherman was very pleased. He went into his house and led out his daughter, Satyavati, whom he handed over to the young prince.

Devavrata brought the fisher-girl to Shantanu. Then, before the king and the people of the realm, he repeated the solemn oath he had taken upon the river-bank—that he would give up his claim to the throne and to the kingdom, and that he would never marry. Thus he would remain childless and with neither his sons nor grandsons to claim Shantanu's throne, Satyavati's descendants would rule the kingdom of Bharata.

When he had repeated this great oath, his father embraced and blessed him, saying, "Live for ever, noble prince! May you never know defeat and may you be so strong that death itself shall not come to you, unless you wish it."

Thus it happened that Satyavati, the fisher-girl, was married to King Shantanu. She bore him two sons, Chitrangada and Vichitraveerya. And after Shantanu, they each, in their turn, came to the throne to rule the kingdom.

2
The Unhappy Princess

True to his word, Bhishma, as he shall now be called, renounced his claim to the throne of Hastinapura. He neither married nor had children. Instead, upon Shantanu's death, Bhishma placed the sons of Satyavati on the throne. Chitrangada, the elder son, did not rule long, for he met with an early death. When he died, his young brother Vichitraveerya succeeded him. Bhishma himself remained at the royal court, loyal and faithful to his younger brother, the king. He helped the young ruler to govern his kingdom, giving him wise advice. During this time there was peace in the land, for the fame of Bhishma's strength and skill in warfare had spread so wide and men so feared his might that the enemies of Hastinapura dared not attack it.

One day there came news to the royal court of Hastinapura that the beautiful daughters of the ruler of Kashi were to be given in marriage to whoever won them in battle. There was to be a tournament in Kashi and all the royal princes of the country could take part in it.

When Bhishma heard this, he decided to go to Kashi and win the girls for his brother Vichitraveerya. When he arrived, he found hundreds of princes already gathered from all parts of the land, each hoping for a double victory: glory for himself and a beautiful princess for a bride.

The other princes taunted Bhishma, for they thought he had broken his vow and come to win a bride for himself. But Bhishma said nothing. He took his seat among them and, when the signal was given, joined in the fierce battle. So skilled and excellent a warrior was he that he overcame them all, one after another, until there was no one left to challenge him. Then, flushed with the pride of victory, Bhishma came forward and lifting the three beautiful princesses of Kashi into his chariot, rode away with them towards Hastinapura.

He had not gone far when he was overtaken by the young king Shalva, who had come in hot pursuit. He barred the way and challenged Bhishma to battle, declaring that Amba, the eldest of the three princesses, had been promised to him. Bhishma accepted the challenge and a fierce fight took place in which, once more, Bhishma emerged victorious. Shalva drew back, his face dark with shame and anger, mounted his war-chariot and rode swiftly away, while Bhishma continued on his way Hastinapura with the three beautiful princesses.

All Hastinapura rejoiced over Bhishma's victories. Preparations were made for the marriage of Vichitraveerya to all the princesses. Amba did

not share in the happiness; she did not care for the weak and sickly Vichitraveerya, even though he was king of Hastinapura. Her heart was set upon the young and handsome King Shalva. Ceaselessly she wept and then, at last, she came before Bhishma and cried out to him in anger and sorrow.

"I cannot marry Vichitraveerya, for I do not love him! Shalva was chosen for my husband. How can I marry another? You are famous for your righteousness, Bhishma, and yet you keep a defenceless woman here against her will."

"What do you wish me to do, child?" Bhishma asked her gently, for he pitied her and wanted to help her. She answered without hesitation:

"Send me back to Shalva, for I was promised to him."

Bhishma realised the truth of her words, and he sent her with attendants to Shalva's kingdom. But when she came before Shalva the sight of her brought to his mind his disgrace at the hands of Bhishma and his heart grew bitter with anger.

"Why do you come here to me?" He asked her unkindly. "Do you feel no shame! Go back to the man with whom you went!" And he told her he would never marry a girl who had been captured by a rival.

Amba stood dazed for a while. Then she turned away, her heart weeping at the shame that Shalva had brought upon her. Sadly, the poor girl returned to Hastinapura.

"Shalva has turned me away," she cried to Bhishma. "What shall I do now?"

Bhishma felt guilty and troubled, for he knew that he was to blame for her unhappiness. He was anxious to do right by her, to help her out of her distress. So he brought her now before his younger brother Vichitraveerya. But the young king refused to marry Amba, declaring scornfully that he did not want as a wife a girl who loved another man. Thus, the proud Amba was refused a second time. Even Vichitraveerya, whom she despised, would not have her!

In despair, Amba turned to Bhishma. "It is you who have brought this upon me!" she cried. "Make amends. Take me as your wife."

Bhishma was deeply sorry for the poor, unhappy princess. But he was bound by his oath never to marry and he could not break his word. Gently, he explained this to the unhappy Amba.

"Go back to Shalva, child," he said. "Perhaps he can still be persuaded."

10

Amba did not have much hope of that. But she swallowed her pride and went to Shalva's country with a heavy heart.

Once more she came before Shalva and begged him to marry her. "I do not ask to be your chief wife. Let me be just one of your wives," she pleaded. "Do not turn me away."

Shalva laughed scornfully.

"Never," he answered. "Never shall I marry a girl who was captured by another in battle—a girl who has been the cause of my defeat and shame. Is one answer not good enough for you? Go back to Hastinapura."

Amba's cup of sorrow was full. The humiliation she had suffered on all sides made her bitter and angry. And she cursed her fate.

When she reached Hastinapura, she tried once more to persuade Bhishma to marry her.

But Bhishma shook his head and said, "How can I break my word, Princess? How can I do a false thing?"

Repulsed on all sides, Amba began to brood upon her sorrow and loneliness. She was young and beautiful, a princess of royal blood; yet her life had been blighted. Her heart swelled with anger against all the world, but especially against Bhishma whom she blamed for all this shame and misery.

11

Thoughts of revenge rose powerfully within her. She felt that she would never again find peace until she had brought about Bhishma's death. The thought began to haunt her and, day by day, she grew more desperate, until she began to seek some way by which she could achieve her purpose.

The embittered princess began to travel. She went from one kingdom to another, begging the rulers to make war upon Bhishma.

But they shook their heads and would have nothing to do with her, for they all feared Bhishma's strength. There was no one who dared face Bhishma in battle.

With each failure, the princess grew more and more and more bitter. Her hatred for Bhishma was like a living entity, consuming her from within. Nothing else seemed to matter. The world no longer interested her. Her eyes took on a wild, crazed look, and her heart echoed with cries for revenge.

One day Amba left the royal palace and retired into the forest. Since the world had failed her, she determined to seek the help of heaven. She lived the hard life of an ascetic, fasting and doing penance, torturing her body until she became thin and old before her time. Her face grew lined with wrinkles, her soft eyes turned harsh and her hands became coarse. Her long, glossy hair grew matted and brown with dust. But she cared nothing for her appearance, for she lived only for revenge, praying for it day and night. For many years she lived on roots and fruits and berries. Then she ceased to eat even this food and began to live on water alone, and then as the years passed, without even the water, as she sat never moving, lost in meditation.

So great was the power of her penance that, at last, the day came when Lord Shiva appeared before her and asked her what she desired.

"That Bhishma may be defeated and laid low," she cried out. "I wish that I may with my own hands bring about Bhishma's death, for he has destroyed me!"

The Lord answered gently, "There is no one in the world, dear child, who can defeat Bhishma, for he is blessed by the Gods."

Then Amba sobbed wildly, "Lord, is all my penance then in vain? Have I spent all these years for nothing?"

Lord Shiva, who is also the great God of Destruction, gazed upon the unhappy woman with compassion in his eyes.

"Penance is never in vain, Amba," he said. "And your desire shall be

fulfilled. All men and everything that is born must die. That is the supreme law; and one day even Bhishma must die, for Bhishma is a mortal. But Bhishma is so good and so great and so pure that no ordinary death can touch him. Disease and old age will not hurt him; weapons will be of no avail against him. Only you can bring about Bhishma's death, Amba, for you have spent all your life acquiring the strength for it by your penance and prayer. Be at peace now, for the day will come when you shall, with your own hands, bring about Bhishma's death."

"How?" cried Amba impatiently, "Lord, tell me how and when?" Then Shiva told her that she could not achieve it in that life. Bhishma was so pure and so powerful that in order to slay him she must be born once again. "You must die first and be reborn," said Shiva. "And in your next life you shall be born as the daughter of King Drupada of Panchala and be the cause of Bhishma's death."

"In my next life," she echoed. "Lord, how can I wait so long? And then how would I know that these things will truly come to pass?"

The Lord smiled at her impatience. "See," he said, removing from around his throat the string of *rudraksha* beads and putting them around her neck. "These beads shall be your sign." And he vanished.

Amba's withered heart stirred and rejoiced as she left the forest and made her way to Kampilya, Drupada's capital city. Here she hung on the gate-post of the royal palace the beads from around her neck. Then, as the astonished guards gazed terror-stricken at her gaunt, ochre-clad figure, she made her way into the hall where Drupada was performing a sacrifice. He hoped by this means to please the gods so that they would bless him with children. The orange flames of the sacrificial fire

crackled and leapt up to the rafters, as the priests chanted their mantras and prayers. As Amba stood there and stared, a strange look came into her eyes. The assembled people heard a cry escape her. Then as they looked on amazed, the figure in orange darted across the room and leapt into the flames. In a second the sacrificial fire had consumed Amba. But it was only her mortal body that died. Her desire did not die. It lived on strong as ever, enabling her to be born again. And in keeping with Shiva's promise, she was born as the daughter of Drupada, king of Panchala.

The princess grew up in her father's royal palace. They named her Shikhandini. She was a dark and secretive child, silent and mysterious. Often she wandered alone, deep in her melancholy thoughts which she shared with no one. One day as she went past the palace gates, Shikhandini found on the door-post the necklace of beads that Amba had left there. The child stretched out her hand and reached for it. She put it around her neck and, as soon as she had done so, she remembered the past—all of Amba's sorrows, all her intense desire for revenge. Her former life returned to her and she began to recall the purpose of the birth she had now taken. A quiet determination held her. Once again she, who had been Amba, began to pray and to meditate and this time she wished that she might be changed into a man.

Her prayer was granted to her. In the forest, the princess Shikhandini found a Yaksha who agreed to exchange his manhood for her womanhood. Thus, Shikhandini returned to Drupada's palace changed into a man.

And now her restless heart was at peace; for she knew in a strange way that the wrongs Amba had suffered would be avenged, and that Bhishma would meet his end at last.

3

The Birth of Karna

One golden morning, another young princess sat at her window gazing at the eastern sky that was streaked with crimson and gold. The sun was rising and the earth was stirring to life at his magic touch. The dewdrops hung glinting like diamonds from the leaves, and all the birds were singing. It seemed to the young girl that she had never seen anything more beautiful in her life than the Sun God, who rode across the sky in his golden chariot. As she thought this, she remembered a prayer charm that a sage had once given her. By the power of this charm, the sage had said, she could call the very gods in the heavens to her side to make her the mother of their sons. The princess, whose name was Kunti, wondered what would happen if she uttered the charm now. Would the Sun God really come? She had never used the charm before, for she was still very young.

Her heart beat fast at the thought of seeing the Sun God. Then, timidly, not quite believing, she whispered the magic words. She held her breath, scared by what she had done, for she knew it had not been right for her to utter the charm before she was fully grown. She did not want any sons as yet. She knew she was too young.

But even as she was thinking this, she saw the shining God of the Sun descending in a great blaze of gold. The next minute he was beside her and his eyes looked upon her with love.

Kunti trembled with fear. She covered her face with her hands and begged him to return to the Heavens, from where he had come. But this the Sun God could not do, for he was held by the power of the magic charm she had uttered. The Sun God gently made love to Kunti, and when he returned to his kingdom in the sky, she became the mother of his little son, a beautiful, shining child, bright as the Sun God himself. And because he was the Sun God's child, he was not like other babies: even at birth he wore armour which shone like gold and strange earrings in his ears which glowed with a reddish light.

But Kunti was not happy. She knew that her father King Kuntibhoja and the people around her would be angry with her, and she wished she had never met the Sun God nor borne the child. She would have liked to hide the baby just as she had concealed his birth, but that was not possible. Full of fear, she thought at last of a plan by which she could get rid of the baby. At the dead of night, she placed the child in a wooden box and hurried out of the palace gates with it. She came to a river, and there she set the box afloat upon the water. Then she hurried

back to the palace. But her heart was very heavy at the thought of what she had done. She knew that as long as she lived, she would never have any peace or happiness, for the memory of the innocent little baby whom she had set afloat upon the river would always be with her.

Days passed and Kunti grew into a beautiful young woman, but her eyes remained sad and she rarely smiled. Often, she wept to herself at night, thinking about the wooden box upon the river.

When the time came, she was given in marriage to Pandu, the second son of Vichitraveerya of Hastinapura. Vichitraveerya was dead, and his eldest son, Dhritarashtra, was blind. The elder statesmen of the kingdom, among whom was Bhishma, had therefore placed Pandu upon the throne of Hastinapura to rule in Dhritarashtra's place. Kunti lived in the royal palace. She served her elders dutifully and won the love of all those around her. But no one knew the sad, dark secret that lay heavy on her heart, and all her life she lived under its grim and terrible shadow.

But Kunti's baby son, who had so cruelly been abandoned, was not fated to die. The wooden chest that carried him floated down the river with the current towards Hastinapura. As it drifted, it was seen and hauled ashore by a man named Adiratha, a humble charioteer. He was greatly surprised to see a baby inside the chest. When he lifted the boy and saw his shining beauty he was filled with great joy.

Adiratha took the little baby home to his wife, Radha. When she heard the story he had to tell, her eyes filled with grateful, happy tears, for Radha had no children of her own, and now, it seemed, Heaven had miraculously answered her prayer for a child.

Radha and Adiratha decided to adopt the little foundling. They named him Karna, because of the wonderful rings in his ears. They knew in their simple hearts that he could not be an ordinary child, for no ordinary child had earrings such as his. No ordinary child was encased, as he was, in armour—a coat of mail that shone like gold.

Under their loving care, Karna grew up to be a fine youth, quick and clever in his ways. Early in life he learned to draw the bow and wield the sword. So skilful was he in the use of weapons that the charioteer and his wife and all who saw him were filled with wonder.

The boy spoke little and kept his deep, melancholy thoughts to himself. Yet he was always upright in his dealings, faithful, generous and bold. They found him quick-tempered: when he was roused to anger his hand trembled upon the hilt of his sword. But he was equally quick to forgive and forget. He would never betray a friend, nor break a promise, nor forget a kindness done to him.

And so, though some feared him, and some secretly hated him for his quick anger, there were many who admired him in their hearts.

But no one, not even his foster parents, knew the story of his birth, of his immortal father, the Sun God, and his mother, the beautiful Queen Kunti of Hastinapura.

16

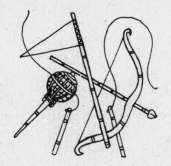

The Pandava Princes

King Pandu of Hastinapura was a man of frail health. But he ruled the State wisely with the help of many experienced and able counsellors. Of them all, the ablest were his uncle Bhishma and his half-brother, Vidura, who was born of a humble slave-girl but had grown to be wise and rich in understanding. Pandu took their advice on all matters. During his reign, Hastinapura was like a strong ship guided by a trusty captain and manned by faithful sailors.

King Pandu had married Kunti and Madri and the two wives loved each other dearly. All went well and the days passed peacefully, until the king's health worsened and he retired to the forest with his wives. For many years they lived a quiet life there, while the blind Dhritarashtra held the throne as regent. The Pandava princes were born while Pandu, Kunti and Madri lived in the forest.

The five Pandava boys were not ordinary children. They were the gifts of the gods and when they were born they shone with a heavenly light. Yudhishthira, the eldest, was given by Dharma, the Lord of Justice, and the God of Death. Indra, the king of the gods, gave to Kunti the brave and noble Arjuna. The valiant Bhima was the gift of the Wind God, Vayu. Nakula and Sahadeva came to Madri from the Ashwini twins. They grew up in their forest home; and Pandu, who with each passing day grew weaker and paler with his illness, was full of joy to see them before him.

But Pandu did not live long, and his sons were still children when one day he suddenly died. The two queens were grief-stricken. They gathered their fatherless boys around them and mourned for their husband.

The sages who lived in the forest hurried to their side to comfort them. They went to Hastinapura with the sad news. Madri's sorrow was so great that when they lit the funeral pyre of Pandu, she entered the flames and ended her life. Her two little sons she entrusted to Kunti.

Kunti gathered the children to her. She was dressed now in the white garments of a widow. Her beautiful face was lined with sorrow, her eyes ringed with dark lines. Fear was in her heart as she looked upon the five fatherless boys; the days ahead would no longer be easy. The sages advised her to take her sons back to the ancestral home in Hastinapura where it was right and natural for them to be.

Bhishma, Vidura and the other elders of the realm, who had hurried to the forest on hearing the news of the king's death, also begged Kunti to go back with them to Hastinapura. And so with her sons, the widowed queen followed the elders to the capital city.

As they approached it, they could see its golden rooftops gleaming in

the sun. Great crowds of people had gathered to receive and welcome them. Though the people grieved for the beloved king who was dead, they were proud and overjoyed to see the five noble princes. "God bless the sons of Pandu," the people whispered to one another, "they are good and noble. They are as handsome as the gods in the Heavens."

Now when these words reached the sons of Dhritarashtra, they were not at all pleased. There were a hundred of them and they were called the Kauravas. Duryodhana was the eldest. A proud and haughty boy, he was not happy about his cousins' return. When Duryodhana heard what the people of Hastinapura said about them, he frowned darkly. His eyes clouded over and the canker of jealousy began to eat at his heart. He knew he was expected to receive his cousins and welcome them; it was a bitter thought. He ground his teeth as he went down the palace steps towards the Pandavas. He hated them and it angered him to see the love the people showed them; it tortured him to see the joy and pride on the faces of Bhishma and Vidura. It was a bitter day for Duryodhana—this day of the Pandavas' return to Hastinapura. But he swallowed his anger and held out his hand. He smiled and called them his brothers; he embraced them and led them up the palace steps, hating them secretly all the while.

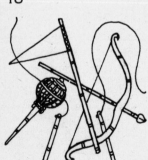

18

The blind king Dhritarashtra tottered up to them and when they bent down and touched his feet in respect, the old man raised them to him and embraced them. Then Gandhari, Dhritarashtra's wife and the mother of the Kauravas, held out her arms to them. So great was her love and devotion to her blind husband that from the day she had married him, Gandhari had bound up her own eyes with a cloth and refused to see the loveliness of the world because she could not share it with him. Gandhari embraced the sobbing Kunti and spoke many words of comfort to her. She gathered the Pandava princes to her kindly and lovingly. And all the time Duryodhana watched with a smile upon his lips and hatred in his heart.

The Great Archer

Kunti and her sons lived in the royal palace at Hastinapura and the Pandava and Kaurava princes grew up together. The head of their household was their great-uncle Bhishma, and his word was law. He loved the boys as if they were his own sons; and so did Vidura, Dhritarashtra's half-brother. Kunti watched anxiously as her sons grew. Vague fears for their safety haunted her. She did not trust the Kauravas for she knew that they had no love for their cousins. And yet she knew that while Bhishma was there she had nothing to fear, for Bhishma was wise and just in all his dealings.

The princes sported in the palace gardens. They played ball, flew kites, rolled marbles and shot with catapults and slings. And like the true Kshatriyas they were, they had their little bows and arrows and swords.

One day while the princes of Hastinapura were playing together as usual, their ball, thrown far and fast by one of them, fell into an old well in a corner of the garden. The boys gathered round the well and peered into it. They could see the ball but had no idea how to get it out.

As they stood there trying to decide what to do, they saw walking towards them a little dark-skinned man, a stranger whom they had never seen before. His keen gaze, sharp as needle-points, seemed to pierce them through and through. They knew him to be a Brahmin because of the sacred thread around his body.

The stranger came up to them and asked them about their problem. Gratefully, the boys clamoured to tell him.

"We have lost our ball," they chorused. "It fell into the well while we were playing and now we cannot get it out!" The dark stranger smiled.

"Surely that is not difficult for boys so well trained in archery," he remarked, and his eyes seemed to mock them. They looked at him surprised, even a little amused.

"Archery?" they asked laughing. "What has archery got to do with getting a ball out of a well, Brahmin?"

"Everything," answered the stranger, smiling mysteriously. "Everything, as you will now see! Get me an arrow." But the princes had no arrows ready that day. "No matter," said the stranger. "Go, get me from the field beyond, a few good strong stems of the Khusha grass growing there and I will show you such a sight as you have never seen before."

His voice seemed to command them, and they sped off to do as they were told. Then they stood breathlessly around him, watching with rapt attention. The stranger chose the longest and strongest of the grass stems. Then uttering his prayer charm he shot it forth. The grass stem streaked into the well with the speed of lightning, striking the ball in such a manner that it bounded out of the water, hit the wall of the well, then bounced back off the side and up in the air! The Brahmin caught the ball deftly as it rose, and handed it back to the astonished boys. It was a remarkable feat. They stared at him in wonder. Then Yudhishthira, still dazed, said: "There is a ring too, in the well—one that I lost some days ago. When the waters settle you will be able to see it at the bottom. Could you get it out for me as you did the ball?"

"Nothing easier!" laughed the stranger. He picked up the bow and chose another stem. This time he cut a deep notch into it. That done, he drew his bow and shot the grass stem down into the well. Once more the boys saw it speeding down. They saw it strike the earth through the ring, so that the ring was caught in the notch. The stem stuck in the mud and stood upright. Then the man sent the other grass stems one by one after it, first carefully cutting notches into each. So well were the grasses aimed, with such precision and power, that each grass struck the notch of the one before, and stuck fast in it. Thus, the grasses made a long line of arrows with which he was able to pull out the ring.

"Bravo!" cried the delighted princes and they stared at him in admiration. "You are truly a great archer. What is your name, stranger?" But the stranger only shook his head and smiled.

"Go!" he commanded them. "Go and tell your great-uncle what you have seen today." The young princes needed no second bidding. They ran off to tell Bhishma all that had happened.

Bhishma knew at once that this man who had come to their palace was no ordinary archer. He was sure that the stranger in the garden was Dronacharya, the son of Bharadwaja who was believed to have learnt archery from the gods in heaven. He hurried down to the garden and was overjoyed to find that his guess had been correct. Bhishma knew that there was no one in the land of Bharata who could equal Drona as an archer.

Bhishma at once engaged Drona to teach the royal princes the arts of warfare. From then on, Drona lived at the royal palace at Hastinapura.

Drona proved an excellent teacher. One day he called his pupils to him to test their power of concentration. Gathering them around him, he pointed out a target. It was a bird on the branch of a tree. "Bring down the head of the bird for me!" commanded Drona. He told Yudhishthira to come forward alone because he was the eldest. Yudhishthira drew his bow. But at that moment Drona held up his hand: "Wait!" he said, "Tell me first, what do you see?" "I see the bird," answered Yudhishthira, "and the branch on which it sits and the leaves of the tree."

"Go on," Drona commanded, "Is there anything else? Tell me."

Yudhishthira answered, "I see the tree and sky and you, my teacher, and I see my brothers."

Drona said to him: "Stand aside. You have still much to learn."

After Yudhishthira came Duryodhana. He answered Drona's question just as Yudhishthira had done, saying that he saw the bird and the branch, the leaves and the tree, the sky and, before him, his teacher and beyond, his brothers. Then Drona set him aside also, and asked for Bhima. Bhima fared no better. At that Drona was full of sorrow that his pupils had not been as good as he wished. At last he called Arjuna to him and repeated his questions.

"Do you see the bird?"

"I do," Arjuna answered.

"And what else besides?"

"I see only the bird," Arjuna answered. "Nothing else."

"Do you not see the tree and the sky and the earth, myself, your teacher, and beyond, do you not see your brothers?"

"I see only the bird," Arjuna repeated.

Arjuna's answer pleased Drona, for this was what he was hoping to hear from his students. He asked, "What part of the bird do you see, Arjuna?"

Arjuna answered: "Only the eye!" Drona walked up to Arjuna, and patted him on his back. "Lower your bow, Arjuna!" he exclaimed. "You have proved yourself a true archer. For, above everything, an archer must be undivided in his attention; when the true archer concentrates, and his eyes see nothing but his target, his arrow will reach it unerringly."

Ever afterwards, Drona loved Arjuna as his star pupil. After a few months of training, Drona wished to test his pupils again. At the same time he longed to punish Drupada, king of Panchala, for a wrong the king had done to him.

Many years before, Drupada, the prince of Panchala, and Drona had studied under Drona's father, Bharadwaja, in his hermitage. In those happy, carefree days of their youth, the prince of Panchala and the poor Brahmin boy had sworn eternal friendship. At the end of his course of studies, Drupada prepared to return to Panchala. The royal chariot awaited him, with servants and attendants bending low before him. As Drupada walked up to the chariot he could not help feeling that he was above everybody there in rank and status. Nevertheless he embraced his friend Drona warmly and invited him to come to Panchala. Drona agreed. Drupada returned to Panchala and, inheriting its throne, was crowned king.

For many years, however, Drona was not able to keep his promise to visit his friend. He continued his studies, gaining mastery over all the sciences and arts. He was an earnest young man and proved such an apt pupil that people said the gods had blessed him with the knowledge of divine weapons and with the secrets of using them. In time, this earnest and serious young scholar married the sister of Kripacharya, the instructor to the Pandava and Kaurava princes at Hastinapura, and

22

his wife bore him a little son.

Now a new phase began in Drona's life. Until then Drona had not cared for material comfort or for wealth—being content to live a stern, harsh life in his forest hermitage. But the birth of his son changed all that. The boy became the centre of his life. Drona longed to give his son all the comforts he had never wanted for himself. So he determined to find work at one of the royal courts. He remembered his boyhood friend, Drupada, who was now king of the Panchala kingdom, and made up his mind to go to Drupada for help. As an old friend, Drupada would surely come to his aid.

But when Drona, barefoot and dressed only in his loin cloth, came before Drupada on his throne, he found the king very different from the boyhood friend he had known. For wealth and power had gone to Drupada's head and he had grown proud and haughty. He looked at the poor Brahmin before him and was ashamed to own that once they had been friends. In that great royal court, in the presence of all assembled there, Drupada insulted Drona. His lip curled with scorn. "Friends!" he exclaimed. "I do not remember ever having known you. Get you gone, Brahmin, and if it is alms you want, go to the almshouse, where rice is given to beggars."

Drona looked up in surprise and grief. "I have not come for alms, Drupada," he said, and he reminded Drupada of the happy days of their youth. But the haughty king refused to acknowledge that they had once been friends. "You are no better than a common beggar!" he said. "Friendship is possible only between equals. How can a beggar claim friendship with a king? Leave the court at once. We have seen thousands of your kind begging for scraps from rich men's tables. We have no time for people like you." The servants laid rough hands on Drona, and he was turned out of the royal court.

Drona felt utterly humiliated. Anger filled his heart. He went to the house of his brother-in-law, Kripacharya, in Hastinapura. It was while he was there that he met Bhishma and was engaged by him to be tutor to the royal princes.

Drona never forgot Drupada's insulting behaviour. He never forgave him and he longed for revenge. When Drona felt that the princes of Hastinapura had been adequately trained, he called Duryodhana to him and commanded him to make war on the Panchala king. Duryodhana obeyed. But Drupada defeated him and Duryodhana came back in disgrace. Then Drona named Arjuna for the task. Arjuna defeated the Panchalas, captured their king and brought him before Drona. Drupada's pride was brought to dust, and Drona's desire for revenge was at last satisfied.

Now Drona reminded the royal captive of his words. He had said that friendship was possible only between equals. "You can have half your kingdom back, Drupada," said Drona, smiling contemptuously. "The other half I shall keep. So shall I be a king and your equal; so may I claim your friendship." And Drupada winced at the mocking voice. Drona ordered Drupada to be freed to return to his own country. The proud king bowed before him. But in his heart he began to hate Drona.

Humbled and smarting under the disgrace of his defeat, it was now Drupada's turn to plan revenge. He hated to think that he owed his throne to Drona's generosity. With his heart burning with rancour, he began to pray. He prayed that he might have a son who would one day bring about Drona's death.

But Drupada also prayed for a daughter who would one day be Arjuna's wife. For, during the journey to Hastinapura, Drupada had been struck by Arjuna's noble bearing, by his wisdom and goodness. Drupada's prayers were answered and to him were born a dark pair of twins, a boy called Dhrishtadyumna and a girl called Krishna, who was also known as Draupadi.

24

A Wicked Plot

Kunti's fears were not groundless. Though the Pandavas and the Kauravas grew up together and shared all things equally, there was no love lost between them. Duryodhana and his brothers hated the five Pandavas. They looked upon them as rivals and intruders and wished that they had never come to live in Hastinapura at the royal palace. They were jealous of the Pandavas and the love that the people bore them. They envied their good looks and noble bearing. They noticed that by their charm, good manners and friendliness, the Pandavas made themselves popular with everybody. Most of all, they feared that the people of Hastinapura would one day pass over Duryodhana, and choose Yudhishthira to be their king. Duryodhana nursed hatred in his heart, but outwardly pretended love and friendship for his cousins which he was far from feeling. Whenever he had the chance, he tried to harm them, and on one occasion he even tried to kill Bhima.

Bhima was Duryodhana's special enemy. He was a big, strong, simple-hearted boy with a curious sense of humour. He had a turn for practical jokes and he played them upon the Kauravas, to their great annoyance. The Kauravas were vain, pompous youths and Bhima disliked them as heartily as they disliked him. He took it upon himself to humble their pride. Bhima was also something of a bully and secretly Duryodhana feared his great strength. Once it happened that Bhima chanced upon Duryodhana stealing fruit. He went up to the tree and shook it violently, threatening to uproot it, till Duryodhana, white-faced and trembling, clung to the branches and begged him to stop. Bhima seemed to think this extremely funny!

Another time he ducked the Kaurava brothers, one by one, into the icy waters of a river, holding them by the scruff of their necks till each one spluttered and shivered and cried out for mercy.

Often he would engage in wrestling bouts with his cousins, who were like toys in his hands. He would throw them down with ease, one after the other, and would walk away roaring with laughter.

This, of course, did not make Bhima very popular with his cousins. Duryodhana's hatred for him increased day by day. Deep in his heart, Duryodhana nursed a desire to kill Bhima, but Bhima was too strong for him, and Duryodhana knew he had no chance against his cousin in an open fight. So day and night, Duryodhana plotted against the unsuspecting Bhima.

Then at last when his plans were ripe, he approached the Pandavas and suggested that they should all go out and camp for a few days on the nearby river-bank. The unsuspecting Pandavas readily agreed and the party set out in high spirits for the royal summer residence on the river-bank. Here they spent several happy days, swimming, boating, riding and hunting. On the last night of their stay, Duryodhana arranged a feast at which all the choicest dishes that the Pandava brothers most loved were set before them. It was a royal feast and Bhima, who loved good food, fell to it with a royal appetite. For him Duryodhana had had special food cooked and Bhima ate vast quantities of it. Duryodhana watched him closely and was very pleased. For the special food was poisoned.

That night, while the Pandava princes slept, Duryodhana and his brothers came to Bhima where he lay in a deep, death-like slumber—the effect of the poisoned food. Quickly and silently they bound him with ropes and carried him out; they flung him into the river and returned to the palace as if nothing had happened.

The next morning there was a search for Bhima; but when he was nowhere to be found, the Pandavas, thinking he had gone off somewhere and would return on his own, went back to Hastinapura with their cousins. Only Duryodhana and his close friends knew the truth. They rubbed their hands with glee and secretly rejoiced, believing that Bhima was dead. But Bhima had not died. He was too strong for any poison to kill him. It had only made him unconscious. He fell into a whirlpool and was sucked deeper and deeper into it, until he reached the kingdom of the snakes under the river. Now, the snake-people or the *Nagas* are wise, gentle creatures with a vast knowledge of poisons and medicines. They gathered around the unconscious form of Bhima, and they took pity on him. With their double tongues they sucked out the poison from his body until he revived and sat up, dazed and bewildered. Upon hearing his story, the snake-people nodded gravely.

"This is Duryodhana's doing," they said. "Duryodhana and his brothers hate you. They will try every means to kill you."

Bhima stayed with the snake-people until he had recovered his strength. They would have liked him to stay for ever. But Bhima loved his mother and brothers far too much for that. So he thanked the kindly creatures, said goodbye to them, and returned to Hastinapura.

26

Duryodhana and his brothers were amazed to see Bhima alive and well. They had never doubted the success of their evil plan. Kunti and her other sons had waited anxiously for him and then sorrowfully given him up for dead. They were now filled with happiness to see him. The Kauravas came and greeted him too, with smiles upon their faces. But in their hearts they were worried because their plot had failed.

Bhima, however, gave no sign that he knew of the plot to murder him. Duryodhana smiled unsteadily, wondering secretly how much Bhima had found out.

That night, Bhima told his mother and brothers the true story. They spoke in whispers because now they knew they were in danger. They agreed that they must be very careful. Duryodhana and his brothers hated them and would stop at nothing to harm them. They knew that they had powerful enemies in that beautiful palace and things were never what they appeared to be. A smile might mean that a plot was hatching. Soft words might be like double-edged swords. A goblet of sparkling wine might contain death, and behind the sculptured pillars of the palace, murder might be lurking.

So the days passed, filled with suspicion and fear, and in the palace, the children of Pandu and the children of Dhritarashtra grew into manhood.

7

Ekalavya's Training

Ekalavya was the son of the chief of a forest-tribe called the Nishadas, who made their living by hunting and fishing. Ekalavya had grown up in his forest home to become a brave, strong and worthy young man. As he grew up, he longed to learn the skills of Kshatriya warfare, but there was no one to teach him. He had heard about the great Drona who lived in Hastinapura and whom none could equal as a teacher. Ekalavya determined to become Drona's pupil and to learn from him. So he left his forest home and journeyed to far-off Hastinapura.

It was a long and difficult journey, but that did not daunt Ekalavya. After many days of walking, he at last reached the great city and the gates of the royal palace. In the king's gardens, a little dark man was instructing his pupils. Ekalavya saw how they listened to him with awe and respect. He noticed how clear were the teacher's instructions, and how authoritatively he commanded their attention. And Ekalavya knew that this man could be none other than the great teacher, Drona. So Ekalavya walked up and saluted him. Drona returned the greeting, wondering who the young man could be. He saw with pleasure how tall and straight-limbed he was, how clear his eyes were, shining as they did with the light of intelligence. Drona asked him who he was and what he wanted. When the teacher heard how the boy had come asking to be a pupil, he felt flattered and said: "What is your caste, child? What is your family? Where are you brought up?"

"We are Nishadas, sir," Ekalavya answered. "My father is chief of the tribe, and we live in the forests. I belong, therefore, to no caste, for our people are not of the Aryan race. I long to learn the martial arts and to be a soldier in the service of my country."

"A forest tribesman!" At these words Drona drew himself up haughtily, exclaiming, "Do you not know, boy, that I am a teacher of Kshatriya princes? I do not teach tribesmen; I accept only Kshatriyas as my pupils. Please go away, young man. I cannot teach you."

Ekalavya walked out of the garden and stood gazing at Drona's royal pupils. It was a bitter disappointment to him. He had come to Hastinapura with only one purpose—to become a pupil of the renowned teacher. And he had been rebuffed. He walked away deep in thought and sad at heart. He did not feel any anger at Drona's refusal. Indeed, his desire to learn was so great that he had no time at all to waste on anger. The more he thought about it, the stronger became

Ekalavya's desire to be Drona's pupil and to learn from him. But, of course, Drona would not change his mind.

Ekalavya returned to the forest from which he had come. When he arrived there he continued to think, until at last he found a solution to his problem. He set to work with clay and made himself an image in the likeness of Drona. He set up this image, and meditated deeply before it. In his heart he looked upon this image as Drona himself. After he had meditated for a long time, he got up and began to practise the art of the soldier, shooting his arrows at targets that he set up for himself. Every day he did this, praying before the clay image, and studying and practising before it with such concentration and deep intent, that it was not long before he mastered, in that lonely forest, all the skills that Drona taught the princes in the royal palace. Far from feeling anger at the insult he had suffered at Drona's hands, he felt for Drona a deep love and reverence, for he looked upon him as a teacher in spite of his contemptuous attitude.

29

One day, Drona brought his royal pupils into the forest in order to teach them hunting. It happened to be the same forest where Ekalavya lived but Drona did not know this.

As the royal party made their way forward, Drona saw many signs that they were not alone. There were arrows stuck fast in the tree trunks as if someone had been practising archery. There were tracks and footmarks. He was still wondering about the discovery, when one of his dogs began to bark. At that very moment, there came swiftly through the air, one after another, seven shining arrows that struck with the speed of lightning at the dog's open mouth. Drona could see that they had been shot from a great distance, and whoever had shot them had taken aim with nothing to guide him except the sound of the dog's barking. They were the arrows of a true warrior.

The sight surprised Drona very greatly, for he had always believed that there was no one who could equal his pupils. Now he was not so sure. He wondered who the unknown warrior could be and, spurred on by his curiosity, he made his way deeper into the forest, bidding his pupils to follow. They had barely gone some distance when they came upon Ekalavya in a small clearing, standing with his bow drawn and his arrow ready to fly. The youth looked up and saw them. Instantly he put his bow to one side and, folding his hands together, went down on his knees. Drona wondered greatly at his noble bearing and conduct. "Here," he thought, "is a true Kshatriya, one who would make the world proud that he had been born!"

"Who are you, young man?" Drona asked. "And who is your teacher? Surely your teacher must be a great Guru to have trained such a mighty warrior!"

"I am Ekalavya, sir," the youth answered. "My family belong to the Nishada tribe and we live in the forest. My teacher is the great and incomparable Drona."

Drona started.

"Drona?" he repeated, looking upon the kneeling boy, bewildered.

"But Drona lives in Hastinapura. He knows no Ekalavya!" Drona had forgotten the incident that had taken place in the palace garden. Then Ekalavya told him how he had made a clay image of the teacher and looking upon it as the living Drona, had sat before it in prayer and practised the martial arts in its living presence. "Though he does not know it, Drona is in truth my Guru!"

"A clay image?" whispered Drona, and suddenly he remembered the youth he had turned away. He was filled, in spite of himself, with wonder, astonishment and a deep pleasure. But as he stood there with the kneeling boy before him, troubled feelings of envy and fear began to arise in Drona's heart, though he allowed no sign of them to show upon his face. He spoke with a smile. "I have come before you in person, Ekalavya. I am your teacher, Drona, and I wish to test you. Let there be a contest here and now! Match your skill with the Kshatriya princes of Hastinapura. They are also my pupils."

Nothing could have made Ekalavya happier. Joyfully he agreed to Drona's suggestion. The contest started. There in the forest glade the pupils of Drona displayed their skill one by one before the master. Yudhishthira and Duryodhana, Bhima, Arjuna and Dushahsana—all those who had learnt from Drona—came forward to wrestle and fence and shoot their arrows at targets that he named. But, of them all, Ekalavya was easily the best, and there was no one, not even Arjuna, who could excel the forest tribesman. One by one, they retired, defeated by him, filled with shame and jealousy. He alone remained fresh and smiling and clear-eyed, eager and ready for more.

Drona looked around at the royal pupils whom he had trained with such care; he could not bear to think that this forest tribesman, whom he had turned away and refused to teach, had proved their superior. Not one of them could match him. Drona felt bitterly disappointed. But he swallowed his feelings and smiled at the boy. He called him to his side. "Since I am your teacher and have taught you all you know, I must have my fees. A teacher must be paid."

"That he must!" agreed Ekalavya. "Whatever my teacher asks I shall give to him." Drona looked at him keenly, while Ekalavya continued, "My teacher has only to command, and all I have is his."

"Then listen, Ekalavya," said Drona and he did not for a moment takes his eyes from that eager, young face. "In return for my teaching I will take from you your right thumb."

30

The boy started slightly. Drona wished to maim him, so that he could never draw his bow again as well as he did. With Ekalavya maimed, Drona's Kshatriya pupils would have no rival and Arjuna would have no match. Ekalavya understood this, but smiled gently.

"What my teacher asks I will gladly give," he said. He drew his sword and with one stroke he cut off his right thumb. The bleeding offering he gave to Drona, his teacher, with a smiling face and an ungrudging heart.

The princes of Hastinapura returned to their city with Drona, while Ekalavya turned back quietly to the forest glades where he lived.

Arjuna's rival had been destroyed.

8

Karna Faces Arjuna

The young princes of Hastinapura grew to be fine and strong. Drona and Kripa taught them the skills that all Kshatriyas had to master. They learned to ride their horses and drive their chariots, to fence and to wrestle, to draw the bow and wield the mace. They learned the formations and movements of the infantry and cavalry during battle. They studied the arts of defence and attack.

They learned too, from their wise tutors, the warrior's code of honour: that a true Kshatriya is, above all, a prince in thought, word and deed; one who thinks no unworthy thought, speaks no lowly word and does no mean or cowardly deed. The princes of Hastinapura learned that a Kshatriya's place is on the battlefield where he defends his people and his country against the enemy. A Kshatriya must always be brave and fearless but never cruel. He must go to battle ready to meet death and he may never, if he is a true Kshatriya, turn his back on the enemy or fly from danger. He must be noble and large-hearted, generous and forgiving. He must not raise his hand to hurt one who is weaker than he; he must not fight a woman or a child, or one of a lowly caste, one who has fallen, or who is asleep; he must not, while mounted, fight one who is on foot, or strike anyone by creeping up from behind. And he must be steadfast and loyal and true to his liege lord and his people, both in good times and bad.

In course of time, Drona felt that his pupils had reached a high degree of skill and had mastered all their lessons. They were now without rivals in the whole land—Bhima and Duryodhana in the art of wielding the mace; Nakula and Sahadeva as horsemen; Drona's son, Ashvatthama (who had grown up with the royal princes) in the science of warfare and of planning the formation of army divisions, the sieges of cities and attacks on and defence of fortresses; Yudhishthira as a chariot fighter and leader of men. But, of them all, Arjuna was the very best, for he excelled in all things. Arjuna was his teacher's favourite pupil and his pride.

Then a time came when, according to custom, Drona fixed a day for a tournament, at which his pupils could display their skill to the world. There would be individual displays by each prince and matches at which they would pit their strength against one another and against any who challenged them.

To this tournament were invited all the people of Hastinapura and they came in holiday clothes, jostling each other and crowding through the public entrances to catch a glimpse of the royal princes. Tents were pitched and brightly coloured pennants fluttered gaily over them in the sunshine.

Beyond, under richly embroidered canopies, were the seats for the royal family and for people of high rank and office who came accompanied by a great procession, with the beating of drums and the music of pipes—first, the blind king Dhritarashtra and then Gandhari, his queen. After her came Kunti, mother of the Pandavas. Kunti was followed by the noble advisers Bhishma and Vidura, and the teachers, Drona and Kripa.

The blare of conch shells rent the air; drums began to beat and martial music played, announcing the arrival of the princes. The crowd cheered and shouted as they entered, dressed in their shining coats of mail; Yudhishthira, the eldest, leading and, following him, his brothers and cousins. The priests began to chant the sonorous Vedic hymns to the lighting of the sacrificial fire, and offerings were made to the gods.

Then the princes stood up and began their display. They showed their marvellous feats of strength and skill and cunning. As they watched, the people held their breath. For never before had they seen such strength, such grace and lightness of movement, such wonderful feats of skill, or such marksmanship. The twanging of bowstrings seemed to tear open the skies and so thick was the shower of arrows that the light of the sun was shut out from the world. Yet, there was not a single arrow needlessly shot, nor was there a single dart that did not go swiftly and surely to its target. Other feats were also shown. Duryodhana and Bhima displayed their skill with their maces. The young Nakula and Sahadeva exhibited their unrivalled horsemanship.

Last of all came Arjuna, and at the sight of him the people roared a welcome. He bowed to his teachers and his elders, and returned the greetings of the crowds before he entered the contest. When the people saw the wonders that he performed with his bow and his arrows and the almost magical quality of his darts, when they saw his swiftness of foot and lightness of movement and his skill and courage, they cheered him again and again and acknowledged him the greatest of them all. The widowed queen Kunti felt her heart stir with joy and pride as she watched; and the people shouted loudly: "There is no one who can equal Arjuna in this world!" But when Duryodhana heard these words he ground his teeth with jealousy. He bit his nails and wrung his hands. "If only Arjuna could be beaten!..." thought Duryodhana.

At that moment, as if in answer to his prayer, there arose from the crowd a young man dressed in shining armour and bearing arms. He strode towards the enclosure where the royal princes stood—a tall, broad-shouldered man, fair of face and keen of eye. Though he came from the common crowd, he walked boldly and stood straight, carrying himself more proudly than any prince. In his ears were a strange pair of earrings. They shone with such a bright red light that his

32

face and his eyes seemed to reflect their glow.

A hush fell upon the crowd as they watched. Under their canopies the royal personages waited. They whispered to each other and to their servants, asking about the cause of the delay. Only Kunti gasped and grew pale, as she saw the strange warrior. Those earrings...that coat of mail! Did she not know them?

The newcomer entered the enclosure, and, bowing quickly before them all, he announced loudly: "I too wish to display my skill before the gathering...for I can prove that Arjuna's feats are child's play to me."

Drona frowned. Who was this unknown warrior who stood in the common crowd and dared to challenge Arjuna? He grew uneasy as he watched the youth's bold manner. Drona did not like the turn things were taking. He felt that a challenge to Arjuna was like a challenge to himself. Arjuna's defeat or humiliation would be Drona's too. He must not let this happen. As he was thinking, however, Arjuna stepped forward. "I accept the challenge!" he said smiling. Drona waved him aside, and went up to the stranger. Ignoring Arjuna's words, Drona said to him: "Before you enter such a contest, you must prove yourself, Stranger! You must display your skill before the assembly."

"Nothing easier!" laughed the stranger. "Shall we start?"

And so the newcomer began to display his skills to all those gathered there. In all that he did, he proved himself fully the equal of the princes. Drona's anxiety grew as he watched the display. The mob, however, cheered wildly, for here indeed was a match for Arjuna. The newcomer's dexterity was as great as the Kshatriya prince's. Indeed, whatever Arjuna could do, the unknown warrior could also do and with greater skill and ease.

All the while Queen Kunti looked on, her heart pounding in her breast, her hands cold from fear and her face as white as death. "Where will all this end?" she thought desperately.

From his place Duryodhana watched, too, and saw how skilfully the unknown warrior handled his weapons. He knew that here at last, was what he had waited for all these long years—a rival to Arjuna! Heaven had answered his wish. Duryodhana came quickly forward and took the stranger's hand. Then, in the sight of all, he embraced him warmly.

"Welcome, Warrior," he said. "Whoever you may be, from now on you shall be as a blood brother to me. Whatever you ask, I shall give, if it is in my power."

The warrior thanked Duryodhana: "I shall not forget your kindness and generosity," he answered. "I have something indeed to ask of you, Prince, and this is it."

Then raising his voice so that everyone could hear, he said, "A duel with Arjuna! That is all I ask. Let me have permission to fight a duel with Arjuna."

Hearing his words, Kunti began to tremble like a leaf. But Arjuna stepped forward.

"I accept the challenge!" he said again, eagerly. "I will fight this stranger."

They stood face to face, Arjuna and his rival, in readiness for the contest. Those who were assembled there were full of wonder to see how greatly they resembled each other, both tall and ruddy and shining-eyed, with perfect limbs and clean, strong features. Except that Arjuna was younger and slighter, while the other had reached full manhood and was bigger built.

As they stood, poised to fight, Kunti covered her eyes with her hands and a wild scream escaped her. The next moment she had fainted in the arms of her serving maid and had to be carried away.

Drona and Kripa were whispering together anxiously; Drona was determined to avoid this contest. Just as the two warriors drew their swords, Kripa arose and held up his hand. He came down to where they stood.

"Wait!" Kripa exclaimed sharply, and he faced Karna—for it was indeed he, the son of Kunti and the Sun God. "Wait!" repeated Kripa. "Do you not know, Warrior, that Kshatriya fighters must make known their ancestry and family before they fight a duel? Do you not know that a Kshatriya may not cross swords with one who is of low birth?"

Kripa turned to Arjuna. "Name your family then, Arjuna," he said. "Tell us what race you belong to, and who your ancestors are."

Arjuna answered in a clear loud voice; he told the assembly the names of his royal ancestors.

Kripa turned to the other. "Stranger, what is your name? What is your family? What is the blood that runs in your veins? Proclaim these things before you cross swords with a royal prince."

"My name is Karna," he answered. "I am a warrior, I cannot claim royal blood...."

"Then you may not fight a royal prince," interrupted Kripa triumphantly. Karna bit his lip. Kripa went on, with scorn in his voice and his eyes: "Go back to the common crowd from which you come; this a tournament for Kshatriyas and men of royal birth!"

But even as Kripa spoke, Duryodhana stepped forward. He put his hand upon Karna's shoulder.

"Common crowd!" he cried angrily to Kripa. "Is not a man made noble by his deeds, and not by his birth? Do not your books say this and have you not yourself often said this to us?"

But Kripa and Drona, fearing Arjuna's defeat, hardened their hearts against him. "Arjuna is a royal prince," said Drona stubbornly, "He will not soil his hands by fighting one who is not of noble birth."

34

Then Duryodhana, roused to anger because his plan would be foiled, faced Drona his teacher and said:

"Very well then—if you say Arjuna may fight only a royal prince, why, that can easily be arranged. If this stranger is not a prince, why, that can easily be set right." He raised his voice and announced: "I, Duryodhana, prince of Hastinapura, bestow upon Karna the kingdom of Anga. He shall be king of that beautiful land and shall be free to fight whomever he chooses." Karna knelt before Duryodhana, tears of gratitude in his eyes. Duryodhana placed upon his head the crown that he had quickly sent for. The priests came forward at his bidding and with song and

prayer and coronation hymns they anointed Karna's head and sprinkled holy water upon it, and he was crowned king of Anga.

The crowds cheered wildly. But in the royal ranks there was silence and no one knew what to say. At that moment there arose from the crowd an old, bent man, dressed in the humble clothes of a servant. It was Adiratha, Karna's foster-father. He tottered up to the enclosure while the crowd made way for him, and came to where Karna and Duryodhana stood. The people looked on, curious and pondering. They saw the tears run down the old man's furrowed cheeks; they heard his trembling voice cry out, "Oh my son! my son!" They saw him hold out his thin, reedy arms and move forward to embrace Karna. "Father!" they heard Karna cry, as he knelt at his feet. The old man blessed him, raised him up and embraced him again, weeping tears of happiness and pride.

Now, the Pandavas had been watching, and when Bhima saw this scene he shouted out in a rude and sneering voice: "King of Anga, is he? Why, he is the son of a chariot driver. He has common blood! A chariot driver—to fight with royal princes! Does he not know that he was born to wield a horse-whip and not a sword, which is the weapon of a prince?"

At these cruel, ugly words, Karna stood silent, breathing hard, flushed with anger and sorrow. His arm tightened around his old father's shoulders. Tears arose in his throat, but he swallowed them back. But Duryodhana would not be silent. His eyes blazed as he answered Bhima.

"Shame upon you who call yourself a prince!" Duryodhana flung at him. "Your words are the words of one who is weak and stupid and unworthy. A true Kshatriya would not soil his mouth by uttering such unworthy words!" He looked round, but nobody spoke. Whether they were unwilling to defy the Kshatriya code, or whether they feared Drona and respected his word, Duryodhana never knew. But at that critical moment, they all remained silent and Duryodhana found himself alone beside the stranger. He turned to Karna.

"Come," he said, in a voice that all could hear. "Come with me. You shall be my brother, and a day will come when these insults shall be avenged. Come, let us go."

He took Karna's arm and the two went off together.

36

The tournament came to a sudden end. The crowd broke up and men talked in excited whispers as they left.

"This is not the end of the story!" they remarked to each other. "It is only the beginning. One day, Arjuna and Karna will come face to face in battle...and who knows what will happen then?"

That night, while Karna slept, he had a strange dream. It seemed to him that he saw a shining being descend from the sky and appear before him. He heard him call his name: "Karna! Karna!" "Who are you?" Karna asked the stranger. And the other answered: "I am your father, the Sun God!"

Karna started. "What is this you say?" he whispered huskily. "My father is Adiratha, charioteer of Hastinapura."

"No, Karna," answered the Sun God. "Adiratha is not in truth your father." And he told him the story of his birth.

"You are no humble chariot driver," he said. "Your blood is royal and noble!" Karna remained silent; a hundred conflicting thoughts were crowding his mind.

Through their din and confusion he heard the Sun God's warning voice begging him to keep secret what he had told him.

"Speak about this to no one, my beloved son, or you will betray and humiliate Kunti, the mother who bore you." "It shall be as you say," murmured Karna. "The secret shall be locked up in my heart, and no man will know it."

But the Sun God had come to speak about other things—to warn Karna about enemies who wished to harm him and would try to make him weak and powerless. He told Karna how Indra, the heavenly father of Arjuna, would come to Karna in disguise and try to get from him his magic armour and earrings.

"Do not part with these, Karna," said the Sun God. "They are my gifts to you; they are charms that protect you and make you invincible." Karna remained silent. "Do not part with them, Karna," the Sun God's voice repeated, and it was still ringing in Karna's ears as he awoke. He looked about him. He was alone. The Sun God had disappeared. Was it really a dream? he wondered.

But that evening in the gloom of twilight, an old wrinkled man came to Karna, declaring that he was a humble beggar come to seek charity. "Your fame as a generous man has spread over the world," said the old man. "And I wish to have proof of your generosity."

Karna remembered his dream, but gave no sign that he did. He only said quietly, "Tell me what you want, and I shall not refuse it to you, for I have never refused any man anything!" Then the Brahmin asked Karna to make him a gift of his earrings and armour.

Karna had expected this. "They shall be yours," he answered, and without a moment's hesitation he cut off his earrings and unlocked his armour and gave him both.

Hardly had he done so, when Karna saw a change come over the old man; he was transformed into a shining being, wearing a jewelled crown and dressed in garments of silk and gold.

"I am Indra," he said. "The King of the Gods."

"Do you think I did not see through you?" thought Karna scornfully, but he said nothing. Indra went on, "Your generosity has filled me with wonder and joy, and it shall not go unrewarded. Therefore, in return for what you have done for me, Karna, you may ask from me whatever gift you will and it shall be yours."

Karna answered, smiling a little, "There is only one thing I desire, and that is your Brahmastra. In return for my earrings and my armour, Lord Indra, give me your Brahmastra, the weapon that never fails!" Indra was taken aback. No mortal had ever touched the Brahmastra before, for it was Indra's special weapon. Whoever possessed it became invincible, and more than that, could destroy the entire earth and all the other worlds besides. The Brahmastra was not a weapon for mortal men; Indra tried to explain this to Karna. "Ask for any other gift, Karna," he begged. But Karna shook his head. "If I cannot have the Brahmastra I will have nothing!" he said stubbornly. In the end Indra had to yield.

"You will have the Brahmastra," he said, "since you have set your heart on it, and since I cannot go back on my word, but you will have it to use only once. You shall destroy with it only one enemy and no more. And when that enemy has been destroyed the Brahmastra will be powerless."

Then he placed the Brahmastra weapon in Karna's hands and vanished.

Karna laughed with joy. He looked at the shining beauty of the weapon and cried out: "With this weapon of Indra shall Arjuna be destroyed!"

For Karna knew that the day would come when the Kauravas and Pandavas would meet in a great war when, once and for all, their bitter feuds would be settled. He knew that Arjuna was his special enemy. The other Pandavas were as nothing to him. His heart longed for a duel with Arjuna, the greatest warrior in the land. His one desire was Arjuna's defeat. To this end all his thoughts and actions were directed. For this reason Karna, disregarding the Sun God's advice, had parted with his earrings and his coat of mail, so that he might bargain for the unfailing Brahmastra. And now he had it and it was his to use. True, he could use it only once. A second chance would not be given him. But what of that? Karna's heart leaped when he thought of the time when he would use it.

But first he must perfect himself in the entire field of archery and find a Guru as great as Drona.

Karna knew that there was only one person in the world who could equal Drona, and that was Parashurama. Indeed, it was said that Drona himself had been Parashurama's pupil. But Karna knew also that Parashurama, who was a Brahmin, hated all Kshatriyas and would have nothing to do with them. He thought over the matter and in the end he went to Parashurama's hermitage disguised as a Brahmin. The unsuspecting Parashurama received Karna and agreed to be his teacher, and Karna lived undiscovered for several years in his hermitage. He served the fiery-tempered sage well, and Parashurama gave him instruction in return.

During all that time Karna guarded his secret, and no man knew him for a Kshatriya.

The day came at last when Karna, having mastered the secret mantra, reached the end of his long course of study. But on that fateful day, Parashurama discovered Karna's secret.

Parashurama was sleeping that afternoon, his head resting upon Karna's lap, when a wood-borer settled upon Karna's thigh and stung

38

him. Not wishing to disturb the master, Karna remained still and unmoving in spite of the pain. The insect continued to sting him until it had bored a hole in his flesh. The blood began to flow, but Karna sat on without wincing, for he had been taught that it is wrong to disturb a sleeping man, especially a teacher. Karna allowed the blood to flow and the insect continued to bore into his flesh.

As last the teacher woke up from his sleep. Parashurama saw the blood flowing down Karna's thigh. It had made a little pool on the ground. Greatly concerned, Parashurama asked his pupil what had happened. When he discovered how the insect had bored through the youth's flesh, Parashurama was aghast. He questioned Karna, who respectfully explained that he had remained still to avoid disturbing his teacher. Parashurama stared at him in amazement. Then slowly a look of comprehension came into his eyes. He continued to scrutinize the young man before him. He was thinking, "Only a Kshatriya can bear pain as this youth has borne it. For the Kshatriyas are trained from childhood to endure pain without murmuring. This youth can never be a Brahmin! He must be a Kshatriya!"

Suddenly he pointed a finger at Karna. "You have tricked me!" he shouted, his eyes blazing with anger. "You have deceived me! You are a Kshatriya—you have tried to get knowledge from me under false pretences! Go away before I reduce you to ashes!"

Karna hung his head. He had spent long years in patient and painstaking study. He had undergone many hardships and humiliations to learn the secret. He had come at last to the end of his long and arduous course, and now he had betrayed himself. He knew Parashurama would never forgive him. He stood before his teacher, humble and speechless, as Parashurama's voice, shrill with anger, fell upon his ears.

"A curse on you for your falsehood!" shrieked the old man. "May all you have learnt here be lost upon you. May all your efforts fail!"

Karna turned pale as he saw his hopes crashing about him. A man of truth, he had been caught in an act of falsehood. Karna fell at the teacher's feet, begging forgiveness, and Parashurama was mollified when he saw how deeply his pupil repented. His curse still lay upon the unhappy youth's head, and yet Parashurama softened it a little. "Go from here," he said, his voice sharp with mockery. "You have learnt much and been a good pupil. The knowledge you have received will be lost indeed, but only in that critical hour when you need it the most!"

Karna arose, heavy-hearted. Then with a last gesture of reverence and farewell he turned sadly away to go. The teacher's voice seemed to ring in his ears. Ill-luck seemed to dog his footsteps. Fate seemed to be against him, everywhere and in all things. Then he felt the shining weapon of Indra in his hands and his spirits rose.

"Arjuna!" he thought, gazing at the Brahmastra. "Here lies your destruction, here in my hands."

9
Duryodhana Plots Again

The happenings at the tournament were only straws in the wind. For, during their early years, the Kauravas never ceased to hate their cousins. Duryodhana brooded constantly. Anything that went well for the Pandavas was something evil for him. And Bhima did not improve matters with his loud bantering and his sneering, outspoken words. Duryodhana never forgave Bhima for what had happened on the day of the tournament. Besides, he feared greatly the growing strength of the Pandavas and their popularity with the people.

During this time Duryodhana found himself surrounded by evil advisers. Small-minded, wicked men, watching Duryodhana's discontent, saw an opportunity to raise themselves in the royal favour. The prince took these people for his friends because they flattered him and spoke as he wished, while he rejected the wise advice of men like Bhishma and Drona who were frank and did not hesitate to point out his faults.

As for his parents, they were good people, but they loved their son with a foolish, doting love and could not bear to deny him anything. That was how he had grown into a headstrong boy; and now he would take no advice from anyone, except when it agreed with what he wanted. Besides, Dhritarashtra himself was uneasy about the growing strength of his nephews.

Duryodhana's false friends whispered to him that his cousins were surely not immortal. They hinted that their death could surely be brought about if one were patient and cunning! They spoke of ways, of how enemies could be done away with if they became inconvenient, and Duryodhana, listening carefully, was heartened. Presently he and his friends put their heads together and plotted a dark and evil deed.

But all this while, the Pandavas were not sleeping. They too were vigilant. Their spies went about the palace, mingled with many people and kept their eyes and ears open, but gave no sign that they saw or heard anything. Thus, the Pandavas came to know that another plot was hatching, a deeper one this time, and more carefully laid. It was intended to catch, at one stroke, the five of them as well as their widowed mother. And so, one day when Duryodhana came up to them beaming and smiling, to tell them of a festival planned at Varnavata, the Pandavas were not without misgivings. But they gave no outward sign of them. The people of Varnavata loved them, said Duryodhana. They waited to welcome them to their city. He himself had given orders that a most beautiful and wonderful palace was to be built for them to live in. "See for yourselves," he added, and he brought them before Dhritarashtra, the king, who also urged them to go.

When they were alone, the Pandavas discussed the matter among themselves and with Vidura, their uncle. They knew very well that Duryodhana's motives could not be honest, but they also knew it would be more dangerous to stay than to go. In the end, they decided to leave. But they watched and listened carefully. On the day before their departure, Vidura came to them with important information. He had discovered Duryodhana's evil plot. In low whispers and using many secret code words, he told them that the palace of pleasure Duryodhana had built for them at Varnavata was in fact a palace of death. For it was made of wax, and within its walls and in many secret places the builders had hidden inflammable materials. Duryodhana's plot was to trap them inside a burning house. One day the palace would catch fire and no one would know it was not an accident. The Pandavas would be sleeping inside and they would be trapped.

Vidura begged his nephews not to panic. "Be brave and calm," he said. "Give no sign that you know. Only wait and watch every minute of the day and night." He went on to tell them how his own workmen had mingled unnoticed with Duryodhana's and noted down every detail of the palace of wax. They were building a secret underground passage which would lead out of that terrible palace into the forest outside. Vidura told the Pandavas that they must watch for the day when the passage would be completed, for it would be their means of escape. He said that he had also employed a skilled miner who would give them the password and warn them.

The Pandavas went to Varnavata and found that Vidura had spoken the truth. For as they walked about the palace, they saw that it was planned to trap them if its wax-and-straw filled walls caught fire. In their hearts they thanked their good uncle and blessed him, remembering how already, even at this very moment, the underground passage was being dug.

Bearing in mind Vidura's warning, the Pandavas spent their days and nights watching and making plans for their escape. Outside Varnavata was a dense forest through which flowed the river Ganga. Beyond the river, the country was even more thickly forested. Few people had set their feet in that land.

The five Pandava princes rode every day through the forest and secretly acquainted themselves with all the paths and tracks. They saw with satisfaction where Vidura's workmen had cut the subterranean passage, working from the forest and digging through the earth until they reached the palace.

For a whole year the Pandavas lived in Varnavata while Duryodhana waited and watched. He was in no hurry to carry out his wicked scheme; this time he did not want to fail. Morever, he wished to lull all suspicion and make it appear to the world as if he had nothing to do with their ghastly death.

The Pandavas waited too and watched. Secretly, from time to time, Vidura sent them word about the happenings in court. "You must fly," Vidura's messengers warned them, "for Duryodhana hates you, and will try every means to destroy you if you return. You must fly and hide yourselves until your evil days have passed. Take refuge in the forest. Disguise yourselves. Let Duryodhana think you are dead."

One day, word reached Yudhishthira and his brothers that on a certain night, the palace of wax would be set on fire. Thereupon the Pandavas set to work to complete their own plans for escape. That night Kunti prepared a great feast, and invited all the inmates of the palace to share it. But the Pandavas had seen to it that the food and the wine were drugged. The guards and the servants fell into a heavy stupor. They did not stir as the Pandavas crept softly down the narrow steps of the underground passage. At a safe distance from the palace, the princes signalled to their friends, who instantly set fire to the palace. As the great structure went up in flames, the citizens hurried about trying to put out the fire. But the flames only rose higher, and within a few hours the palace was reduced to a heap of ashes. When morning came, people searched through the ruins and found many charred bodies. These were the bodies of Duryodhana's servants. But the people of Varnavata wept for the Pandavas, believing them to be dead.

When word reached Hastinapura of the fire and Duryodhana heard that charred bodies had been found, his wicked heart rejoiced, though outwardly he made a great show of grief. In the palace there were many who wept sincerely for the Pandavas, and Duryodhana mingled his false tears with theirs.

Meanwhile, the Pandavas and their mother fled through the underground passage, emerging at its other end in the fearful forest. It was pitch dark and the weird tree-shapes seemed like demons. All around them was the fearsome screech of strange birds, and the roaring of wild animals. When Kunti trembled with fear, her sons consoled her with loving words. But there was little time to waste.

Hurriedly they set out upon that desolate and frightful journey, and walked without resting for long, weary hours. At last, they reached the river Ganga, which they crossed in a boat that the kindly and ever-watchful Vidura had kept there for them.

42

On the other side of the river was a strange country, a dark forest region where no man had ever set foot. Overhead, the branches of the trees were so thick that the sun's light could scarcely pierce through. The ground was marshy and infested with deadly creatures. As the Pandavas walked through this wild country, their feet grew tired and Kunti drooped with fatigue. But they dared not stop, for fear they might be detected.

Bhima, the strongest of them all, went ahead and broke the branches to make way for the rest. He searched through the forest to find them food and water. Often he lifted his frail mother in his arms and carried her through the forest. Indeed, Bhima's strength was so great that he could carry all five of them.

As they journeyed they had many adventures. One day, Bhima went in search of water for his thirsting family and came upon a young woman beside a pool. This woman was really the demon queen Hidimbi who lived with her brother Hidimba in the forest. Unnoticed by them, Hidimbi had kept track of the wanderers. She had, in fact, fallen in love with Bhima. Now, Hidimbi came to Bhima, confessed her love and begged him to take her as his wife. Bhima was greatly pleased. But before he could marry her, he had to fight her brother, who was very angry that his sister had chosen a human creature as her husband. There was a terrible duel between the two in which Bhima vanquished Hidimbi's brother and killed him.

Then Bhima returned to his mother and brothers with his bride. Hidimbi proved a valuable friend to them, for she knew the forest well. She brought them food, attended to their needs and stood on guard while they slept. So strong was this good demon wife of Bhima's that she sometimes carried them upon her big, powerful shoulders. In her gruff voice she told them amusing stories and they grew to like her very much indeed. As for Bhima, he loved her dearly and was full of joy when he heard that soon she would bear him a child. Eventually, the Pandavas reached the city of Ekachakrapura. But Hidimbi could not leave the forest which was her home and her kingdom. She tried to persuade Bhima to stay with her in the forest but Bhima could not leave his brothers and his mother. So, the husband and the wife sadly bid each other good-bye. Some time later, Hidimbi bore Bhima's child, the valiant Ghatotkacha, but it was many years before the father was united with his son.

A Silent City

A strange gloom enshrouded the city of Ekachakrapura. There were no sounds of chattering or laughter, and the people walked as if bowed down with some terrible burden. It was a silent city, and each person seemed to carry a mysterious sorrow.

The Pandavas moved unrecognised among the people, and reached the house of a poor potter who offered them a room. Here they lived for several months.

One day, Kunti heard a great noise of weeping and wailing from the potter's family. Hurrying to see them, she persuaded them to tell her the reason for their sorrow. They told her that Ekachakrapura was under the sway of a demon named Bakasura who had come from the forest one day and gone about the city looting and pillaging, killing people and devouring them. The king of Ekachakrapura and all his ministers had fled, leaving the citizens to defend themselves as best they could. The fear-stricken citizens had finally made an agreement with the demon. Daily, they would send him one human being and a quantity of food in a bullock cart. The citizen, the food and the bullocks made up Baka's meal, while the empty cart was brought back for the next trip. "Tomorrow it is my family's turn," said the potter in anguish. "One of us must go—and leave the rest to mourn. There is no one who can help us, good mother."

Kunti slipped away and returned to her room. In the evening, when her sons came home, she related to them what she had heard, and told them how the shadow of death was falling at that moment upon the little house where they lived. When Bhima heard the story, he resolved to go in place of the potter and meet the monster Baka. He was confident he could destroy the demon.

At first the brothers were reluctant to let Bhima go. They feared that they would be discovered and that Duryodhana would come to know their whereabouts. But after a while they agreed that Bhima should fight the tyrant. "Are we not Kshatriyas? Is is not our duty to protect the defenceless?" they argued among themselves.

The potter and his family were overwhelmed when they heard of Bhima's offer. "How shall we ever show you our gratitude?" they cried.

"By silence!" said the Pandavas gravely. "Speak no word about it to anyone, and thus we shall know that you are grateful."

The next morning Bhima drove the bullock cart with its vast quantity of food to the cave where Bakasura lived. He was very hungry after his long ride and, without further ceremony, fell to eating the food meant for the demon. As he ate he called out in his great bellowing voice, "Baka, evil one, devourer of human flesh, where are you? Come out and show yourself! Your food is here."

At this, a tremendous roar was heard from inside the dark cavern. "Who dares to call me by name?" cried Baka. "I do," laughed Bhima. "Come and see for yourself. But of course, you may take your time, for in the meanwhile, I will finish your dinner for you. It is uncommonly good and I am hungry."

"Dinner? Dinner?" bellowed the demon in a mad rage. "Who are you, fool, that speaks to me in such words?" He had never been addressed so insolently, and he was as surprised as he was angry.

"Come and see for yourself," roared Bhima. "I am only a poor human being, sent to be served up for your dinner."

A deafening cry rent the air. The earth shook violently. Slowly, the fiery-eyed monster emerged from the cave.

Baka was a huge, ugly creature towering above the trees. His face and body were covered with coarse red hair and sharp, long fangs like those of an animal hung out of his mouth in a fearful grin. His breath was foul and his eyes were bloodshot. Bhima looked up at the ugly monster and calmly went on eating. He scooped up a mouthful of rice and spoke to the beast. "Will you wait till I finish dinner? It is hardly fair to disturb a man while he is eating." For a second, Baka gaped at him in wide-eyed surprise. Then with a loud howl, he charged at Bhima, and began to rain blows upon his back while he ate.

"Ah!" said Bhima at each blow, "that feels good; it makes the food go down better!" And he went on eating with great relish. Then he washed down the food with a full goblet of wine, and burped aloud to show his appreciation and satisfaction. "That was quite a good meal," said Bhima as he wiped his mouth with the back of his large hand, while Baka rushed about, up and down and round and round, working himself into a wild rage.

"Come now, Baka! I am ready. Shall we fight?" Bhima roared out. In reply, Baka threw a big tree at Bhima. But Bhima brushed it away, as he would have done a troublesome insect.

"Oh, surely not this children's game, Baka!" he smiled. "You will not refuse me a hand-to-hand fight?" Baka did not answer. He continued to hurl trees at him. Then suddenly he changed his tactics and lunged at Bhima. With one blow Bhima sent the demon reeling far from him. Baka came right back and the two of them grappled and wrestled until the earth shook. They fought many rounds but, at the end of each, Bhima threw Baka down. Again and again, Baka returned to the fight, until at length Bhima caught him and broke his back.

A little dazed but otherwise not much the worse for his adventure, Bhima returned to Ekachakrapura. They garlanded him and adorned his forehead with vermilion powder. Bhima pledged them to secrecy, saying, "That's all you can do for us in return," and the grateful potter gave him his word to keep silent.

46

Draupadi's Swayamvara

All through the days of their absence, the Pandavas kept in touch with Hastinapura. Faithful friends came secretly from time to time to visit them and inform them of events at the royal court and in the country.

That was how, soon after the slaying of Bakasura, news reached them that King Drupada of Panchala (whom Arjuna had once captured in battle) was inviting the princes of the land to the Swayamvara of his daughter, Princess Draupadi. A Swayamvara was usually a ceremony at which a girl chose her husband from a gathering of suitors. King Drupada, however, proposed to hold a contest whose winner would be given Draupadi in marriage. When the Pandavas heard the news, they knew that the time had come to reveal themselves. They decided to travel to Kampilya, Drupada's capital, and take part in the contest. So they said goodbye to the kind potter and his family and, disguising themselves as poor Brahmins, set out on their journey. On their way they mingled with other Brahmins bound for the same destination, and, upon arriving in Kampilya, went to live in a humble quarter of the city.

The city of Kampilya was bustling with preparations for the royal marriage. The streets were festooned with flowers and leaves. Thousands of little wick lamps illuminated the night. In the bazaars, trade was lively and brisk because thousands of visitors had thronged the city to be present at the royal Swayamvara. Everywhere there was talk of the contest in which the greatest warriors in the land would take part. The festivities would continue for sixteen days. In Drupada's palace, his royal guests were entertained with sumptuous food and rare wines, with song and dance, puppetry and drama, with athletic feats and hunting trips. For Draupadi was the king's only daughter, and he loved her so much that he would spare nothing for her happiness. In his heart, Drupada still secretly hoped that Arjuna was not dead but would come to the Swayamvara and claim the royal princess.

Great and powerful princes and chieftains from all over the country came to Kampilya, and Drupada knew just why. Beautiful as Draupadi was, he knew that it was not her beauty alone that brought the princes to compete for her hand. He was aware that the kings who had assembled there had come to win his friendship and support, and to strengthen themselves by an alliance with him. For Drupada was strong and powerful, and Panchala was a force to be reckoned with.

The sixteenth day was the day of the Swayamvara. Drupada had arranged, high above a pool of water, a set of revolving wheels, and placed a fish beyond it. The winner would be the one who could shoot five darts, one after another, through the exact centre of the wheels into the eye of the fish. The contestant could not look directly at his target; instead, he was to shoot looking at its reflection in the water. Duryodhana, his friend Karna, Jarasandha, the king of Kashi, Krishna and his brother Balarama, king of the Vrishnis, Shishupala, Shalya and many others were present in the distinguished gathering. But nobody knew the Pandavas as they stood disguised as humble Brahmins, chanting hymns and collecting alms in their begging bowls.

At the auspicious hour, the royal elephant carrying the princess was led in by Draupadi's twin brother, Dhrishtadyumna. All who were assembled saw with wonder the beauty of the princess. She was dark as a rain cloud and her skin was clear and smooth. Under thick, brooding lashes her large black eyes shone like twin stars. Her mouth was full and proud. And though, as was thought right for an unmarried girl, she lowered her gaze before the people, there was pride in her noble bearing, and a queenly dignity about her, in spite of her tender years.

Dhrishtadyumna led the elephant round the enclosure where the royal guests sat and called out each man's name, his family and clan and the name of the kingdom over which he ruled. As Draupadi passed before them in all her youthful beauty, each prince felt his heart beat faster. Each vowed to himself to win her for his bride. But when they went to shoot, one after the other, the warriors failed in the task that Drupada had set them, and returned crestfallen and ashamed to their places. When Karna, king of Anga walked up and took the bow, five humble Brahmins held their breath and looked at each other with anxious eyes, while the assembled kings waited tensely in their seats. They felt that now the contest would surely end for, as an archer, Karna was considered second to none. Karna drew the mighty bow; but as his dart was about to fly, the voice of Princess Draupadi rang out and broke the silence.

"Wait!" she commanded sharply. "I will not wed a charioteer's son. I am a royal princess—I will not have a low caste man contesting for my hand!" Her voice dripped with scorn as she pronounced the word "charioteer". Karna flinched and put down the bow. The arrow slipped from his fingers. He retired to his seat, humiliated. Once again Karna felt cheated out of his chance. Once again, just at the moment when it seemed that he would succeed, luck had deserted him!

Now, a Brahmin youth stepped into the arena.

He called himself a Brahmin, but even in his humble attire he held himself as proud as any Kshatriya and walked like a prince. The princess saw him and held her breath. The youth was Arjuna, but no one knew him in his lowly dress. He came forward, seeking permission to enter the contest, and Drupada, after a moment's hesitation, assented.

The proud Kshatriya princes moved uneasily in their seats; they did not like to be challenged by a Brahmin. Many among them grew sullen

and murmured that Drupada should not allow such irregularities. "These contests are for Kshatriyas, and people of royal blood," they said. But Arjuna, as he stood in the arena, noticed nothing. He drew the great bow and took careful aim—and the darts he sent flew like lightning through the revolving circles and struck the fish in the centre of the eye. As he did so, Arjuna heard the joyful applause break over his head. And yet there were some who did not join the general acclamation. For on their golden thrones, many of the princes began to murmur to each other, saying "What kind of Swayamvara is this, where a beggar is allowed to stand beside a prince and compete? Drupada seems to have invited us only to shame us. Shall we not punish him for bringing disgrace on us?" They looked on with displeasure as the princess descended from the elephant and, led by her brother, stepped forward to garland the winner.

By now, loud angry voices filled the air. "Who is this impostor? This Brahmin cub? What right does a Brahmin have to compete with warriors? Drupada, you have played foul! We have been humiliated!" Arjuna saw the Kshatriya princes, their faces dark with anger, approach Drupada, shaking their fists and brandishing their weapons. Drupada fell back before their numbers. Arjuna, Bhima and Dhrishtadyumna rushed to his aid and protected him from the anger of the princes. Meanwhile, Yudhishthira, fearing they would be recognised, had slipped away with Nakula and Sahadeva. The fighting slowly subsided and the princes started leaving in anger. Among them was Krishna. Watching keenly, he guessed that things were not what they seemed. He smiled a little as he whispered to his brother Balarama, "There is more to this drama than meets the eye, my brother!"

"Why do you say so?" asked Balarama. Krishna's eyes twinkled as he answered, "Because these Brahmin brothers we have seen today are not Brahmins at all. Did you think that those arrows were the arrows of peaceable, gentle-hearted scholars?"

"Who then do you think the young men are?" Balarama persisted.

Krishna leaned close and whispered in his ear, "That one is Arjuna, the Pandava prince: none other. And that mighty one there is Bhima."

"But the Pandavas are dead!" exclaimed Balarama in astonishment. "Did they not die in the burning house at Varnavata many months ago? Duryodhana planned it, I am told."

Krishna shook his head. "Mark my words, brother. These men are the Pandavas. Do not ask why or how I know. Wait and see. The drama is only about to begin!" Then he put his forefinger to his lips and would not say another word.

At the end of the festivities, Arjuna and Bhima left the assembly quietly with Princess Draupadi, declining the escort that Drupada offered them. But Drupada himself, suspecting that things were not what they seemed, was anxious to know about the family his daughter had married into. He sent his son, Dhrishtadyumna, secretly behind them.

Dhrishtadyumna followed them to the threshold of a lowly house. "Mother, see what alms we have got today!" they said. From inside the house a woman's voice came in answer, "My sons, share whatever you have equally among all five of you." At this they gasped and cried out, "Oh, Mother, what is this you have commanded us to do?"

Then Dhrishtadyumna saw a gentle-faced, grey-haired woman come out to greet them. "We have won a bride and you have asked us to share her among ourselves!" said her two sons in dismay, while she embraced the princess and drew her inside.

Dhrishtadyumna observed how the five sons, in obedience to their mother's words, decided to take Draupadi, his sister, for their joint wife. And from where he lay crouched down, he heard them talk till far into the night and describe and discuss the happenings of the evening. Such was their talk and so full was it of soldiers' expressions and knowledge of weapons and of war, that Dhrishtadyumna knew these men to be true warriors and princes. The knowledge filled him with joy. He returned to the palace and reported everything to his father,

Drupada. The king was overjoyed, for he quickly realised that these unknown mysterious brothers could only be the Pandava princes.

Drupada speedily sent messengers with Dhrishtadyumna to welcome the Pandavas and bring them to his royal palace, where he celebrated the marriage of his daughter to all five of them. They stayed with him at his court and met the other kings who had come at Drupada's invitation to the wedding. Among these was Krishna of Dwaraka. When Yudhishthira came before Krishna and spoke to him, he realised that here was one who, because of his wisdom, was greater than all the kings in the world. Deep in his heart he worshipped Krishna, and loved and honoured him. Ever afterwards, Yudhishthira and his brothers put all their hope and trust in Krishna, who remained their wise counsellor and their greatest friend.

The Pandavas found themselves now surrounded by powerful and wise allies. The news of their marriage to Draupadi and their alliance with Krishna and Drupada spread rapidly. It was not long before it reached the royal court of Hastinapura. Duryodhana was livid with rage when he heard it.

"Oh miserable fate!" cried Duryodhana, weeping angry tears. "What is the use of living? For the Pandavas are alive, and that poisons the air I breathe!" He would not eat or play or take pleasure in anything. His friend Karna sat by him. Karna was not much happier than Duryodhana, for he too had no love for the Pandavas. Indeed, the remembrance of Draupadi's scorn and his public humiliation still rankled in his mind.

"We must destroy the Pandavas," moaned Duryodhana. "How shall we do it? We must seek some way to make them quarrel among themselves and destroy one another. If they stay united, they will destroy us!"

Karna shook his head. He did not think it possible that the five

52

brothers would ever quarrel; they loved each other too well for that. Besides, they were shrewd men and had grown wise to the ways of the world. They knew Duryodhana and did not trust him.

"Let us bribe Drupada!" suggested Duryodhana. "Let us make him our friend. Let us break this alliance they have made."

"Sooner try to break the hand of fate!" laughed Karna without mirth. "These are childish schemes, friend Duryodhana. The Pandavas will never be taken in by them."

"What other course is left to us then, Karna?" cried Duryodhana, wringing his hands, and Karna answered, like the warrior he was, "Fight them face to face. Meet them in battle and overcome them or die in the attempt. That is the best way and it is the Kshatriya's way."

But when Duryodhana went before Bhishma, Drona and Vidura with his suggestion, the elders advised him differently. "Are you mad, Duryodhana, that you wish to destroy your cousins? Do you not see that by following this path you will bring about your own destruction? Your thoughts are neither good nor wise. Already the people of the kingdom blame you and murmur against you, suspecting that the fire in Varnavata was your doing. They wait to welcome the Pandavas into the capital, and their anger will turn against you if you try to harm your cousins."

"What do you wish me to do then?" Duryodhana exclaimed bitterly, hating them in his heart, yet knowing he could not go against their advice.

"Send an escort to the court of Drupada and welcome your cousins home again," Drona advised him. "Make friends with them and do what is right and just by them. Make amends for the wrongs they have suffered at your hands."

It was a bitter pill for Duryodhana to swallow. But he dared not go against their word. He was furious and made no secret of his feelings. But he finally agreed to send a message to the Pandavas at Kampilya. Vidura happily consented to go with the messengers and invite the Pandavas back.

But Drupada would not permit his sons-in-law to leave. For he feared this was still another murderous ruse of Duryodhana's. He laid down many conditions that Duryodhana must fulfil before the Pandavas would go to Hastinapura. It was only when Vidura assured him that Duryodhana would be bound by his promises, and when Krishna himself declared it wise for them to go, that Drupada gave his consent.

So the Pandavas returned once more to Hastinapura bringing with them the lovely dark princess who was their bride. Once again the citizens of Hastinapura poured out joyfully into the streets to welcome them.

12

Imperial Indraprastha

The elders in the court of Dhritarashtra advised the blind old king to make peace with the Pandavas and to give them what rightly belonged to them. So, when the five brothers came before him, Dhritarashtra welcomed them and congratulated them on their escape from the burning house and on their marriage to the Panchala princess, Draupadi. Then he gave them a small tract of land called Khandavaprastha, some distance away from Hastinapura. It was a barren place, desolate and uninhabited. By day the land lay dusty and dry under the burning sun, and at night jackals came out of their lairs, and filled the silence with a weird howling. People said that this land was the resting place of demons and ghosts, and avoided it in fear. This was the land that Dhritarashtra presented to his nephews. In his heart he hoped he had seen the last of the Pandavas.

The blind king was secretly pleased with his plan and relieved that Yudhishthira did not complain about the injustice of their treatment. He wanted the Pandavas both out of sight and out of harm's way.

The Pandava princes, with their mother and a few faithful followers, set out for their new home. Far from being deceived, they knew well the difficulties they would encounter. But they had stout hearts and great faith, and wished at all costs to avoid a quarrel with their cousins.

When they reached their destination, they set about planning and organising the construction of their capital city. Yudhishthira spared himself neither trouble nor money for this great work; he sent for the master town-builders and architects of the time. As news of the venture spread, more people came looking for work—engineers, sculptors and carvers, painters and landscape gardeners, as well as masons, bricklayers, carpenters and tradesmen. What was once a silent, lonely desert, now became the scene of busy human activity. A city grew; a beautiful and noble city, set amid green parks and wooded gardens. People quickly settled down there and set up trades which grew and prospered. Others cultivated the land that lay outside the city. Kind weather favoured them and, with hard work, they found that the soil was not as poor as it had seemed to be. They reaped good harvests and sold the produce in the capital at fair and honest prices.

Yudhishthira, young though he was and without experience, proved himself to be a very capable and energetic ruler, devoted to the welfare of his subjects. He set up a wise administration, appointing honest and efficient ministers, and together they made the laws of the land. So just

and wise were these laws that men saw no reason to break them. Yudhishthira's kingdom therefore became known for the honest and law-abiding nature of its people.

Visitors to the kingdom were full of wonder, and went back with marvellous stories of the magnificent new city, Indraprastha. For this was the name Yudhishthira gave to his capital.

As the years went by, more and more people from the surrounding areas began to acknowledge Yudhishthira as their sovereign. Tribute filled the royal coffers, in return for friendship and protection. Throughout, Drupada, the king of Panchala, and Krishna, of Dwaraka, remained the young king's trusted friends and advisers. Yudhishthira sent his brothers to the four corners of the country to extend his empire and influence.

At this stage, friends began to advise him to perform the Imperial Sacrifice, the Rajasuya Yagna, and proclaim himself emperor of the country.

But Yudhishthira knew that he must be sure of his strength before he could perform the Rajasuya sacrifice and call himself emperor. If any ruler challenged his right to this title, there would be trouble and war. Failure or defeat would easily make him an object of ridicule and scorn, and a prey to the schemes of jealous enemies. He spoke to Krishna about the matter.

Krishna told him that there was one king in the country who would challenge his right to empire—Jarasandha, king of Magadha. Jarasandha was a tyrant and a threat to the whole world. Eighty-six princes captured by him in war lay in his prisons. Jarasandha had to be defeated before Yudhishthira could claim the title of sovereign of the earth. But the peace-loving Yudhishthira drew back at the thought of enmity with another. He had no wish to pick quarrels with his neighbours. "Let us give up the idea of the Rajasuya," he reasoned.

But Bhima and Arjuna thought differently. The quiet life of peace they led irked them, and they longed for action. They felt that it was their duty as Kshatriyas to make war upon the wicked and come to the help of the defenceless, and they told Yudhishthira so. They begged leave to march upon Jarasandha's city.

But Krishna knew better. "Your armies will be driven like chaff before the wind by those of Jarasandha!" he warned.

"What then?" Bhima and Arjuna asked, and were told that Jarasandha must be slain in hand-to-hand combat.

Yudhishthira was greatly distressed to see his brothers so eager for war and power. He himself did not care greatly for foolhardy adventure, for battles and quarrels. But Krishna argued long and persistently and pointed out the danger of allowing evil to grow in this world. Reluctantly, Yudhishthira agreed to accompany Krishna and his brothers to Jarasandha's royal city, Girivraja.

As they travelled in disguise to Magadha, Krishna told the Pandava brothers the strange story of its ruler. Jarasandha, it was said, had been born not whole, as other people, but in two halves. A medicine-woman named Jara had magically joined the two pieces together and restored the child to his grateful parents. Jara had blessed him with long life and superhuman strength. All men would fear him, she said. No weapons would touch him and he would excel in wrestling and in feats of strength.

But there would be one flaw in Jarasandha's strength; his body, which was made up of two separate halves, could easily fall apart. But, as often as his body was torn in two, so often would the pieces come together. He would die only if the pieces were so placed that they could never come together again.

Jarasandha grew up into a reckless and wilful man, ambitious for power, greedy for wealth, ruthless and cruel towards all who came in his way. He made war upon his neighbours, and his empire grew steadily in size and strength. So powerful had Jarasandha become that Krishna himself had yielded to him, retreating from his capital city Mathura right to the shores of the western sea, where he established a new capital, Dwaraka. But in the east, Jarasandha's power grew, along with his pride and wicked deeds.

Disguised as Brahmin priests, the Pandava brothers neared the capital of Magadha. Krishna warned them that Jarasandha was strong and cunning and it would not be easy to overpower him.

The gates of Jarasandha's capital were heavily guarded. The king had of late felt a strange anxiety; bad dreams had troubled his sleep, and it had been foretold by soothsayers that the days to come were inauspicious for him and filled with dangers of many kinds. For this reason, he had ordered the gates of the city and royal palace to be closely guarded. He had invited Brahmin priests from far and near to come and perform sacrifices to please the gods. Krishna and the Pandavas made their way past the guards, entered the palace gates and stood among the Brahmins around the sacrificial fire. But as Jarasandha went among his guests, he stopped before the Pandava brothers and looked at them curiously for a long time. These men did not look like Brahmins and men of peace. He noticed that their hands were scarred and blistered, as if by the continual use of weapons of war. His suspicions were roused and he watched them carefully as they moved about. Very soon he guessed the truth. He came to Bhima and laughed. "I have discovered you beneath your disguise, Pandava! And you, Krishna, I have discovered you too. You are indeed at the root of all this!" Then, growing stern, he demanded to know what they wanted from him and why they had come.

"A duel, Jarasandha," cried Bhima, no longer able to keep up the pretence. "I wish to wrestle with you!"

Thus challenged, Jarasandha had no honourable course open to him but to accept, and he did so, for he was no coward.

"Do you think I fear you, you brat?" he sneered, "Come, come! In a few minutes your bones will be ground to powder."

So saying, Jarasandha led them to the arena where wrestling matches were held. Yudhishthira prayed that all would go well; he wished in his

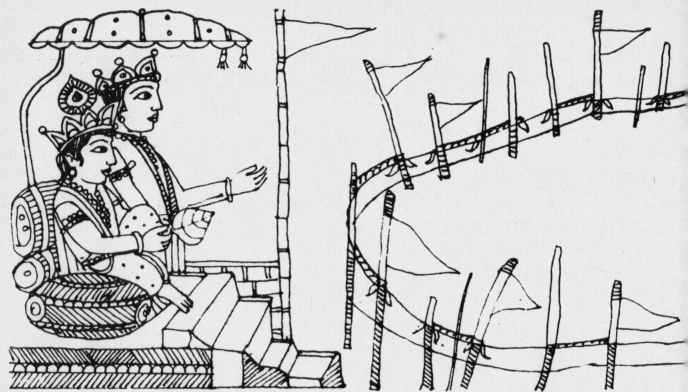

heart that kingship did not carry with it so many burdens. News of the
bout spread quickly and the people flocked in great numbers to see it.

At the given signal, Jarasandha and Bhima advanced towards each
other and came to grips. As they wrestled, it was hard to tell who was
the stronger of the two. Their strength and their skill were so evenly
matched that if now Bhima overcome Jarasandha and threw him upon
the floor, it was not long before Jarasandha dealt with him in similar
fashion. Each evening the heroes would retire, neither victorious and
neither vanquished. Each succeeding morning the wrestling would
continue. Thus it lasted for fourteen days and it seemed that the fight
would never end.

Then one day, something happened; the wrestlers had taken so close
a grip of each other that no one could tell which limb was whose. It
was a tense moment and in the silence there could be heard only their
heavy breathing. Suddenly, Bhima slipped his hand out of Jarasandha's
grip. In a second, he had caught his opponent's foot. He struggled from
Jarasandha's grasp and, quicker than it takes to tell, threw him upon the
floor. Then, with a mighty roar of triumph, he put his foot upon the
fallen Jarasandha, and tearing him into two, flung the pieces away.
"Victory! Victory is ours," he roared. But he cried out too soon. For to
his amazement, he saw the two pieces move closer until they were
joined together.

Jarasandha rose up again, ready to continue the fight. Three times
did Bhima tear Jarasandha into pieces and three times did the pieces

58

join together, making Jarasandha whole again, many times stronger than he had been before. Bhima was nonplussed. He was growing tired. Never had he seen such a monster as this, who, even when torn into two, recovered his life and increased his strength.

Jarasandha laughed. "Surrender, Bhima!" he sneered. "Though I have eighty-six kings in my dungeons, there is still room for more. Nothing would please me better than to spare your life and make you and your brothers my prisoners!"

"I have come here to wrestle, Jarasandha," Bhima roared back, "not to exchange words. Come forward and fight...or have you had enough? Are you tired? If you are, shall I carry you now through the dust, to surrender before your visitors?"

In response, Jarasandha angrily advanced again, his arms stretched out, his bull-like head bent aggressively to the fight. The two of them wrestled many rounds together, until once more Bhima caught his opponent by the legs and tore him into two. At this moment, Krishna made a sign to Bhima. He took a betel leaf between his thumb and finger, tore it into two and crossed his hands, before he threw the pieces away. Bhima took the hint and he too crossed his hands before he threw down the two halves of Jarasandha's body. The pieces moved farther and farther from each other, unable to unite, and Jarasandha breathed his last. Then the Pandavas went down to the dungeons and set free Jarasandha's prisoners. The people of Magadha hailed the Pandavas as saviours who had freed them from their yoke, and blessed them with flowers and festive vermilion powder.

Jarasandha was cremated solemnly by the Pandava brothers. After the period of mourning was over, Yudhishthira placed Jarasandha's son Sahadeva upon Magadha's throne, and the young prince readily acknowledged the Pandava as his overlord.

With Jarasandha dead, the way was open for Yudhishthira to perform the Imperial Sacrifice, the Rajasuya Yagna, for there now remained no one in the country who could challenge him. With powerful allies on all sides, and an empire of many subject states, Yudhishthira felt strong enough to claim the overlordship of the entire country. So he now made preparations for the Rajasuya Yagna. To this great ceremony were invited all the kings and princes of the realm. To refuse the invitation would have been equal to an insult. All the rulers were there, including Duryodhana of Hastinapura, Shakuni of Gandhara and Karna of Anga. Yudhishthira and his brothers welcomed their guests cordially, and showed each of them the honour and respect due to him. Every day there were festivities and ceremonies and celebrations.

On the last day, Yudhishthira was to receive the imperial crown.

But an ugly quarrel broke out which marred the entire celebration. On that day, Yudhishthira, wishing to do homage to each of the assembled princes in turn, according to their rank, led Krishna to the foremost seat of honour. Krishna and Balarama were Yadava princes of Dwaraka. Their friendship with the Pandavas was deep and warm. And when Arjuna won for himself the love and hand in marriage of their sister, Subhadra, this friendship was strengthened further by ties of kinship. But Krishna was not, in that assembly, a king as the others were. It was his brother who was the crowned head of Dwaraka. For that matter, Dwaraka itself was not the foremost of the states represented. Yudhishthira's action therefore, giving Krishna the first place, surprised many people. It seemed to them to be a blunder, and there were several uplifted eyebrows as Krishna was led to the place of honour. But Yudhishthira knew what he was doing. He knew that Krishna was greater than all the people assembled there, though his greatness did not stem from material things like wealth; Krishna did not have the ordinary trappings of power. But Krishna was wise and

60

godly. Yudhishthira felt that it was Krishna's wisdom and goodness that entitled him to the first place in the assembly.

But there was a murmur of protest from among the guests, soft at first and then louder, until Krishna's cousin, Shishupala, king of Chedi, stood up angrily. Shishupala hated Krishna bitterly; he could not bear to see him thus honoured. He broke out into such a volley of angry words against Krishna that the assembled people held their breath in fear. There were some, however, who felt the stir of old jealousies and were secretly pleased.

Yudhishthira looked around him in dismay. After a while, Bhishma arose and held up his hand for silence. He warned Shishupala sternly of the consequences of his behaviour and related to the assembly a prophecy made at Shishupala's birth, that he would one day meet his death at Krishna's hands. Shishupala, he continued, had come into the world with three eyes and four hands. Soothsayers, looking into the future, had predicted an early and violent death for the boy. The slayer, they said, would be the person who would cure him of his deformity. The anxious parents had travelled around the country with the baby.

But no one had been able to cure him. One day his cousin, Krishna, happened to lift the child, and at his touch the boy was cured. But the joy of the parents was clouded as they remembered the prophecy; they knew that Krishna, who had healed their son, would also be his slayer. Shishupala's mother, who was also Krishna's aunt, fell at his feet and begged for mercy. "Though he may wrong you a hundred times, Lord, you must forgive him and spare his life," she sobbed. Krishna gave her his word. "For your sake, gentle lady," he said, "I will forgive him a hundred wrongs. But the day may come when he may offend me once too often and then he will force my hand!"

The sad mother knew then that in fairness she could ask no more.

Shishupala grew up to hate Krishna, who had healed him, as fiercely as only the evil can hate the good. Hearing Bhishma relate his story, Shishupala grew even angrier. He advanced before the assembly and continued to shout against Krishna, insulting him and calling him names. The assembled people sat tensely in their places; a few tried to stop Shishupala, but in vain. Meanwhile, Krishna sat unruffled and silent, looking at the angry youth with calm eyes. Krishna's lips were moving. Shishupala did not know it, but Krishna was counting each insult. When he had reached a hundred, he stood up and held up his hand, commanding Shishupala to stop and warning him of the consequences of not doing so. But Shishupala's hatred had made him reckless. He responded with a dark look and yet another vile term of abuse. At this insult, the hundredth and first, Krishna threw his shining discus at him. Before the eyes of the assembled people, it flew across the great hall, flashing like lightning. Shishupala fell to the floor, his head slashed from his body.

A stunned silence fell upon the assembly. The friends of Shishupala looked fearfully at Krishna, but no one raised a voice, for they knew that the angry young king had brought this calamity upon himself.

Funeral rites due to a warrior and a king were performed at Yudhishthira's command. All the great personages followed Shishupala's bier upon the last journey and mourned for him. He had been a hot-headed and misguided youth, but it could not be denied that he had been a brave prince.

The funeral over, Yudhishthira took up again the performance of the sacrifice which had so rudely been interrupted and the festivities continued to the chanting of hymns and prayers. Holy water was sprinkled upon Yudhishthira's head, his body was anointed with perfumed oil, and he was crowned emperor. The elders who were assembled there came and blessed him, while the younger people did him homage as he sat upon the imperial throne.

But Yudhishthira's heart was heavy and he was full of foreboding. The future seemed dark and uncertain. The killing of Shishupala had been a stain on that beautiful day. Around him he saw the unsmiling faces of his cousins, the Kauravas. There was so much hatred and hostility around him that he began to doubt if, after all, kingship and empire were worthwhile things. He resolved then and there that he, as king or emperor, would never start a quarrel with anyone of his own accord, and would do nothing to provoke a war. Always he would seek to keep the peace, whatever the cost. But still his heart continued to be heavy and uneasy.

The Rajasuya sacrifice completed, the guests went home to their kingdoms. But Duryodhana stayed on in Indraprastha at his cousin's invitation. Yudhishthira showered him with kindness and courtesy and entertained him royally in the palace. He was taken around the capital and shown its wonderful sights. But when Duryodhana saw all the things that the Pandavas had built, when he saw how vast quantities of tribute came from the four corners of the empire to the overlord— gold and silver and pearls and precious stones; perfumes and incense; grains and cereals; metalware and crystal and articles of wood and ivory; silk and muslin cloth; the furs of rare animals, woollen shawls, carpets and leather goods; camels and horses, elephants and peacocks—when Duryodhana saw how hundreds of people waited upon Yudhishthira's word, and how thousands of slaves bent low before him, and how his subjects praised him, honoured him and loved

him, his jealousy flamed afresh like a fire that was fanned to new life.

Duryodhana went about the palace, sulky and out of temper, nursing his anger and self-pity. As he wandered in and out of the corridors, he found that the palace was so vast and cunningly built, that he could not easily find his way around. Its magnificence quite took his breath away, for in all his life he had not seen anything like it. As he wandered, it seemed to him that he saw a pool of water before him. He carefully raised the hem of his clothes to avoid getting it wet; only to find that there was no water, but a floor polished so smooth that it looked wet. Feeling rather foolish, he hoped no one had seen him; but at that moment, Nakula passed by and explained to him carefully that there was no water. Nakula's tone was kind enough, but Duryodhana was sure he saw a glint of amusement in his eyes. Further on, Duryodhana blundered again, mistaking a crystal door for open space and bumping his head into it, so that tears sprang to his eyes—whereupon Bhima suddenly appeared and held the door open for him, looking greatly concerned; but Duryodhana felt that Bhima was really laughing.

A little later, Duryodhana landed with a splash in a lotus pool which he had not seen, and as he came up spluttering and clutching his wet clothes, he heard the giggling of women and saw, behind a latticed door, Draupadi with her ladies-in-waiting. They fled when he saw them, but he heard their laughter following him all the way to his apartment.

Duryodhana gnashed his teeth with rage. The thought of the Pandavas' prosperity was like a thorn in his flesh. Secure on his throne, Yudhishthira had built up a powerful empire and strengthened himself with many alliances.

His power was so great that Duryodhana knew no armed might, could hurt him and bring him down. Yudhishthira had escaped every trap that Duryodhana had laid for him, and now he was emperor. Duryodhana could not sleep for jealousy. Bitter thoughts filled his mind and he had no joy in living.

If only, he thought, if only the Pandavas could be destroyed! How he would love to see Yudhishthira's empire come crumbling down; how he would love to see Yudhishthira and his brothers reduced to beggary! But Duryodhana knew that in the normal course of things, this would never happen.

64

13

The Gambling Match

Duryodhana returned to Hastinapura to his loving parents, to his kingdom and people. But his mood did not improve. Indeed, the sight of his own surroundings, so poor and ordinary in comparison to his cousins', only increased the depth of his misery. Discontent, hatred and envy made him wretchedly unhappy.

And as he brooded in this manner, there came to him a man with the sly, slinking ways of a jackal: Shakuni, Duryodhana's maternal uncle, the brother of Gandhari and the prince of Gandhara. Shakuni did not love Duryodhana, for his nephew had done him much harm. Once, long ago, he had seized Shakuni and his ninety-nine brothers and put them into a prison cell. There they had languished while Duryodhana gloated over their fate. He sent them food that was just enough for one person to live on . When the gaoler brought it, they fell upon it like a pack of wolves—one man's portion for a hundred men! But there was one among them who saw how this would destroy all of them.

"Let such a thing not happen," he said. "Let one man among us be fed and let him live, and one day when ninety-nine of us are gone, this one man will avenge our cruel death." So they cast lots and Shakuni's name was drawn. Then the brothers called out to Shakuni and declared that he must be the one to live and avenge their death. Shakuni wept. One by one he embraced his brothers and solemnly vowed to destroy Duryodhana. Then he ate the single meal that was sent each time, while his brothers died slowly of hunger. One after another they died while he held them in his arms, and with their dying eyes they begged him to remember his promise. Shakuni never forgot. When Duryodhana found that ninety-nine of the princes were dead, he had Shakuni released. Thereafter, Shakuni lived at his nephew's palace.

He moved about the palace corridors like an evil shadow, smirking and whispering as he kept Duryodhana company. He fawned upon Duryodhana and continued to poison his heart and fan his jealousy and anger.

"You must not despair!" he whispered to his nephew. "Yudhishthira and his brothers can be destroyed."

"How?" asked Duryodhana morosely. "They have vast armies and loyal subjects. Their power is much greater than ours."

"Never fear!" answered Shakuni, grinning evilly. "There are other ways of destroying a man. It is true that Yudhishthira will never be defeated on the battlefield, but his downfall can be brought about by cunning."

Duryodhana pricked up his ears and Shakuni drew closer and whispered. "Invite Yudhishthira here for a game of dice. You know that Yudhishthira has a weakness for gambling. I will play for you against him. I will play skilfully and, if necessary, I will cheat. I will stop at nothing to win from Yudhishthira the stakes he will offer; I will goad him into staking all his possessions, even to his kingdom and his subjects. I will bring him to his ruin."

Duryodhana was delighted. It seemed to him an excellent way to lay Yudhishthira low. Then a doubt arose in his mind. He recalled that Yudhishthira, when he became king, had taken an oath never to touch the dice. But Shakuni chuckled, rubbing his hands together. "What is it worth, the oath of a gambler?" he spat contemptuously, and his nephew nodded, smiling in agreement.

And so the two put their heads together and hatched the plot. Yudhishthira was to be persuaded to come to a gambling match. Shakuni was to play against him and, by fair means or foul, win all his possessions. Then, reduced to nothing, Yudhishthira and his brothers were to be driven into exile.

Duryodhana came to his blind old father, Dhritarashtra, seeking his consent to the whole scheme. But, as Dhritarashtra listened to what his son had to say, he grew uneasy and afraid. His conscience told him that what his son planned was neither right nor wise. Yet, the old man was secretly not unwilling to see the plan succeed. He tried at first, though rather half-heartedly, to persuade Duryodhana to change his mind.

But, of course, Duryodhana would not heed the old man. He treated his advice with contempt and brushed it aside. He argued at length with his father to make him believe that what he planned was not wrong. He fretted and fumed and sulked and stormed until at last the weak Dhritarashtra gave him permission to invite Yudhishthira to the gambling match.

66

Duryodhana was beside himself with joy. He had a great hall of pleasure built especially for the match. He ordered a palace to be made for the Pandavas to stay in when they came. Deciding that the best person to take his invitation to the Pandavas was Vidura, Duryodhana had him summoned before Dhritarashtra, and the old king asked Vidura to proceed to Indraprastha. When Vidura heard the reason he was shocked, for he saw through Duryodhana's plan. He spoke out his mind quite frankly and sternly.

"What you seem to be planning is not only wicked but foolish and dangerous as well," he warned.

But Dhritarashtra was weak and stupid, and easily led by his son. Besides, he did not like Vidura, who was only a commoner of humble birth, to tell him, the king, what to do. So he drew himself up haughtily. "Your sovereign commands you," he said coldly from his throne. Vidura bowed his head, for he knew he must obey the word of the king.

As he moved away, Dhritarashtra murmured to him, "This is fate; all is fate. No man can change fate. What has to happen, will happen."

But Vidura sighed heavily and made no answer. He knew that men blame fate when they lack the courage to take the right action. When disaster results, they blame fate when they should, in fact, blame themselves.

Soon afterwards, Vidura set off for Indraprastha. A warm welcome awaited him at the palace of the Pandavas. But Vidura remained sad and spoke little. At last, Yudhishthira asked him what the matter was, and Vidura told him of the invitation he had brought for the gambling match.

Yudhishthira listened gravely.

"Men bring ruin upon themselves by such play," he answered slowly. "Has it not been said that wise men do not play games of chance? Why does Duryodhana seek this kind of war with us? Is it not more honourable for a Kshatriya prince to fight on the battlefield than to gamble at a dice board?"

But even as he spoke these words of wisdom, Yudhishthira was wavering. In his heart, the desire to gamble, which he had held in check for so many years, began to stir again.

His resolution weakened; for Yudhishthira loved the dice. He began to find excuses for breaking the vow he had made years ago never to touch the gambling board again.

"A Kshatriya must not refuse a challenge," he murmured. "It would look like cowardice. And then what harm could there be in an innocent game?" Then again: "It would be awkward to refuse an invitation to play. They would laugh at me for being a coward. Worse, they might be offended and that might lead to the very quarrel I wish to avoid."

"I will come," he said at last. "It will be neither right nor courteous to refuse." His brothers tried to hold him back, but Yudhishthira would not heed their advice. The lure of the gambling board was too strong and he allowed himself to fall into the trap that Duryodhana and Shakuni had set for him.

The dice used in that fateful gambling match were made of the bones of Shakuni's ninety-nine brothers. When they died in prison, and their flesh was reduced to ash, Shakuni whittled their bones, carving them into the most beautiful and seductive dice ever seen. And into the dice had gone the dead men's fierce, hot desire for revenge. Shakuni had kept the dice hidden away until the day of the gambling match.

As the Pandava brothers journeyed to Hastinapura, they were heavy-hearted and anxious, for they knew Yudhishthira's passion for gambling only too well. They knew too that Duryodhana's invitation could not have been prompted by friendly feeling. But Yudhishthira was their king and elder brother. They could only advise him. They could not forbid him to do what he chose.

Yudhishthira was not without his own doubts. He had given in to Duryodhana partly to avoid discourtesy and partly because he loved the game. In the manner of gamblers, he was sure in his mind that he would win. But he was not at all sure whether he was right to have agreed to play.

Duryodhana was all smiles as he welcomed his cousins. He took care to see that they were entertained with all honour.

On the day appointed for the gambling match, the Pandava brothers came to the newly-built hall where all was in readiness for the game. Duryodhana stood waiting impatiently near by. Shakuni stood clutching the dice in his hands. His small eyes gleamed like a rat's. Around the hall sat the men of the great Kuru clan, the royal family and their ministers, the councillors, the teachers and all the high officials. Their faces were full of anxiety as they waited for the drama to begin.

They had all tried to draw Duryodhana away from the evil path he was taking. They had talked to him about the duty and the code of a Kshatriya, reminding him that a true warrior fights on the battlefield and does not seek victory in games of chance. Bhishma had warned him that he was letting loose forces of evil, which would one day bring about his own ruin. "Do you not understand that the result of evil action can only be evil?" he pleaded, speaking to both Duryodhana and Dhritarashtra. But Duryodhana tossed his proud head scornfully. He would have none of the old man's advice. "Yudhishthira has accepted my invitation," he said angrily. "What is wrong with a friendly match?"

Drona and Bhishma now sat with the blind king and watched in silence as the Pandavas came in. Yudhishthira's eyes were troubled as

68

he greeted the assembled people. "Gambling is evil," he murmured. But when Duryodhana taunted him with wanting to back out, Yudhishthira took his seat at the gambling board and called out to Duryodhana to come and begin the game. But Duryodhana answered, "My uncle Shakuni will play for me. I shall sit beside him and his losses will be my losses as his gains will be my gains."

Yudhishthira looked up quickly. "That is not fair," he protested. "This was not part of the agreement. I did not come to play against Shakuni." For Yudhishthira knew how sharp Shakuni was, how cunning and clever and also how unscrupulous. Shakuni cared nothing for principles, for right and wrong. He cared only for his own self-interest. To gain his advantage, Shakuni would stoop to any evil.

Yudhishthira did not wish to play against this shrewd and cunning man.

But Duryodhana laughed and taunted him again, asking if he was afraid of losing. Duryodhana's words were like a challenge to Yudhishthira, as indeed he had meant them to be.

"I am not afraid," said Yudhishthira proudly. "Though you do not play fair, I shall play with you." Duryodhana was pleased. They sat down to play.

Yudhishthira laid his stake upon the board — a necklace of rich and rare pearls. He took the dice and flung them down. Then Shakuni rattled his dice and played. At the end of the first round, Shakuni had won, and Yudhishthira handed the stake over to him. He had lost his pearl necklace, but it did not matter. His treasure-chests were full of money and rare jewels and the game had just begun. At the next round, Yudhishthira staked all the jewellery in his treasury. They played and he lost again.

"The jewels in your treasury are mine," said Shakuni softly. Yudhishthira laughed. The excitement was mounting to his head. Not to be daunted, he played again. He staked the gold and silver in his treasure-houses and these also he lost. One by one, Yudhishthira staked his chariots, his elephants and horses; his cattle; his slaves and his servants. One by one, he lost them all on that luckless day. Shakuni's crafty eyes gleamed. The dice seemed to obey him; he was well pleased. Shakuni was adept at the game and he cheated without shame.

"Will you continue to play?" Duryodhana taunted his cousin as he watched him lose repeatedly. Yudhishthira answered, breathing hard, stung by the mockery in his voice, "Yes, I will continue." For now he was seized with a kind of madness and could not stop. He must win, somehow he would win. He would not give up until he had made good all his losses.

He played again. This time, he pledged the wealth of his kingdom, the villages of his empire and his lordship over his people. And one by one, he began to lose them all.

Day after day the game went on, Yudhishthira pledging his worldly possessions and losing them to Shakuni. Still he would not stop. Then the dark hour came when he had staked and lost all, and had nothing left of his own; he was like a penniless beggar in the street. But even then he would not give up.

His brothers crept up to him slowly and begged, "It is enough, brother! Come, let us go; there is nothing left now to stake."

Yudhishthira hardly heard them. He stretched out his trembling hand for the dice.

"I will still win back all I have lost!" he cried, looking around him wildly. His eyes lighted upon his brothers and suddenly he cried out, "I now pledge my brother, the handsome Sahadeva."

In the hall the people held their breath. A royal prince was being used as a pawn in the game! A human being had been staked as if he were an object! But nothing mattered to Yudhishthira. He seemed to have taken leave of his senses. He rattled the dice in the cup and threw them down—and he lost.

"Ha," chuckled Shakuni softly. "Sahadeva is lost. Now he is our slave!"

Yudhishthira clenched his teeth; no one moved in their seats as Sahadeva was led over to Shakuni. "What will you pledge now? Sahadeva is gone! Will you not try to recover him?" whispered Shakuni leering.

Yudhishthira answered, speaking hosrsely: "I have lost Sahadeva. But Nakula is left. Nakula, who is skilled in the arts; Nakula, who is the best horseman in the country. I pledge Nakula. With him as my stake, I shall win back what I have lost." Nakula came forward, and he too was lost in

70

that desperate game. Shakuni laughed. "The game must stop now!" he taunted Yudhishthira. "Surely you will not pledge your full brothers. You can afford to give away the sons of Madri who are only your half brothers, but naturally the sons of Kunti would be too precious?"

"My brothers are all equally dear to me!" cried Yudhishthira. "Prove it then!" Shakuni challenged and Yudhishthira fell into the trap. "I will pledge Bhima!" he said, "I will prove to you that the sons of Kunti are not dearer to me than the sons of Madri!"

Again they played, with the same result. Bhima too was lost.

Shakuni's eyes glittered with greed. He leaned forward. "And now, Yudhishthira? Who now?"

71

"Arjuna!" cried Yudhishthira, despair in his eyes and cold sweat upon his forehead. His voice sounded high and shrill. His hands trembled violently as he held them out for the dice.

"I will win yet. All that I have lost I will win," he thought desperately.

But he lost Arjuna too.

All his faithful brothers had been pledged and lost, and Yudhishthira was alone.

"Yudhishthira! What now?" Shakuni mocked.

"Myself!" Yudhishthira cried out. "I will pledge myself and win." But when Yudhishthira played, he lost again. Now he and all his brothers were the slaves of Shakuni.

Still Shakuni would not let him stop. He leaned forward and reminded him that there was still Draupadi who had not yet been staked.

"It may be that she will bring you good luck today!" he whispered.

Then the desperate Yudhishthira cried out, his voice choking with sobs, "Draupadi! I pledge Draupadi this time!"

All this while there had been a tense silence in the assembly, and the people had sat looking on helplessly as Yudhishthira gambled away his liberty and that of his brothers. But now the silence was broken with loud shouts of protest.

"No!" they cried out. "For shame, Yudhishthira! Stop the game. Duryodhana! Stop Shakuni! A woman must not be dishonoured."

But Yudhishthira clutched the dice in his hand as a drowning man clutches at a straw. He could not stop now. The blood pounding in his head, his heart racing within him, Yudhishthira played, this time with Draupadi as a stake. And once again he lost.

Then Duryodhana, laughing aloud, commanded Vidura to fetch Draupadi. "From now on she is our slave!" he said. "She shall sweep the palace floors!"

But Vidura refused to go. He spoke out his mind sternly and openly to Duryodhana and warned him of the disaster that would result from his evil ways. Other people spoke too, among whom was Vikarna, the youngest of Duryodhana's brothers, reproaching him for the wrong he was doing.

But Duryodhana's triumph had gone to his head. He would heed no one. Since Vidura would not go, Duryodhana sent his charioteer to fetch Draupadi from her apartments. When the charioteer came before Draupadi, the proud princess refused to go with him.

"Go and tell them," she said, holding her head high, "that Yudhishthira was already a slave when he pledged me. A slave has no rights and no belongings. The instant Yudhishthira became a slave, I ceased to be his wife. Therefore, since I did not belong to him, he had no right to use me as his pawn!"

Gathering up her silken skirts, pride and anger flashing in her dark eyes, Draupadi ordered Duryodhana's charioteer out of the house.

"Go and tell your master I will not come," she said. When Duryodhana heard her message, he commanded his brother Dushahsana to bring Draupadi before the gathering. Dushahsana did not hesitate. At his brother's bidding he swaggered out of the hall, boasting that he would drag the proud Draupadi through the dust and bring her to her knees before them.

He went to Draupadi's apartments, calling out to her mockingly, and followed her into the inner rooms where she fled from him. Catching her by her long, dark hair, he dragged her out of the house, down the steps and through the dust into his chariot. And he brought her thus into the hall before Duryodhana and forced her to her knees before him.

But she, proud woman, rose up again and stood before the assembly, her hair streaming behind her, her large eyes flaming. She spoke to the elders and declared she was no slave, for Yudhishthira had lost his freedom before he had pledged her. And in a clear, ringing voice, she reproached them for the wrongs they were allowing.

But the world seemed to have fallen on evil days, for the elders only bent their heads and her protests went unheeded in that company.

Duryodhana's pride and wickedness had gone beyond all bounds. He had neither pity nor mercy nor good sense. In his madness, he even ordered that Draupadi's clothes should be stripped from her as she stood in the assembly; he thought this would be the best way to disgrace the proud queen and bring her to shame.

When he gave the order, a great shout went up in the assembly and the elders begged Duryodhana to desist. Even Dhritarashtra added his weak voice to their protests. But Duryodhana's heart seemed to be made of stone. Nothing would move him. With an arrogant laugh he commanded Dushahsana to tear away Draupadi's clothing.

In a daze, Draupadi heard the order as she stood in that assembly, alone and helpless. Fear filled her. Suddenly she knew that there was no one in the world who could come to her aid—neither the five stalwart princes who were her husbands, nor the wealthy nobles and courtiers, not the wise elders of Dhritarashtra's court, nor even King Dhritarashtra himself. No one would or could come to her help. In that terrible moment of distress, Draupadi turned all her thoughts to God. She reached out to Him for help, knowing Him to be man's final refuge.

Lord Krishna then came to her rescue and worked a miracle. As Dushahsana stripped her of one garment, another one appeared upon

her. As that was torn away, another came in its place, and another and another and another! Dushahsana's swarthy hands grew tired as he pulled. Rivers of sweat ran down his face and body. The pile of garments he had pulled from Draupadi grew so high that it reached the ceiling. The people were stunned. But Draupadi knew nothing. For she stood rooted to the spot, her eyes closed, her hands clasped, all her thoughts and all her being fixed on God.

In the end Dushahsana grew so faint and tired that he had to stop. Then, as Draupadi opened her eyes, the great pile of glittering garments went up in flames, leaving nothing but smoke and ashes.

All this while the Pandava brothers had stood helpless. Their wife had been dishonoured and they had been powerless to protect her. They hung their heads in shame and sorrow. The mighty Bhima felt his heart breaking. His great frame shook; he gnashed his teeth and clenched his hands and swore a great oath, that one day he would tear open the wicked Dushahsana's breast with his bare hands and drink his blood.

As these happenings took place within, there came from outside the fearful sound of asses braying and vultures screeching; a wild wind arose; the sky grew dark with an eclipse and a great storm burst. Hearing these sounds and knowing them to be omens of evil, the blind Dhritarashtra grew pale and began to tremble. For now he was thoroughly frightened by the extent of his son's folly.

Dhritarashtra was feeble. He could not say "No" to his wayward son. Equally, he could not ignore the stern warnings of the counsellors or the voice of his own conscience. When Duryodhana was absent for a while, Dhritarashtra summoned Draupadi before him and began to cajole her with soft and kind words, trying to soothe her anger. He asked her to name whatever she wished and promised that he would give it to her. At that, Draupadi stood before him with her head held high, eyes proud and fearless. She demanded from him the freedom of Yudhishthira, her husband.

Dhritarashtra was only too glad to grant her wish. "Ask more, child," he begged her. "Ask more and you shall have your desire."

Then Draupadi spoke again and asked for the Pandava brothers to be set free and for their arms and weapons to be restored to them. Dhritarashtra, anxious to undo the wrongs his son had done, hastened to give the order to set the Pandavas free.

74

"Ask more, child, ask more!" he continued to wheedle. "Ask for your husband's kingdom."

But this Draupadi would not do. "A Kshatriya may ask for two gifts only and no more," she answered haughtily, "I do not want a kingdom as a gift from my enemies. My husbands are free men now. Armed with their weapons they can conquer the world."

Her words and the voice in which they were uttered made the old king quail.

"Nevertheless, even though you do not ask for it, the kingdom of Indraprastha is yours," he quavered in a persuasive tone. He begged the

Pandavas to accept the offer and return to their kingdom in peace. He begged their forgiveness for the wrongs Duryodhana had done them, pleading with them to forget what had happened.

Draupadi did not answer. But her eyes blazed fire as she left the hall with her five husbands.

So the Pandavas left the assembly hall, free men again because of Draupadi's courage, for it was she who had won them their freedom. For once, in his son's absence, Dhritarashtra had acted with some courage and firmness.

When Duryodhana returned, however, he was furious.

"What a foolish thing you have done!" he stormed at his father. "What madness is this? You have set free enemies, whom we have insulted and dishonoured. Can you not see that they will have their revenge?"

"What shall I do, then?" Dhritarashtra began to whimper again. He was like a leaf in his weakness, blown about by every wind. Then Duryodhana asked his father to send for the Pandavas again for a second game of dice. At that the people in the assembly all cried out, "No, no, not again! Now, at least, let there be peace!"

But Duryodhana, headstrong and foolish, would have his way.

"We shall play one more round," he announced. "This time the loser shall go into the forest for twelve years and live there as an ascetic. The thirteenth year, he shall spend in disguise and hiding. If he should, during that thirteenth year, be discovered or recognised, then he shall spend twelve more years in the forests."

It was a strange wager. Nobody had heard of such a thing before. Everyone in the assembly, even the valiant Karna, begged Duryodhana to give up his madness and allow the Pandavas to go in peace. But the advice fell on deaf ears, as Duryodhana prevailed upon his father to agree to his fantastic proposal.

So messengers were sent once more to the Pandavas. The five princes and their wife were still upon the road when the messengers overtook them.

It would be expected that after the misfortunes he had brought upon himself and his family, Yudhishthira would have learnt prudence. But the love of dice was as strong in him as ever. He did not like the thought that he owed his freedom and that of his brothers to a favour of Dhritarashtra. He wanted to play and win. He still felt that luck would favour him if he tried once more. His brothers cried out in despair, begging him not to accept, but Yudhishthira said:

"I will come and play one more round."

There was no dissuading him. He seemed bent on his own destruction. Sadly the Pandava brothers turned back and came once more to Hastinapura.

Once more, while his brothers looked on in gloomy silence, Yudhishthira played; and once more he lost. And now, in accordance with the terms of their wager, the Pandavas had to go into exile.

Then the Pandava princes and Draupadi bowed before the elders and walked slowly out of the hall, eyes lowered, speaking not a word. All stood silent, watching them go. But when they reached the street, there came before them great crowds of weeping, sorrowful people, who cried out and begged them not to go. Their weeping and their lamentations were so loud that the blind king Dhritarashtra trembled with fear on his throne.

Even the strong-willed Duryodhana began to feel uneasy and fearful of the future, He came running to Drona and begged him with tears in his eyes not to forsake him.

"I will stand by you, Prince," Drona said wearily, "for I have eaten of your rice and I owe you loyalty. But what you have done is wrong." Drona then spoke frankly and pointed out to Duryodhana the foolishness of his action. He counselled him to undo it by making peace with the Pandavas and returning their kingdom to them. Duryodhana turned away from him angrily.

"Make peace with my cousins!" he cried. "This I will never do."

He turned and strode out of the hall and the council came to an abrupt end.

76

14

The Pandavas in Exile

When the news of the Pandavas' banishment reached Drupada, he hurried to meet them, accompanied by his son Dhrishtadyumna. Krishna too came quickly to their side, full of concern at the events that had taken place. At the sight of them, the memory of her sufferings and the wrongs done to her returned to Draupadi in waves of grief. Weeping bitterly, she related to them the story of Duryodhana's wickedness, of the gambling match and how she had been dragged into the assembly and shamed. Hearing her, Dhrishtadyumna's face grew dark with anger. He swore to her that he would avenge the wrongs she had suffered, even though he might die for it. Krishna spoke too, promising her that those who had caused her sorrow and brought about her disgrace would surely be destroyed.

Then Drupada and Dhrishtadyumna returned to Panchala, taking the young sons of Draupadi with them. Krishna returned to Dwaraka with his sister Subhadra, wife of Arjuna, and her infant son Abhimanyu.

The exiled Pandavas made their way into the forests where they were to spend the days of their banishment. Travelling westwards, they reached the wild, unexplored territory called the Kamyaka region on the banks of the river Saraswati. No Aryan except for a few rishis and hermits had ever before set foot in it. The Pandavas came across hermitages scattered here and there in forest clearings and on river-banks, and from time to time, they stopped to visit the good and wise men.

Life was hard in the wilderness. But the Pandavas were brave and stout-hearted. Draupadi went everywhere with them, sharing their hardships. The memory of the sorrows and humiliations she had suffered remained fresh and raw. She would neither forget the wrongs the Kauravas had done her, nor would she let her husbands forget. She did not think much of Yudhishthira's meek and submissive behaviour, and she was often impatient with Arjuna too, for the manner in which he allowed his elder brother to impose his authority on him. Bhima was more after her heart. For Bhima thought and felt like her.

From the Kamyaka forest they travelled to the Daivatvana lake, on the banks of which they lived for five years. From there they went on to the holy site of Prayag, then eastwards again until they came to the ocean. After they had lived for some time in that region, they travelled back to the forests of the Vindhyas. As they wandered through the wilderness, they discussed among themselves the ways and means to get back the kingdom Duryodhana had wrested from them.

Duryodhana had driven them into exile, and he now ruled over their domains. Duryodhana was greedy and cunning. The Pandavas did not think that he would return their kingdom to them at the end of their period of exile. There would be a dispute which would surely lead to war. They knew they must arm themselves now and strengthen themselves by alliances with friendly rulers.

Meanwhile they lived the life of hermits and, as they wandered from place to place, they came to know well the surrounding country and its people.

Far away in Hastinapura, Duryodhana's heart still burned with jealousy and allowed him no peace. One day he called Shakuni and Karna, and told them of yet another plan to destroy the Pandavas.

"Unarmed and helpless they wander through the forests," he said, "and if we attack them now, we shall certainly defeat them." Shakuni and Karna were delighted. The three of them agreed to keep the elders in the dark as to their real intention.

"Let us pretend that we are going to our cattle stations to count our cattle," suggested Duryodhana and the others applauded him warmly.

Having secured the necessary permission from his father and the elders at court, Duryodhana and his companions set out in high spirits from Hastinapura and arrived at the Daivatvana forest where the Pandavas lived in exile. But when they tried to enter it, they found their way barred, for there, guarding the forest and the Pandavas within, stood the heavenly armies of the Gandharvas under their king Chitrasena. Indra, who had seen Duryodhana's evil intention, had commanded them to protect the Pandavas. Duryodhana and his companions thus had to do battle first with these heavenly warriors. Duryodhana had not foreseen this conflict. His army was completely routed by Chitrasena. Karna and Shakuni fled, while Duryodhana was taken prisoner and dragged in disgrace before Yudhishthira.

When Yudhishthira saw his cousin in chains and thoroughly humbled, he pitied him. He begged Chitrasena to release him and, turning to his brothers who were clamouring for revenge, reminded them that Duryodhana was, after all, their cousin and flesh of their flesh. "We cannot forsake him in his distress," said the gentle Yudhishthira. He ordered Duryodhana to be released, and speaking to him kindly, gave him permission to return to Hastinapura.

78

Duryodhana gnashed his teeth as he turned to go. There was no joy in his heart, and no gratitude. His anger against the Pandavas increased a hundred-fold, for he hated to have to be thankful to those he considered his greatest enemies on earth.

Back in the palace he sulked and brooded all day, refusing to eat or drink or sleep. Karna tried to console his broken spirit, but Duryodhana turned heavily away.

"Better far to die," he groaned, "than to owe my life to the man I hate."

Then Karna, grieved to see his friend so unhappy, swore to him a great and terrible oath, declaring that the day would come when he would surely destroy Arjuna. By his honour, and all that he held dear, he swore that he would live the life of an ascetic, eating no meat and drinking no wine until he had killed Arjuna.

"If Arjuna is removed," said Karna, "the strength of the Pandavas will be cut at the root!"

Duryodhana's fainting heart lifted at Karna's words. He embraced his loyal friend warmly.

"We will defeat the Pandavas yet," he said. "We will vanquish them and lay them low."

But the Pandavas, serving their term of exile in the forest, were learning much and growing rich in experience and wisdom through their many adventures.

Once, a wise sage spoke to them and advised them to obtain from the gods certain heavenly weapons which would be useful to them in the time to come. Arjuna, who was always ready for adventure, took him at his word. He took leave of his wife and brothers and set off alone for the Himalayan regions, where he hoped to do penance to please the gods and so obtain their weapons from them.

Armed with his bow, his quiver of arrows slung on his back, Arjuna walked through the forests alone for many long and weary days, suffering many hardships. He learned from his heavenly father, Indra, who revealed himself to him, that he would be given the weapons of gods only if he could obtain the blessing of Mahadeva, the three-eyed God of Destruction. Then Arjuna made a clay image of Mahadeva and sat upon a rock before it in deep meditation. For many days he prayed and did hard penance. He grew so thin that the bones showed in his body, and his beard grew matted and long, and the clothing fell from him in tatters until he was naked in the Himalayan winter. At last Mahadeva appeared before him in the guise of a forest tribesman. But before he revealed himself, Mahadeva wished to test him. He challenged Arjuna to a fight and the Pandava accepted; for all his prayer and meditation, for all his fasting and penance, Arjuna was still a Kshatriya and the hot blood of the Kshatriya which flowed in his veins could not be subdued. He would never refuse a challenge to fight.

So they strung their bows and the arrows began to fly. But though a hundred arrows pierced Arjuna's body till the blood ran down his limbs in great streams, Arjuna's arrows did not so much as touch the hunter. Instead, they fell at his feet as if they had been flowers. After a while Arjuna's quiver was empty and he had no more arrows to shoot. Then he rushed at his adversary with his bow, but the hunter wrenched it away from him without effort, as if it had been a toy. Arjuna drew his sword, but the sword broke and fell from his hand.

So they fell to wrestling. Once again the tribesman proved invincible, for Arjuna was scarcely able even to touch him. On the other hand, the hunter again and again brought him to earth. But as many times as he was knocked down, so many times did Arjuna spring up, refusing to acknowledge defeat. There was no part of him that was not injured. His bones were like pulp inside his battered body. Still Arjuna would not stop. Still he fought on.

Then at last came his darkest hour, when he was thrown upon the ground and had not the strength even to get up. At that moment Arjuna remembered his God and surrendered himself completely to him, praying humbly and desperately for help. Finding a garland of flowers near him, he threw it upon the clay image of Mahadeva, but even as he watched, it flew to the neck of the hunter. Arjuna stared at the marvellous occurrence, and realised with a strange sense of awakening that this was no forest hunter at all, but Mahadeva himself.

Arjuna cried out in joy and crept up to the tribesman's feet, begging forgiveness. Mahadeva smiled and raised him up; at his touch, the

strength flowed back into Arjuna's body, his wounds healed, his skin grew smooth and he became whole again. Mahadeva, who was pleased with Arjuna's valour, gave him the weapons he had prayed for and blessed him, declaring that final victory would be his. After the great God had blessed him, there appeared before Arjuna the lesser gods, who also gave him weapons; Yama gave his noose, Kubera, his arrows of sleep and Varuna his mace. Overwhelmed by the kindness of the gods, Arjuna struggled in vain to find words to thank them. But they understood his gratitude, smiled and vanished from his presence, leaving him alone with their wonderful gifts.

Indra, the king of the gods, returned and took Arjuna in his winged chariot to his kingdom in the heavens. Here Arjuna lived in comfort for five years, learning the use of the weapons he had won and many other sciences and arts, including music and dance from Chitrasena, the

heavenly musician. Arjuna proved an apt pupil and it was not long before he became an accomplished artist. When he felt he had learnt all the things that had to be learned, Indra sent him back to earth with his blessings, promising him and his brothers victory over their enemies.

Another time, it so happened that the Pandava brothers, in pursuit of a deer in the forest, wandered far from their dwelling place. The sun was hot overhead and they grew thirsty. The deer had vanished, and now, footsore and weary, they came at last to a stop, knowing that their search was in vain. Their mouths were parched; they scanned the earth in all directions for some sign of water. But seeing none, they trudged wearily onward until at last Yudhishthira, unable to go any further, sank down under a tree to rest and sent Sahadeva in search of water. The youth went readily enough, but when he did not return for a long

time, Yudhishthira grew concerned. He sent Nakula to see what had happened. Nakula obeyed—but he too, like Sahadeva, did not return. Then one by one, Yudhishthira sent his remaining brothers after the others but when they all went and none returned, he grew very anxious, not knowing what evil fate had overtaken them. At last, he decided to go and see for himself. Following their footsteps, he walked on for a distance until he came to a pool in a clearing. Its clear, still waters reflected the blue sky, while the pink, white and blue lotuses that grew in it raised their smiling heads to the sun. But as his eyes looked upon the lovely scene, Yudhishthira saw another sight at which the blood froze in his veins. For there, upon the earth, lay his four brothers, cold and still, either dead or unconscious. Their eyes were closed, and when he called to them they would not answer. Sorrow filled the king's heart, and he fell on his knees by them and wept bitterly for them, wringing his hands in his grief and crying out to heaven to take him too, for he could not live without his brothers.

Unknown to Yudhishthira, his brothers had failed a strange test at this forest pool. The first to come was Sahadeva. Full of joy at seeing water, he knelt upon the bank and bent down to quench his thirst. Suddenly, a voice broke through the silence of the grove. "Stop, Sahadeva!" said the voice, "Do not drink, for this is an enchanted pool." Startled, Sahadeva looked about him, but he could see no one. He turned to the water. It looked cool and inviting. He was very thirsty. As he paused, undecided, the voice rang out again.

"I am a Yaksha," it said, "and this enchanted pool belongs to me. No one may drink of its water until he has answered my questions."

Sahadeva rose up and waited.

He could still see nobody. He seemed to be alone except for the birds chirping in the trees and the dragonflies zooming over the water.

"It must be my fancy," Sahadeva thought. "The hot sun makes my imagination work."

He decided to ignore the voice of the invisible speaker. He was too tired and thirsty to wait. He made a cup of his hands and kneeling down, began to drink. But hardly had the water touched his lips, when he felt himself struck down. Sahadeva's senses reeled. The world went dark and he fell down unconscious.

When Nakula arrived shortly afterwards, he was grieved and surprised to see his brother in this condition. But so great was his own thirst that he did not wait. He rushed to the water's edge to drink. But as he stooped, he too heard the Yaksha's warning voice. However, he too paid no attention. He drank and instantly he too was struck down and rendered unconscious. When Bhima came to the spot, the same fate overtook him, though he was strong and mighty and sent a shower of arrows in all directions in search of the hidden enemy. Arjuna fared no better.

For a long time Yudhishthira wept on the bank. Then feeling his thirst overpower him, he dragged himself to the edge of the water. But as he bent down, Yudhishthira heard the Yaksha's warning voice. "Who are you?" he called and looked around. "Ask your questions; I shall answer them as well as I can."

The voice continued: "I am a Yaksha, Yudhishthira, and it is well for you that you heeded my warning. Now listen to my questions.

"What makes the sun shine?"

"The power of God!" Yudhishthira answered.

"What is man's surest weapon against danger?" Yudhishthira quickly replied, "Courage! Courage is his surest weapon in danger."

"What gives more to man than even the earth does? What feeds him and sustains him and makes him strong?" the Yaksha persisted. Yudhishthira did not hesitate. "A mother, surely. It is only a mother who gives a man life, feeds him and sustains him. A mother is more than the earth."

"When does a man become loved by his fellows?" asked the Yaksha,

and Yudhishthira responded, "When he gives up pride." "What is that which makes a man happy when he has lost it?" the Yaksha went on. "Anger," said Yudhishthira with certainty, for he knew that when a man gives up anger, he is full of peace. The Yaksha continued. "What can a man give up and immediately become rich?"

"Desire," answered Yudhishthira. "It is only the man without desires who is really rich. Even if a man has a thousand possessions he will be poor if he is not satisfied." So it went on, until at last the Yaksha said, "I am well pleased with your answers, and I shall restore to you one of your brothers. Choose who it shall be."

Yudhishthira looked at the unconscious forms of his brothers. It was hard for him to decide. But he spoke at last.

"Kind Yaksha," he said, "restore to me my brother Nakula." "And why Nakula?" the Yaksha's voice asked. "Is not Bhima more useful to you? Will you not benefit from his great strength in the war that will surely come? And Arjuna—why do you not choose Arjuna? Is he not dearer to you than all? Is he not the most handsome, the most skilled among them all in the use of arms? Why then do you choose Nakula?"

Then Yudhishthira answered: "Listen, Yaksha," he said. "Righteousness and truth are a man's only weapon and protection. The strength of Bhima and the skill of Arjuna would be of no use to me if I acted unrighteously. Indeed I would be unrighteous if I looked to my own benefit and begged for Bhima's life or Arjuna's in preference to Nakula's. For Nakula is Madri's son, and Bhima and Arjuna, like me, are Kunti's children. Of Kunti's children I at least live. But if Nakula and Sahadeva should both die, then Madri's line would end. Therefore, Yaksha, it is right that Nakula's life should be restored rather than Bhima's or Arjuna's."

When he had said this, in that very moment there appeared before Yudhishthira a shining, crowned person whom he knew at once to be a god. The divine personage was none other than Yama, the God of Justice and Death, Yudhishthira's heavenly father. Yama embraced Yudhishthira and told him that he had come to help the Pandavas in their hour of need. He told him how pleased he was with Yudhishthira's noble conduct and wisdom. He restored to life not just one of the brothers, but all of them.

Yudhishthira knelt at his heavenly father's feet and his heart overflowed with gratitude. Yama blessed him and promised that he and his brothers would be protected by heaven in their hardships.

"No harm shall come to you," he said. "Neither will you be discovered while you live in hiding during the last and thirteenth year of exile."

He advised Yudhishthira to go with his brothers and Draupadi to Matsya, where the good king Virata ruled, and to live there in disguise. There they would be safe from their enemies while they awaited the end of their long period of exile.

15

The Year in Hiding

According to the terms of the agreement with Duryodhana, the Pandavas had to disguise themselves and remain in hiding during the thirteenth year of their banishment. If discovered, they would have to remain in exile for another twelve years. They held anxious consultations about the disguise each was to take.

Yudhishthira declared that he would go to Matsya as a nobleman who had seen better days but through misfortune had lost all his wealth and fallen from high estate. He would be a companion to King Virata, amusing him with his conversation and playing games of dice with him.

Bhima said that he would go disguised as a cook to work in Virata's royal kitchens.

Nakula was to work in Virata's stables while his twin, Sahadeva, would work as a herdsman and look after Virata's large herds of cattle. Arjuna, who had studied under Chitrasena at Indra's court, decided to disguise himself as a teacher of music and dancing. He would teach these arts to the king's children and remain in the inner apartments dressed like a woman. The battle scars upon his rough hard arms were to be hidden under bangles and ornaments. A strange woman he would seem—gruff-voiced, tall and ungainly. Perhaps they would laugh and poke fun at him. But he would go about his work cleverly and he would not be discovered.

Then Draupadi spoke. "I will go as Queen Sudeshna's serving-maiden and companion," she said. Yudhishthira hung his head in shame as he heard her and his eyes filled with tears, remembering how all her life Draupadi had been brought up in comfort and luxury. As her husband, he had vowed to protect her and look after her. Yudhishthira knew he had failed his wife. He saw now, as he had never done before, where his folly had led them. But Draupadi begged him to take heart, and Yudhishthira knew there was no other way.

Then the Pandavas sent their lamps and idols of worship to King Drupada's court and said goodbye to Dhaumya, their priest. Collecting their arms and weapons in a bundle, they brought them at midnight to a cremation ground where the people burned their dead. Here, moving softly and stealthily, they hung the bundle upon the topmost branches of a tall tree. Then, each disguised himself and silently, one after another, taking different paths, they left the forest.

King Virata of Matsya was a good and kindly man who harmed no one. He honoured the gods and tried to live according to the law. But without strength of mind or character, he proved a weak ruler. Though he sat upon the throne of Matsya, the real power lay in the hands of Kichaka, brother of Queen Sudeshna. Kichaka was a greedy, cruel man, but he was also strong and brave. People feared him and he kept law and order in the country. The neighbouring people dared not make trouble upon Matsya's borders, for if they did, Kichaka would come down on them with a heavy hand. So they kept their hands off Virata's territory and respected its boundaries.

The five Pandava brothers came separately into Matsya, as if each did not know the other. The kindly Virata employed them all in his service: Yudhishthira as a companion to him, a courtier who could amuse him and play games with him; Bhima as a royal cook; Arjuna as a teacher of dance and music; Nakula and Sahadeva respectively as groom and herdsman.

Last of all, Draupadi came before Queen Sudeshna and begged to be employed as her companion and serving-maiden. Queen Sudeshna was pleased with the young woman's noble bearing and appearance. She wondered who she was. Draupadi told her that she was the wife of five gods who lived in the heavens and watched over her and protected her constantly. She told her that once long ago, she had served Queen Draupadi at Indraprastha. But when evil days had fallen upon the Pandavas, she had had to leave Indraprastha and seek employment elsewhere. Draupadi also told Queen Sudeshna that she would work for her only on one condition: she would serve no one but the queen or the king. Greatly struck by the serving-woman's manner and good looks, Sudeshna agreed to her condition and employed her.

So Draupadi and the Pandavas lived and worked unrecognised at Virata's royal court. They moved about with care, watching their actions and their words to make sure they would not be discovered, and they gave no sign to anyone that they knew each other.

It was not easy, however, to live as lowly servants taking orders from others, where they had always commanded; but they bore their lot without complaining. This last year which they must spend in hiding was perhaps the hardest of all, but they felt that the end of their troubles was now in sight. Remembering this, they took courage.

Thus ten months went by, and they rejoiced that nobody suspected their identity. Then an unfortunate incident took place which nearly brought them to ruin.

One day, Kichaka's eyes fell on Draupadi, who worked as his sister's serving-maiden under the name of Sairandhri. He was infatuated with her beauty and wanted to have her as his slave. But Draupadi fled from his unwelcome attentions. Kichaka, who was used to having his own way in everything, came to his sister and asked for her beautiful serving-maiden. Queen Sudeshna demurred, pointing out that since the woman did not care to go to him, it would not be right to force her.

Kichaka, however, did not think that a slave's feelings mattered in the least. And Sudeshna, who was fond of her brother, gave in to him.

That evening Sudeshna commanded Draupadi to go with a goblet of wine to Kichaka's house. Draupadi pleaded to be excused from the hateful task. She recalled her one condition of service—to serve only the king and queen. But all entreaties and threats about the anger of her invisible husbands were of no avail. Sudeshna would not be crossed.

She thrust the goblet into Draupadi's hands and commanded her to go, her haughty face dark with anger. Draupadi, however, had no intention of becoming Kichaka's slave. She took the goblet to Kichaka's house but would not enter its doorway. She saw him at the entrance, and thrusting the goblet quickly into his hands, she fled. Thwarted and taken by surprise, Kichaka ran after her, calling to her to stop. But Draupadi continued to run until she reached the pleasure hall where King Virata sat playing dice with Yudhishthira. With a cry, she flung herself at the king's feet, begging him to protect her.

Kichaka was not far behind. Swiftly, he came upon her. He had no regard for king or court. His anger had been sparked, and his pride wounded. Before Virata could say anything, he kicked Draupadi where she knelt.

No one dared to move: neither the king nor the nobles, for they all feared Kichaka too much to intervene when he insulted a serving-maiden. Yudhishthira, of course, had his own reasons for not coming to Draupadi's help. He knew that he must give no sign that he knew Draupadi or that she meant anything to him, for if he did, they might all be discovered before their time. Duryodhana's spies were everywhere and one could not be too careful. So though his heart ached for his wife, Yudhishthira too remained silent like the others.

When he saw how they all feared him, Kichaka laughed aloud, proud and satisfied, and strode away. After a while, poor Draupadi crept away, weeping, to her quarters.

That night, when everyone was asleep, Draupadi tiptoed out of her room and made her way into the servants' quarters where Bhima slept. She shook him and whispering his name softly, woke him. Then she beckoned him to a secret place. Weeping hot, bitter tears, she poured out to him the story of the day's happenings and begged him to avenge the insult she had suffered. Hearing her, Bhima, who loved her more than his life, ground his teeth in anger.

86

"Kill Kichaka if you have any love for me!" she cried out, "or if you will not kill him, say so, and I will kill myself. This disgrace is more than I can bear." Bhima nodded grimly. "Kichaka shall not live," he promised her. His words comforted Draupadi.

Bhima laid his plans carefully, for he knew that if they were discovered before their time they would have played into Duryodhana's hands.

He told Draupadi that she must go to Kichaka and appear to be sorry for what she had done. She must pretend to feel love for him and entice him cleverly into the dancing hall at dead of night. There, he would get what he deserved.

Draupadi calmly carried out her part of the plot. When Kichaka swaggered up to her the next day, she sidled towards him, pretending to admire him. Kichaka, who was as vain and conceited as he was stupid, smirked with delight and fell headlong into the snare. Draupadi flattered him and spoke sweetly to him until she made him promise to meet her secretly in the dancing hall that same night.

"Now you are properly fixed!" thought Draupadi grimly as she watched him go. "It is lucky that your wits do not match your strength!"

That night Kichaka met his death. For, when he came to the dance hall, he saw a muffled figure on a couch. Believing it was Sairandhri, he went close and called her name. Kichaka never knew what happened next, for it all happened too swiftly. In a flash, he was caught in arms stronger, it seemed, than iron. He was still struggling to get free when a sharp, swift blow on his face sent him reeling to the floor and a heavy form was upon him gagging and strangling him.

Quickly recovering his presence of mind, Kichaka struggled to rise. Whatever his faults, he lacked neither strength not courage. But Bhima would not let go his hold. He fell upon him and pounded his head mercilessly till the blood flowed.

When he was sure Kichaka was dead, Bhima got up and slipped away as noiselessly as he had come. He returned to the servants' quarters where he washed his blood-stained hands. Then, quietly, he returned to bed.

The next morning, the palace was astir with the news of the murder of Kichaka. An unknown enemy had made short work of the mighty commander-in-chief of the Matsyan army, whom all men had feared because of his great strength and power. People whispered in fear, not knowing what to think. Queen Sudeshna mourned for her brother and looked darkly at 'Sairandhri'. In her heart, she felt sure that this mysterious woman had something to do with his death. But when she questioned her, Draupadi answered sullenly, "How should I know? Did I not warn you that my invisible husbands are strong and jealous?" Queen Sudeshna would have dismissed her from service, but Draupadi reminded her that according to the conditions of her service, she had been appointed for a year and could not be turned away before that time. So Draupadi remained.

88

There was mourning and grief in Matsya. Though Kichaka had been a cruel tyrant and an arrogant man, he had kept Matsya strong and had protected her from enemy attack. Now that his strong hand had been removed, people feared that Matsya's neighbours would start their mischievous activities again, raiding her border villages, stealing her cattle and crops and terrorising her people. Perhaps there would be an invasion and war. There was trouble in store for them now, and no one to lead the people.

16

The Besieged City

The fears of the Matsya people were not groundless. Even as they were mourning the death of their commander-in-chief, enemies who had been waiting and watching for an opportunity started preparations to attack the defenceless country.

Among these enemies were Susharma, king of Trigarta, and Duryodhana, ruler of Hastinapura. Duryodhana had not dared to attack Matsya when Kichaka was alive.

But when he heard the news of Kichaka's death, he went over the details in his mind again: A mysterious person, they said, had killed Kichaka — an invisible Gandharva, reported to be one of the five husbands of a beautiful and proud serving-maiden, Sairandhri.

Duryodhana frowned to himself. It all seemed to fit so well. He felt sure that the mysterious killer of Kichaka was none other than Bhima, for it was known that in all the world there was only Bhima who could equal Kichaka in strength.

Duryodhana's mind began to work busily away as he hatched his plan. When he had worked out all the details, he announced his intentions to the elders.

"I do not think that the Pandavas are dead," he told them. "I think they are living in Matsya and that the killer of Kichaka is Bhima. However," he went on, "whether the Pandavas live there or not, one thing is certain: Kichaka, defender of Matsya, is dead. Now is the time to strike at Virata's kingdom, before he can recover and build up his strength. Virata will never be able to withstand us alone. Let us, therefore, attack Matsya and carry away her cattle."

His eyes gleamed as he continued: "If Virata has given shelter to the Pandavas, then they will surely give him help and fight for him. Then, of course, they will be discovered before their time and that will be their doom. Either way we stand to gain by making war."

A roar of acclamation greeted Duryodhana's words. Susharma and Karna cheered again, brandishing their shining weapons, till the assembly hall resounded with the noise.

The voices that pleaded for peace, for restraint, for caution were drowned that day in the clamour for war. War was what Duryodhana and his friends wanted, and they had their way. It was agreed that Susharma would attack Matsya on her southern frontiers and engage her armies in battle, while Karna and Duryodhana launched a surprise attack on the north.

In accordance with this plan, Susharma's armies struck Matsya in the south, laying waste the countryside and harassing the people. As they began to make their way towards the capital, the people panicked, defenceless as they were against the marauding soldiers. They sent messengers to the king with appeals for help.

The messengers arriving at the palace found Virata in the dice room playing a game with his favourite courtier Kanka — who was really Yudhishthira. They cried out to him to save them from the plundering armies.

Virata listened to their tale of woe. "Now our troubles have started," he thought, "and I am not strong enough to lead the country against the invaders." He wished Kichaka had been alive, and said so to his companion. "Kichaka was headstrong and often wicked in his ways," he said, "but he was strong. As long as he was alive, no one dared to touch our frontiers."

Yudhishthira answered him, "Sir, you do not need to fear. Indeed we cannot waste time thinking over what might have been. Now is the time for action."

"I do not feel equal to it," Virata protested weakly. "I am a peace-loving man. I like to be left alone."

Yudhishthira cut him short. "This is not the time for talk or for explanations," he said briskly. "Now we must act. You must get your army together and march upon the enemy."

"How?" cried Virata frantically. "Susharma is strong!"

"Listen!" said Yudhishthira. "I will help you. I have been in the service of the Pandavas in Indraprastha and I know the art of warfare. Besides, there are others. There is Ballava your cook; Dharmagranti, who is in charge of your horses and Tantripala, who looks after your cattle. They too have been, like me, in the service of the Pandavas. They will come to your aid. Appoint them officers in your forces. Give them power and authority and they will drive out the invaders."

Virata was too distracted and frightened to argue. He was willing to give over charge to anyone who would take it. He readily did as he was told. Bhima, Nakula and Sahadeva were given charge of army units. Yudhishthira was placed at the head of the forces and Virata, being the king, rode in his chariot beside him.

Thus, the Matsya forces came out to fight the invaders. Nobody knew who the mysterious military commanders were. But whoever they were, they proved their valour and skill on the battlefield that day. The armies of Susharma fled before them like chaff in the wind. But when they re-grouped and in a sudden surprise attack captured Virata, the tide seemed to turn against the Matsyan forces. Then Ballava, riding into the thick of battle and piercing through the enemy formations, rescued him from the jaws of death and brought him to safety. Susharma's soldiers fled in confusion.

The news of the victory spread on wings. The people went wild with joy and began to make preparations for Virata's triumphant return to the capital. Everywhere there was rejoicing in which the recent misfortunes were forgotten.

90

And now, while the citizens were making merry, Duryodhana struck at Matsya's northern frontiers and advanced upon the unsuspecting people. As Susharma had done in the south, so the Kaurava armies did in the north, plundering and looting. And, as before, messengers came flying to the capital to beg the king for help.

But the king was away and all the citizens were busy with preparations for his triumphant entry after his victory. The capital was deserted and there was no one to whom the messengers could speak, except the young prince Uttara Kumar, Virata's son and heir to his throne.

Uttara Kumar was in the women's apartments with his mother. A young lad, hardly more than a child, he was much loved and spoilt by the ladies of the court. When messengers were brought before him he listened carefully to them. "There is no one who can help us now, Prince," they cried, "except you."

Uttara Kumar flushed with pride and his eyes sparkled. "I will lead the people," he answered, full of boyish enthusiasm. The ladies laughed delightedly and applauded him, charmed with his ways. And Sudeshna's heart went out to him in motherly pride.

Only Sairandhri said, "You will no doubt win the war, prince, but before you go, I would request you to take with you Brihannala, the dancing teacher. She will prove a useful companion, for it is said that she is skilled in the charioteer's art."

Prince Uttara pouted a little. "Whoever heard of a woman on a battlefield?" he protested; but Sairandhri answered firmly, "She will be useful to you, Prince, for she is skilled at chariot-driving and you have no chariot-driver."

So at last Prince Uttara was persuaded, and Brihannala was given armour to wear and a whip to hold. Then, bidding the ladies goodbye, the young prince and his companion mounted the chariot.

Brihannala cracked the whip, shouted to the horses and away they sped northwards to face the Kaurava army.

Much to the young prince's surprise, Brihannala proved a skilled charioteer. They sped swiftly over the countryside and Uttara Kumar chattered to the disguised Arjuna freely, boasting in boyish fashion about what he would do upon the battlefield. But when on the third day they sighted the Kaurava army in the distance, when they heard the war cries of the soldiers and the dreadful clamour of arms, the twanging of bowstrings, the rattling of sabres and the blare of conch shells, when he saw the fierce ruddy faces of the warriors, Prince Uttara Kumar lost heart and began to tremble. For he was young and inexperienced, and had never before left the shelter of his home in the palace. He clung to Arjuna, begging him piteously to take him back home, and all Arjuna's attempts to encourage him were of no avail. "They will jeer at you if you return now!" he said. "Even the ladies will laugh." "Let them laugh!" cried the prince, hiding his face in his hands. "I cannot fight the Kauravas."

Arjuna would not let him give way to his fear in this manner. "You must take hold of yourself," he said. "You must not be a coward."

"I cannot help it," sobbed the prince. "Take me back, Brihannala. Take me back, I implore you."

Arjuna tried again: "I will give you weapons," he promised him, "weapons like those the Pandavas used."

Uttara Kumar struggled in his grasp. "I do not want weapons," he cried, "I want to go home. Take me to my mother."

"I will do no such thing," Arjuna answered him firmly. "You are a Kshatriya; you have warrior blood in you. Your duty is to fight for your people and country. I will give you weapons such as you have never seen in all your life. Only take heart."

And he turned a deaf ear to the poor boy's entreaties. He caught Uttara Kumar's hands and tied him to the chariot so that he could not escape.

Then, ignoring the boy's cries, he steered the chariot to that lonely cremation ground where earlier that year, he and his brothers had tied their weapons in a bundle and hung them up on a tree.

"Look!" he pointed out to the prince. "Do you see that object hanging from the tree?"

"It is a corpse!" screamed the terrified prince. "Why have you brought me to this fearsome place, this haunt of evil spirits? Take me back!"

"Listen," said Arjuna, "in that bundle are the weapons of the Pandavas. Climb the tree and bring down the bundle."

His voice was so stern, so commanding, that Uttara Kumar dared not disobey. Trembling, he climbed the tree and brought the bundle down.

"Untie the knots," the charioteer went on in the same stern note. Uttara Kumar obeyed. When he did so he found inside the shining weapons the charioteer had promised.

"These weapons belong to the Pandavas," said the charioteer, and seeing them the prince felt his heart lift with new hope. He turned to the charioteer.

"Who are you?" he asked huskily. "Surely you are no humble dancing teacher! Surely you are no charioteer! Tell me who you are."

Then Arjuna revealed himself to the youth, who thrilled to see him and felt courage surge through him again; for he knew that victory was now certain with the great hero to fight on his side. He knelt down before the warrior with deep humility and reverence. But Arjuna raised him up and embraced him. He spoke stirring words to him, reminding him of his great heritage as a Kshatriya. Hearing them the boy took heart. He climbed back into the chariot and together the two went into battle.

92

The Kauravas saw from afar the chariot in which Prince Uttara Kumar rode with Arjuna. Duryodhana, seeing the boy riding into battle with no better companion than a mannish woman, was completely confident of victory. But even as he was crowing over his chances, and chuckling to himself, the fearful twang of Arjuna's bowstring filled the air, and its resonance seemed to reach the very heavens.

Hearing it, the Kauravas exchanged looks in silence. They each knew that terrible sound and recognised it now. For there was no sound in all the world like that of Arjuna's bowstring

Slowly they began to voice their doubts. At that moment, three swift arrows came speeding through the air and fell, one each at the feet of Bhishma, Drona and Kripa. The elders looked at each other and nodded. Drona announced, "It is just as I had thought; Arjuna stands on the other side of the field. These arrows are proof of the truth of my guess, for with these arrows Arjuna sends his salutations to his elders and teachers. We must move with care."

Drona's words of caution angered Karna, who felt that Drona's heart was not in the fight. It seemed to Karna that Drona was giving this counsel because he loved the Pandavas. Karna taunted Drona and charged him with disloyalty to the Kauravas. Ashwatthama, Drona's son, stung by the taunts, answered him back sharply. Duryodhana joined the duel of words on Karna's side. "What does it matter even if it should be Arjuna?" he said to Drona. "According to the terms of the wager, the Pandavas agreed to return to the forest to serve another twelve-year period of exile if they were discovered before their time. Arjuna has been discovered and the Pandavas will have to pay for his bravado by returning into exile!"

But while Duryodhana was speaking, Drona had been calculating rapidly. "According to the movements of the stars, Duryodhana, the thirteen years ended at the very moment we heard the bowstring! The

94

Pandavas have fulfilled the terms of their pledge!"

His words infuriated Duryodhana. "Karna is right!" he shouted. "Your heart is with the Pandavas. You are a traitor!"

Ashwatthama sprang to his father's side and drew his sword, but Drona held him back. "Mind your words, Duryodhana!" he warned. "Mind your words!"

Karna stood by Duryodhana. "Why else does he always speak in their favour?" he questioned angrily. "Why does he not prove his loyalty to us by his deeds?"

Thus hot words were flung at each other and, even before the battle had started, there was a rift in the Kaurava camp. While they squabbled, Bhishma came up and spoke sternly to them, reminding them that this was not the time to quarrel over petty issues. "Now we must close our ranks and come together, for we are standing on a battlefield," said Bhishma. The quarrel was patched up on the surface, but the anger and suspicion remained within.

The battle that followed was short but decisive. Arjuna's arrows sped in all directions, so swiftly that the Kauravas could not advance. Taken completely by surprise, they retreated in confusion, broke cover and fled. Duryodhana, driving before him the cattle they had stolen, found himself pursued hotly and was forced to give up all he had — the cattle, his weapons, even the very clothes that he wore! The other Kauravas fared no better. It was a complete and crushing defeat.

A broken and dispirited army made its way back to Hastinapura, humiliated and in disgrace.

95

17

The Exile is Over

Arjuna and Uttara Kumar had won a great victory. They turned back to return to the capital. But the glad news of their triumph had gone before them. Crowds of people thronged the streets to greet them as they came. Conch shells boomed and drums throbbed. Everywhere they received a hero's welcome.

In the palace King Virata was beside himself with joy. He gave orders for a great welcome to be prepared for the prince. He talked incessantly about his son, bragging about him with fatherly pride, especially to Kanka, his favourite courtier.

Kanka had always echoed the king's sentiments. During the one year that he had been in Virata's service, he had never displeased him by expressing any opinion that was contrary to his. Virata was therefore surprised when Kanka did not respond with his usual enthusiasm. The truth was that Yudhishthira had made up his mind to reveal his identity, now that the period of exile had ended. But Virata did not know this. Each time Virata spoke in praise of his son's courage and heroism, the courtier, instead of assenting, answered in a very different tone. He referred pointedly to Brihannala's part in the battle, declaring with a little smile that but for Brihannala, the victory would have been impossible. King Virata was greatly annoyed. He felt that Kanka was belittling his son's part in the battle. He could not believe that the victory was won by a woman. Virata wondered if this courtier was not overreaching himself and growing rather insolent. He decided to ignore Kanka's remarks. But when Kanka repeated them several times, Virata lost patience. They were sitting at their usual game of dice and Virata, suddenly angered, flung the dice at Yudhishthira's cheek so hard that they cut him and the blood began to trickle down.

Draupadi who was in the room, gave a little cry of distress and hurried to her husband's side. With a silken cloth she wiped the blood and squeezed it out into a cup of gold.

"Why, what a fuss!" cried Virata impatiently. "What foolishness is this, woman? Why do you collect the blood in a golden cup?"

"Because he is a king, Virata," Draupadi answered, "and royal blood must not fall upon the earth. If it does there will be evil for the land. There will be famine and pestilence and sorrow. Have you not heard this saying, Virata?"

"A king!" Virata cried out, puzzled "What king?" He was finding it hard to control his anger. He could not understand anything.

At that minute the door burst open and with a loud, joyful cry the young prince Uttara Kumar entered and fell at his father's feet. Virata raised him up, all other things forgotten in his happiness at seeing his son returned from the field of battle.

"My valiant boy!" Virata exclaimed, "You have proved your worth today, defeating the most powerful princes in the land...."

But Uttara Kumar interrupted him, "Father!" he said, "it was not my doing at all. See, here is the one who led us to victory."

"Brihannala, the dance teacher!" uttered Virata, completely stupefied.

Prince Uttara Kumar said in a husky voice, full of reverence, "Father, this is no dance teacher, though for a year he lived among us as such. This is Arjuna, the Pandava returned from exile!" And he told his father the story. Virata's amazement was equalled only by his great joy. His eyes filled with happy tears.

"Arjuna!" he repeated again and again. "It is as if you have returned from the dead."

Then Draupadi's words came back to his mind. "He is a king, and royal blood must not be allowed to soak the earth." In a flash, he understood it all! He went up to Yudhishthira and, standing before him with folded hands, humbly begged forgiveness for all the harsh words he had unknowingly spoken to him.

But Yudhishthira bore Virata no ill-will. "You have given us shelter in your kingdom, Virata, my brother," he said, embracing the king. "We who were homeless and pursued by powerful enemies. How can I hold anything against you?"

Then Virata led Yudhishthira to the throne, and Sudeshna, the queen, came forward and begged Draupadi to forgive the many wrongs she had done her. King Virata did the Pandavas great honour, in gratitude to them for having helped him against powerful enemies that day.

He then led his daughter, the princess Uttara, to Arjuna and begged him to accept her as his bride. But this Arjuna would not consent to do. "She is only a child," he said, "and I am no longer young. While I have lived here I have looked upon her as my daughter."

He put his hand upon the girl's head. "One day, there will come one worthier of this pure and gentle creature than an old battle-scarred warrior like me." Arjuna was thinking of his young son Abhimanyu, son of Subhadra.

During the days that followed, there was feasting and merry-making in Matsya to celebrate the victories and welcome the Pandavas. Virata sent invitations to all the friends and kinsmen of the Pandavas to come and greet them after their long sojourn in the forest. They came in their golden palanquins and chariots, bringing with them presents and tribute and tokens of good will. Among them were Drupada of Panchala, and Krishna and Balarama of Dwaraka. With Drupada came the children of Draupadi, while Krishna brought with him Arjuna's son, Abhimanyu.

Arjuna's heart swelled with love and pride to see how the boy had grown. His eyes were bright and clear, his brow noble and good. He held himself straight and stepped forward with such grace and modesty, with such princely dignity, that tears caught in Arjuna's throat. He pressed him to his bosom, unable to speak. And then Arjuna thought of Uttara, Virata's daughter. It seemed to Arjuna that heaven had made these children for each other. He spoke his thoughts to Virata and the king was delighted with the proposal.

Soon preparations were in train for the marriage of Abhimanyu to Uttara. The news was carried by drummers to the furthest corners of the land. There was music and dancing and the gaily decorated streets were crowded with revellers. Everywhere there was laughter and merry-making as the marriage was celebrated with great pomp and splendour.

The sun shone brightly that day from unclouded skies and, for a time, men forgot their sorrows and hatred, put aside their doubts and misgivings and wished the young couple happiness and a long life.

As for Abhimanyu and Uttara, they were well pleased with each other. Each looked into the other's eyes and saw there a deep and loving tenderness. Yet, bitter days were to follow and their young lives were to be clouded over with grief and tragedy. Violence and treachery and death were to cut short the slender thread of their happiness.

98

18

Envoys and Missions

At the end of the marriage festivities, Abhimanyu led his sweet young bride before each of the assembled persons to receive their blessings. Then, the young couple retired into the inner apartments.

In the royal hall, the atmosphere took a serious turn. The men now gathered closer to discuss weighty matters. Hardened warriors they were, grave with many fears and anxieties.

The Pandavas had redeemed the pledge they had made to their cousins. What were they to do next? How should they set about their task? Should they go before Duryodhana, and demand from him the kingdom he had wrested from them by such foul means? Or should they go humbly on bended knees and take what he chose to give?

How much of their territory should they claim? What if Duryodhana refused to acknowledge their rights and restore them their kingdom and belongings? What course were they to take in that case? The Pandavas and their friends knew that Duryodhana would not easily part with his unlawful gains.

In Virata's council chamber there were two views expressed upon these matters. There were some people, led by Krishna, who declared that the Pandavas, having served their sentence and redeemed their pledge, should demand their kingdom as a matter of right. But there were others who felt that the Kauravas should not be offended. They argued that as the Pandavas had been foolish enough to stake their kingdom in a game and lose it, they had forfeited their right to it. All they could do was to beg for kindness from Duryodhana and request a gift of land from him. The chief spokesman for this view was Krishna's brother, Balarama.

Drupada, swarthy-faced, proud and vengeful, was all for action .

In the end, Krishna, supported by the Pandavas and several other princes, suggested that they should try all means to avoid war. "Let us try every means to persuade the Kauravas," he said, "for the ways of peace are the best, and war is never an answer to a problem."

There were murmurs of approval from one section of the assembly, but Krishna had not finished. He went on. "The ways of peace are indeed the best. Yet there are times when men must choose war. For war is to be preferred to a cowardly peace bought at the price of men's honour." At this Drupada and his friends applauded.

"That is just what I say!" exclaimed Drupada. "War cannot be avoided. Do we not know the Kauravas and their crafty ways? We will have to wrest our rights from them by force, by war!"

Krishna, however, spoke firmly in favour of negotiations. "Seek the ways of peace," he advised them, "for war is a dreadful thing in which millions of lives would be sacrificed. It is in our hands to try and prevent it."

Krishna's words raised a murmur of satisfaction among the assembled people. There was so much wisdom in them that even the proud and warlike Drupada had to agree reluctantly with what he said. On this note of peace the conference ended.

Only Draupadi, listening intently, felt anger rise up in her like the fires of hell.

"Peace," she cried out, turning on them with the fury of a tigress. "How can there by peace after the dishonour we have suffered?" Her voice broke and tears streamed down her face as she fell at Krishna's feet. "How can I forget their shameful treatment of me in their assembly? Can you not see that now is the time to avenge the insults I suffered? Oh, how can you talk of peace?"

Krishna drew her aside and spoke words of comfort to her.

"Do not despair," he told her. "It is our duty to seek all ways of settling our demands peacefully. But mark my words! Duryodhana will reject every offer. In his pride and foolishness he will choose war instead of peace and in doing so, will bring about his own destruction."

"So be it!" uttered Draupadi fervently.

During the days that followed, the Pandavas and the Kauravas sent envoys to each other and exchanged messages in the hope of securing fair and honourable terms and of avoiding a fratricidal conflict. The first to go on behalf of the Pandavas was a trusted officer from Drupada's court.

He came before Dhritarashtra and the Kauravas and, in the arrogant tone that Drupada had wished him to use, delivered his master's message faithfully. He reminded the Kauravas of the grievous wrongs they had done their cousins. In Drupada's name, he demanded the kingdom Duryodhana had wrested from them by cunning and trickery. In no uncertain terms he warned them that if peaceful means failed to secure the Pandavas their rights, they would resort to war.

"Make no mistake about it!" he thundered. "The Pandavas are not afraid. They are fully armed and strengthened by many alliances!"

Duryodhana's anger flamed as he heard the envoy. But before he could answer, Bhishma pointed out the error of holding on to what did not rightly belong to him. He warned Duryodhana of the disaster that would overtake him if he did not act righteously. "Justice is justice," Bhishma concluded, "in however offensive a guise it may present itself."

Duryodhana turned on the old man, his face crimson with fury. "You love the Pandavas too much!" he accused him. "That is why you speak in this way!"

Karna sided with Duryodhana. Walking over to where he stood, Karna added his voice to that of his friend. "The Pandavas lost their inheritance by their own foolishness!" he said hotly. "How can they come now, demanding it back! If they are prepared for war, why, so are we! Do they think we fear them?" He looked around with his usual swagger.

Bhishma, however, was not impressed by Karna's fine words and show of strength.

Dhritarashtra held up his hand. "I will send an envoy to Yudhishthira," he quavered. "Let us persuade the Pandavas to accept Duryodhana's decision and give up their claim to their inheritance. In this way we may avoid a war." Bhishma answered nothing, for he recognised Dhritarashtra's suggestion as an unworthy one. The foolish king was trying all kinds of dubious ways to avoid a conflict, instead of facing the truth and doing the right thing.

101

Dhritarashtra's suggestion did not please Karna any more than it did Bhishma, for Karna felt that it was cowardly. "Why should we be afraid of war?" thought Karna. "What is a Kshatriya worth if he will not face death and destruction with a smile?" But he too remained silent, for it was the king who had spoken. Dhritarashtra begged Sanjaya to go as his messenger to the Pandavas and persuade them to give in to Duryodhana. He was to speak to them in a mild and flattering tone, to appeal to their feelings of love for the family and respect for himself, and somehow prevent war.

Sanjaya came to Upalavya, the Matsyan city where the Pandavas had camped, and spoke to Yudhishthira as he had been asked to do.

"What is material wealth before the danger of death, Yudhishthira?" he said. "It is in your hands to avert a terrible war. Duryodhana will not listen to reason, but you are wise and good and thoughtful. Withdraw your claim to your inheritance and you will avert a great disaster."

Listening to these words, Yudhishthira felt confused and troubled, as Dhritarashtra had meant him to be. Yudhishthira was a man of peace and now Dhritarashtra was requesting him to surrender his rights and those of his brothers for the sake of that very peace which he so passionately loved. He was persuading him to yield to wrongdoing, in the name of brotherly love and respect for elders; to give up his lawful inheritance and that of his brothers in order that Duryodhana might keep his unlawful gains.

Yudhishthira thought deeply and for long. Though he yearned for peace, he knew that if he chose Dhritarashtra's way he would be running away from his duty.

When he spoke at last, his voice was grave and earnest. "How can I do what you ask, Sanjaya?" he asked. "We wish our cousins well, for we belong to the same clan. We beg no more from them than that half of the kingdom which is our lawful inheritance." His voice shook with emotion and with sincerity. For a while he paused, unable to speak for the depth of his feeling. Then he stood up before Sanjaya and continued: "No more than our inheritance; but if Duryodhana will not agree even to this, then let him give us only five villages—one for each of us—as a token of his goodwill. Let him not deny us even a place to rest our limbs! Surely we cannot ask for less than that."

Sanjaya went back to Hastinapura, bringing Yudhishthira's message to the Kaurava court. "They ask for just five villages!" he pleaded. "Their cause is just and they are strong."

"Strong!" Duryodhana laughed mockingly. "Is it their strength that makes them give up their claim to the kingdom and beg for five villages?"

Dhritarashtra tried to plead with his son. "They ask for so little, my child," he said. "Give them five villages and they will be content."

Duryodhana lost his temper. "The Pandavas will have nothing," he shouted. "Not even the space of land that can be occupied by the point of a needle."

For one second a hushed silence fell on the hall. Then the voice of the elders rang out, warning Duryodhana. "Consider what you are doing!" they said. "You must be mad. Surely the time of your destruction must be near, for you seem to be intent on rushing to your death."

But Duryodhana would listen to no advice. It seemed as if he had totally lost his reason.

Now, when it seemed that all hope of a peaceful settlement was lost, Krishna himself decided to go to Hastinapura and speak to the Kauravas. The Pandavas—even the lion-hearted Arjuna and Bhima—agreed that peace was to be preferred to war. Only Draupadi, remembering the great wrongs that had been done to her, cried shame upon her husbands for their hesitation in marching upon the men who had dishonoured her. "If my husbands are afraid," she taunted them, "let them say so, and I will go to my father Drupada and my brother Drishtadyumna. They and my five brave sons will come to my aid."

The Pandavas pitied her, for they understood how she felt. But they were wise and knew the dreadful destruction that war would bring. They were not cowards, but they did not wish to bring about such a great disaster. They sat silent, with bowed heads, unable to answer. But Krishna, who could see into all hearts and understand all things, drew her gently aside and begged her to take heart.

"There will be no peace, Draupadi!" he assured her, as he climbed

102

into his chariot. "The Kauravas are drunk with power and will reject all our offers of peace." Hearing his words, Draupadi felt happier. Krishna rode away while the Pandavas looked in the direction of the receding chariot with grave, anxious faces.

Krishna came before the assembly of the Kauravas where the members of the great Kuru clan sat waiting, and was led to the place of honour. From where he sat upon a beautiful throne, encrusted with jewels and precious stones, Krishna spoke to the Kauravas. In moving and eloquent language, Krishna recounted how time and again the Kauravas had wronged and persecuted their cousins. He spoke of the game of dice and of the humiliation of Draupadi and of how, true to

their word, the Pandavas had lived in exile for thirteen gruelling years.

"These thirteen years have gone by," Krishna reminded the Kauravas. "The Pandavas have returned and now they claim the kingdom that was theirs! The world looks to you for justice."

As Krishna spoke, Duryodhana looked around him, and noticed how all who sat there listened to him with respect. He bit his lip fiercely. "How can the Pandavas claim what once they lost, O Krishna?" he demanded angrily. "Go back and tell them that they will get nothing from us!"

Once again the elders tried to persuade Duryodhana to see the error of his ways, and do right. Gandhari, his mother, came into the assembly hall and implored him to be reasonable, but Duryodhana, headstrong and proud, paid no heed to her entreaties.

Krishna tried again. "Duryodhana!" said Krishna, "If you will not return to the Pandavas their kingdom, let them have at least five hundred villages!"

"No!" Duryodhana cried out, his voice bitter with hatred. "The Pandavas will have nothing!"

"Let them have fifty then!" Krishna pleaded. "It is not too much to ask, for the Pandavas are kings and sons of kings. Give them fifty villages, Duryodhana, and they will be satisfied."

"No!" cried Duryodhana again. "No! No! No!" In the great hall the atmosphere was tense as a drawn bowstring.

Krishna spoke again, begging Duryodhana to think well and act rightly for the sake of peace, but Duryodhana only glowered at him and did not answer.

Krishna paused for a while before he resumed his speech.

"Listen, Duryodhana," he said finally, "if you will not let them have even fifty, then let them have five villages."

Duryodhana flung back angrily, "Why do you waste your time babbling in this manner, Krishna? Have I not already said that the Pandavas will get nothing? Not even as much territory as will cover the point of a needle! Go and tell the Pandavas that."

He turned on his heel and left the hall. With him went his friends, Karna, Shakuni and the evil-minded Dushahsana.

Krishna turned to the elders of the court. "You are wise and good men. You have knowledge and foresight," he appealed to them. "Duryodhana's greed and selfishness will lead to certain destruction. War will mean the annihilation of the entire race. I plead for your better understanding and judgment. If it is only Duryodhana who stands between the Kuru race and disaster, then you must sacrifice Duryodhana. For he is only one individual and an individual may be sacrificed in the interests of the larger group. If you remove Duryodhana, you may yet save the situation and avert war."

At this point Duryodhana burst into the room. "A plot," he cried. "It is a plot to kill me! Seize him, Dushahsana, seize Krishna!" A plot it was indeed. But not to kill Duryodhana; it was Krishna's life which was in danger. At Duryodhana's words, Dushahsana sprang upon Krishna to

bind him with ropes while the elders sat aghast; for all knew that it was against the universal law to lay hands upon an emissary.

"Stop!" they cried out, their voices resounding in the hall. "Stop, Duryodhana! Stop, Dushahsana!"

At this terrible moment a miracle happened. Krishna revealed himself in his divine form. Suddenly it seemed to those gathered there that he was everywhere and in all things, even in their own minds and hearts; and that all things were in him—the universe itself with the earth and the heavens and all creation. As for Duryodhana, wherever he turned he seemed to see Krishna, while Dushahsana saw Krishna in everyone who sat there, even in Duryodhana himself. He felt his senses reel. "Where are you, O Krishna?" he roared, "I will seize you and bind you and make you prisoner. Where are you? Where? Where?" But, dazed with the vision of Krishna in his divine form, he never found Krishna. He never seized him and never took him prisoner, and in the end he gave up in despair.

105

"It is a ruse!" Duryodhana muttered. "A trick to frighten us. But we will not yield an inch of territory."

In the midst of all the clamour and confusion, Krishna left the hall in a cloud of smoke. He climbed into his chariot, and drove away from the Kaurava court.

In the assembly hall, all was as it had been before the miracle took place. In their hearts, men had caught for an instant, a glimpse of God. And the next minute, nothing seemed to have changed.

The miracle was forgotten, while fear and foreboding hung in the air like a living thing.

When Kunti heard that Krishna's mission had failed, that only war would decide the quarrel between the Pandavas and Kauravas, she was full of anxiety.

"Is it for this, my sons," she thought sadly to herself, "is it for this that you suffered so bravely for so long, that you might be killed at last upon the field of battle, and your inheritance wrested from you by deceit and force?" She knew that Bhishma and Drona would never wish to kill the Pandavas; they loved them too dearly. It was Karna whom Kunti feared—Karna, that proud, invincible soldier whose steadfast loyalty to Duryodhana was matched only by his implacable hatred for the Pandavas. Remembering Karna, Kunti's heart quailed. "Karna," she cried, "my son, Karna! What cruel fate is this that finds you and your brothers on opposite sides of the battlefield? What unhappy fate has made you the foremost enemy of the Pandavas?"

All night Kunti lay awake tormented by conflicting thoughts. When dawn came, she rose from her bed and slipping out of the palace alone and unseen, walked to the river-bank where she knew Karna came each morning to say his prayers. Standing near him, she waited patiently until he had finished. When he turned round at last and greeted her courteously, she gathered up her courage and spoke to him. In a voice husky with emotion, she told him the story of his birth and of how she had cast him adrift in the river many years ago.

"You are not the son of Adiratha and Radha at all, Karna," she said. "The blood that runs in your veins is as royal as mine!"

Karna cast down his eyes. He said nothing, and Kunti went on. "It is the truth I tell you, Karna: I am your mother."

Still Karna did not reply. Unable to bear the silence any longer, Kunti cried out at last, begging him with clasped hands to forgive her for the wrong she had done him. But Karna harboured no anger against her.

"What is there to forgive, my mother?" he said in a low voice. "Fate rules all men and controls their actions. It has been your destiny to bear me and cast me away; it has been mine to be brought up by strangers and live to see this day." He begged her not to ask for forgiveness and assured her gently that his heart held no resentment.

At Karna's words a great weight seemed to lift from Kunti's heart. She steeled herself to the effort and told him what was in her mind. "You are the eldest of the Pandavas," she said. "Surely you cannot fight against them for you are bound to them by ties of blood."

Then, speaking quickly and breathlessly, she begged Karna to come and join his brothers.

"You are a royal prince," she reminded him, "and you must live like one. At the Kaurava court you are no more than a servant. However high you may rise in their favour, the Kauravas will always be your masters. But if you join your brothers then you will rule and not serve. Your royal birth will be recognised and, as the eldest son, you will be king. You will have wealth and power and all their inheritance. Come, Karna, come and take your rightful place among your flesh and blood."

But Karna was not to be bought over in this manner. Kunti did not know the stuff of which he was made. He faced her boldly and spoke quite simply. "How can you ask this of me?" he said. "For many years I have lived at the Kaurava court, and all that I have today, all that I am today, I owe to the Kauravas and to Duryodhana. Now, when they depend upon me to bring them victory in the war, would you wish me to forsake my lifelong friends and change sides? Would this be conduct befitting a prince, a Kshatriya, an honourable man?"

As he went on, his voice was like a whip lashing her. "If I were tempted by your offer of crown and wealth, and acted in this low and cowardly manner, how could I show my face to the world? Do you not see, Kunti, that by acting as you advise me, I would bring ruin and not glory upon myself? Do you not see that I would know no peace? And if a man is not at peace with himself, then what would he gain even if he had all the wealth of the world?"

Karna spoke boldly and as she heard him, Kunti felt her heart stir with pride. She knew that here before her stood a true Kshatriya, a prince among men, one who could never be bribed or bought. She was torn between admiration for him and anxiety for the Pandavas. And yet she would not give up. She tried another way. This time she appealed to his duty as a son.

"By the laws of Dharma," she persisted, "children owe their parents

love and respect and obedience. Surely you, a just man, will not disregard your mother's plea?"

At these words a look of deep bitterness came over Karna's face. There was a long silence before he could bring himself to say anything. At last he spoke in a low voice, "What duty do I owe you, my mother?" he said. "Forsaken in infancy, I was left to die by you who gave me birth! Have you done a mother's duty by me? Have you given me a mother's love? I grew up among strangers, and all these years your son mattered nothing to you. Do you not see that my real parents are Adiratha and Radha? How can I forsake them who have loved me and cared for me so long?"

Kunti covered her face with her hands, and the scalding tears flowed down her cheeks. She could not bear to hear his words, but he went on relentlessly.

"For years you have had no thought for me. But now that the lives of your other sons are in danger, you come to me. Even at this moment it is for them that you plead!"

Karna did not speak in anger, only in sorrow. Hard though it was to hear his reproaches, Kunti knew that he spoke the truth. She had never given him a mother's love. How then could she claim from him a son's duty? Weeping softly, Kunti turned to go.

Karna looked at her and suddenly felt his heart stir with pity. She seemed so weak, so helpless. She had begged a favour from him, and he who had never refused anyone anything had turned her, his mother, away. "Wait!" he said at last, "wait, Mother!" Kunti waited, trembling to think that he would reproach her again. But when he spoke this time, his voice was quiet and gentle.

"I cannot join the Pandavas," Karna said. "But this I will promise you, my mother, since you come to me begging for their lives: I shall spare the lives of four of the five Pandavas—Yudhishthira, Bhima, Nakula and Sahadeva: these four, I shall not kill. But I cannot promise more than this. I cannot promise you Arjuna's life. Arjuna I shall fight and try with all my strength and power to kill. Either Arjuna or I must die, for there is no room on this earth for both of us. And so, my mother, when one of us is gone, you will still have five sons, for one of us will live!"

Tears flowed down Kunti's wrinkled face. "How noble you are, Karna!" she whispered. "How can I ask more than this? May the Gods bless you!"

Karna prostrated himself before her, and she touched his head in blessing. Then before he could rise, she turned and walked swiftly back to the palace.

19

Preparations for War

To the Pandavas waiting anxiously at Upalavya Krishna brought the terrible news from Hastinapura that all his efforts to secure an honourable peace had failed and that Duryodhana was adamant. All paths were closed to them now, save that of war.

Listening to him, the Pandavas grew heavy-hearted, but Draupadi gave a cry of joy. "Revenge!" she cried out. "Oh sweet, sweet revenge that now will be ours. Now our wrongs will be answered for. Now Dushahsana's blood will flow and soak the earth! And Duryodhana's life will end at the hands of Bhima! Now the Kauravas who brought me shame and sorrow will be cut down root and branch!"

But Yudhishthira did not share her feelings. The news that Krishna brought left him unhappy and disturbed. For a long time he turned it over in his mind, but there was nothing he could do at this stage. The die was cast; there was no turning back. Krishna left the Pandavas and returned to his capital, Dwaraka.

Now both parties began to prepare for war. They sent their emissaries to the courts of other rulers of the day with a view to gaining support and military help.

The kings of the various realms listened attentively to their messages. For many of them it was not easy to decide. Two branches of the same family were going to fight a war. To many kings, both the Pandavas and the Kauravas were related by the same ties of blood. Many people who sympathised with the Pandavas were afraid of the military power of the Kauravas. There were others who felt that the Pandavas had no right to a throne which they had gambled away through their own foolishness.

Balarama and Krishna were related both to the Kauravas and to the Pandavas. Balarama felt he could not join either side without doing injustice to his relatives on the other. He declared himself neutral, and Yudhishthira, seeing the truth of his reasoning, did not try to persuade him against his will. But there was Krishna to be reckoned with. The Yadava armies were large and well-trained. Duryodhana was anxious to secure them. He came personally to Dwaraka to meet Krishna and gain his support.

Now it happened that, by a curious coincidence, Arjuna also arrived on the same day at Krishna's palace with the same purpose in mind. The guards, knowing them to be relatives of the prince, showed them both into the inner rooms. As they entered, they saw Krishna lying asleep on his silken couch. The story goes that they took their seats—

Duryodhana, haughtily choosing the golden chair that stood at the head of the bed; Arjuna happy to sit on a low stool at the sleeping Krishna's feet. Thus they waited, in silence, each thinking in his heart thoughts unknown to the other. Arjuna's mind dwelt on Krishna—on Krishna's goodness and wisdom and power. But Duryodhana's mind was full of bitterness and anger against his cousins, full of his own importance and wealth and might. Presently Krishna awoke and sat up, and his eyes first rested on Arjuna. There was such warmth and pleasure in his voice as he greeted Arjuna that Duryodhana, sitting high on his golden chair, felt a stab of anger and envy. He coughed gently to attract attention and Krishna turned round and saw him.

"What good fortune is mine!" exclaimed Krishna. "What good fortune to have two of my dearest relatives and friends visit me together!" And he held out his arms in welcome and drew them both to him. Then he placed them on either side of him on his couch and did them equal honour. With his own hands he brought them water to wash their feet; and after they had washed he served them food and drink and he spoke to them and enquired after their own welfare and health and the welfare and health of their families. Then after these formalities were completed, he asked them very gently the reason for their visit.

"I come to seek your help in the war, cousin Krishna," Duryodhana said to him speaking first. "You will do well to come on our side; for we are strong; our numbers are large and our victory is certain." Krishna turned to Arjuna.

"And you, Arjuna, what brings you here?" Arjuna answered, "I came also for the same reason, dear cousin—to beg for your help, for without it we are nothing and less than nothing." His voice was low and humble.

Krishna's brow knitted in mock surprise and his merry eyes twinkled. "This is awkward, my cousins," he laughed, "that both of you should come at the same time for the same thing." Then, growing serious, he regarded them thoughtfully for a minute, looking from one to the other, his handsome face cupped in his hands. Finally he stood up and said, "You know that I and my forces are both at your disposal," he said. "There is nothing I would not spare for either of you, for you are both related to me by close ties of blood. But I would like to be completely just and fair, and give my help to both. Let Krishna never be accused of having helped one brother against the other. Therefore, I will leave the choice to you. The choice shall be between my forces and me. You may have either my forces or me, but you cannot have both. He who chooses me to be on his side may have me, but my armies will then fight for the other. I alone will be on his side, and I will neither bear arms nor take part in the fighting. It is for you to choose!"

Duryodhana was about to choose but Krishna held him back. "You were both here at the same time," he said. "But I saw Arjuna first. So let it be Arjuna who chooses first." Duryodhana protested violently that it was a trick to hoodwink him, but Krishna silenced him, saying that in all games there was always a small element of luck. Duryodhana scowled darkly. He had never trusted Krishna. Now he was sure that Krishna was going to play a trick on him. But all the while that Krishna was speaking, Arjuna had been gazing steadfastly into his face, his heart full of reverence and love. He lost no time in making his choice, for he had no doubts. He chose Krishna. "If you are on our side, what more can we want, Lord?" he said, deeply moved.

Krishna turned to Duryodhana. A few minutes ago that prince had been protesting bitterly. But now he stood looking as if he could not believe his ears. His luck seemed too good to be true. No man—Duryodhana felt—no man in his senses could have thrown away such a chance as Arjuna had done! Well, that was lucky for him. And Arjuna had only himself to blame. He said briskly, to indicate that the matter was ended and there was no more to be said, "Your armies for me then, Krishna. It is settled: Arjuna himself has settled it so." For he was afraid Arjuna might change his mind. Arjuna, however, seemed content with the arrangement. Duryodhana looked at him contemptuously. "This Arjuna is a fool," thought Duryodhana. "Who but an utter fool would make such a choice and throw away the last chance of victory?" He congratulated himself upon having won the victory even before the war had started.

Duryodhana had good reason to be confident. There were others whose support he was sure of. The terrible Jayadratha or Saindhava, giant among men, king of the Sindhus and husband of his sister, was on his side. So were Susharma, king of Trigarta, and his sons, all mighty warriors of the time. Then there was Shalya—king of Madra Desha and the maternal uncle of Nakula and Sahadeva. The wily Duryodhana had tricked and bribed Shalya into promising to fight on the Kaurava side against his nephews. Duryodhana smiled gleefully, remembering how he had tricked the unsuspecting Shalya into the situation.

Shalya, concerned about his nephews, had set out from his kingdom on the journey to Upalavya. Hearing this, Duryodhana hastened to devise a cunning scheme. All along the road that he knew Shalya was travelling, he had wells dug for thirsty travellers and water troughs constructed for animals. He built resthouses and inns where travellers could sleep, eat and refresh themselves. He ensured that slaves and servants waited upon Shalya and his retinue at these resting places and served him the tastiest foods and the choicest wines. Musicians and dancers and acrobats entertained the travellers in the evenings. Shalya's journey, which would otherwise have been long and arduous, became so pleasant that he was enthralled. "Why, Yudhishthira has been kindness itself!" exclaimed Shalya, certain that no one but Yudhishthira could have been so generous or have provided so many comforts—"How can I withhold my help from one who has done so much for me, whose hospitality I have so freely accepted?"

And when people asked him whom he would support in the war, he answered laughing, "Naturally, the prince who has been my kind host." Shalya had a rude shock when he heard that that kind host had been Duryodhana, and not Yudhishthira as he had fondly imagined. Duryodhana met him at one stage of the journey and enlightened Shalya. "If you are a man of your word," the Kaurava reminded him, "then you must fight on our side and give us your support!"

Shalya was completely taken aback. He had never dreamed that things would take such a turn. Nakula and Sahadeva were his sister's sons and he loved them dearly. He had the greatest respect for Yudhishthira, and Arjuna had always been a good friend of his. Duryodhana's trick made him look foolish. Shalya felt he had been cheated, but he could not deny that Duryodhana now had a hold on him. Having accepted Duryodhana's hospitality he could not fight against him. Reluctantly Shalya agreed to fight on the Kaurava side. But he remained uneasy and unhappy. He loved the Pandavas too well to want their defeat and death. Little did Duryodhana realise that this unwilling ally he had bought over would not prove a steadfast, faithful friend. To him it seemed that with the allies he had collected and the armies he had built up, victory was as good as won.

Delighted at obtaining the support of the Yadava armies, Duryodhana hurried away from Dwaraka and returned to Hastinapura in high spirits. Arjuna took leave of Krishna. They would meet again shortly, for Krishna had promised to follow him to Upalavya as soon as he could. Arjuna, arriving at the Pandava camp, found his brother and their allies busy with preparations for the war. He approached Yudhishthira and related to him the happenings at Dwaraka. When he told Yudhishthira about the choice he had made, his brother was full of joy.

He embraced Arjuna warmly and told him he had chosen wisely and well. "With Krishna on our side, armed or unarmed, we have nothing to fear," he said fervently. Then he remembered Shalya and his face grew worried. He decided to speak to Krishna about it when he came.

"Shalya could never have gone over willingly to the Kauravas," said Krishna when he heard. "There must have been some misunderstanding." So indeed there was, as he found out when he went to Shalya's camp. In fact, Shalya had no real sympathy for Duryodhana and was willing to render assistance to the Pandavas. Krishna said to him, "Shalya, there is much that you can do. You know that there is no charioteer in the world like you. It is certain that Karna will choose you to be his chariot-driver. You will drive him over the battlefield and be with him when he faces Arjuna, and thus you will hold Arjuna's life in your hands. Karna will depend on you to render him assistance in the battle between him and Arjuna. He will depend on you to steer his chariot skilfully and bring him to victory. Shalya, if you love Arjuna, you will know what to do."

Shalya, who was listening carefully, nodded. "I know what I must do, Krishna," he said. "I have never loved the arrogant Karna. I am and always shall be Arjuna's friend."

Krishna thanked him warmly and returned to Upalavya. In the Pandava camp he found Yudhishthira going about his duties with energy and determination. His brothers and his allies all looked to him to lead them to victory. Yudhishthira appointed seven able generals to command the seven divisions of their army: Drupada, Dhrishtadyumna, Shikhandin, Virata, Satyaki, Chekitana and Bhima. Of these, Dhrishtadyumna was chosen as Supreme Commander of the entire army. Yudhishthira would have liked Krishna to take this position, but Krishna declined, smiling, "I have promised Duryodhana," he said, "that I will not take up arms or fight. If I must take part in the war, let me be Arjuna's charioteer."

The others looked at him in amazement. "The great prince of Dwaraka, a charioteer?" they thought to themselves. But they said nothing, for they trusted Krishna completely.

So Krishna was Arjuna's charioteer during the eighteen days of the great war of Kurukshetra.

Now, on the eve of Kurukshetra, a hot quarrel flared up in the camp of the Kauravas, and there was angry disagreement among their warriors. Bhishma, the veteran hero of many wars and Supreme Commander of the Kaurava forces, had been given the task of appointing the commanding officers. It was expected that Karna would be appointed to a very high rank. But Bhishma had never approved of Karna's arrogance and high-handedness. Karna, for his part, disliked Bhishma and doubted his loyalty to the Kaurava cause. When the time came for choosing the officers, Bhishma spoke his mind frankly to Duryodhana and showed his open disapproval of Karna. Cut to the quick, Karna answered back sharply—and a war of words followed. Incensed by what Bhishma said, Karna declared hotly that he would not take up arms or fight as long as Bhishma was commander. Duryodhana was vexed and grieved. He tried to persuade Karna to be more reasonable. But Karna's pride would not allow him to swallow what he considered an insult.

112

20

Kurukshetra and after

The day of the battle dawned bright and clear. The banners and pennants of kings and chieftains fluttered gaily in the sunshine. But the air was resonant with fearful sounds: the echo of conch shells, the roll of drums, the neighing and whinnying of horses and the dreadful trumpeting of elephants.

Arjuna sat silent in his chariot, gazing into the distance at the opposing armies. He could make out the figures who stood in the front ranks: Bhishma, his great-uncle, head of the Kuru clan; Drona and Kripa, his teachers; and his cousins, the hundred Kauravas. Looking at these people whom he loved, who were his close relatives, bound to him by ties of blood, Arjuna suddenly felt his brave heart fail him. His eyes filled with tears, his knees started to tremble, and the bow began to slip from his hand. How could he shed their blood? To what purpose? What would he gain by destroying those he loved and revered? What happiness would an empire or kingship or power bring him if, in the end, these things were to be gained by the destruction of fellow human beings, relatives and friends? Arjuna's heart faltered and tears rolled down his cheeks. Suddenly he threw away his arms and sat down, crying out, "Krishna, I will not fight this war! I cannot bring myself to destroy those whom I love and honour. Let us surrender. Let the Kauravas take everything, so that there may be peace and goodwill."

It was a moment of crisis. A great battle was about to begin and all was in readiness for it. And just as the first shot was to be fired, the foremost warrior of the day had suddenly lost courage. It seemed to him so senseless and futile to fight and kill—all for the sake of a patch of land called a kingdom.

Krishna listened to Arjuna's words with compassion. He saw how the blood had drained from the hero's face, leaving it pale and grey. He saw how he trembled and how his hair stood on end. Then Krishna spoke wise and gentle words to his friend upon that field of battle, encouraging him and giving him heart. For Krishna knew that it was too late now to withdraw from the conflict. The Pandavas had committed themselves, and now they must go through with the fight to the very end.

So Krishna spoke to Arjuna of life and death, of this world and the ones that are invisible, of the struggles and conflicts and sorrows of mankind, and the three paths by which men may reach God—for all may reach God, no matter who or what they were. There were endless roads that led to Him, but of them all, there were three that were best known—the path of meditation and yoga, the path of duty and the path of the love of God. Each man, said Krishna, might choose his own path to God, according to his nature. But for the Kshatriya, as for most people, the way to God lay in the path of duty. Men must work, and in their work, find God. Arjuna was a Kshatriya and his duty was to fight for righteousness, whatever the consequences. The time for doubt was gone, said Krishna. Now was the time for action, and there must be no hesitation. Arjuna must act fearlessly. And when he acted, he must do so without the desire or hope of reward or glory or even success. Right action, said Krishna, was that which was free from all desire—even the desire for success.

Last of all, Krishna spoke to Arjuna of the limitless and one God that all men seek. "I will speak to you of my divine forms," he said, "but only of those which are the most important, for I am infinite. I am the beginning, the middle and the end of everything. I am birth and the beginning of all things; I am death, which is the end. I am eternal, for I was never born; neither will I ever die. I exist everywhere in all things, and all things exist in Me. There is nothing moving or unmoving that can exist without Me!"

As Arjuna listened, strange emotions seized him. It came to him like the dawning of light upon darkness that it was no mere mortal who sat beside him, but God himself. Understanding this feebly, he began to long to see God in all His glory and expressed this desire to Krishna. Then did Krishna reveal himself to his friend. Arjuna saw the heavenly vision and was struck with such amazement and fear, that his senses reeled and he trembled violently like a leaf in a storm. For the vision was limitless as the universe itself. All around him was the Divine form, infinite and unending. Across the skies it blazed, and over the earth, in all things—even in the smallest particle—a wondrous form such as he could not describe, for he was blinded by the light of countless suns. There was neither beginning nor end, and gazing upon it, Arjuna felt breathless, as if he was a speck of dust and less than that, drowning in a vast, endless sea. Fear seized him and his voice cried out to Krishna for help. Then the Lord in His mercy returned to his human form. The vision ceased and all things became as they were. Nothing seemed to have changed. All was as it had been before everywhere except in Arjuna's heart, for he had seen the light of wisdom. He joined his hands and worshipped Krishna in his heart. Then, with a new spirit surging through him, he took up his arms again and went into battle.

114

So the war began. It continued for eighteen days, and every day blood flowed in rivers, drenching the earth; and the dead and the dying lay in mangled heaps upon the ground. At sunset each day, the truce was sounded and the warriors rested in their camps while the sentries kept watch outside. During the war men showed their true natures in all their strengths and their weaknesses. Many deeds of valour and chivalry were done. But in moments of crisis, even the great and good men

stooped to unworthy things such as falsehood and treachery, forgetting the noble lessons of Kshatriya conduct.

On the first day, with Dushahsana leading the Kauravas and Bhima the Pandavas, the armies joined battle, and after many hours of fearful fighting, a terrible duel took place between Arjuna's son, Abhimanyu, and Bhishma, the grandsire of the clan. For Bhishma pierced the Pandava army formation that first day, bringing with him death and such terror that no one could withstand him. Swift and sure flew his deadly arrows and men fell before them like insects in a fire. Panic spread among the Pandava forces as they fought desperately to hold their ground. But Bhishma's advance could not be checked, and it seemed that the Pandavas would be routed completely on the very first day. Then, the young Abhimanyu came riding in his chariot to meet the fiery old warrior in combat. He fought with astonishing skill and courage. Here was one who did not know what fear was, and danger only made him the more eager to go out and meet it! Men looked at the boy in wonder, for he seemed to be everywhere, at all times, fighting in turn with bow and mace and sword, with such dexterity that it took the combined efforts of Bhishma, Shalya, Kripa and Kirtivarman to beat him back. Still he fought on, one youth scarcely out of his boyhood, eager-eyed and undaunted amongst these fierce and hardened warriors, until the Pandavas, fearing for his safety, sent to his help Virata and his sons Sweta and Uttara Kumar. Then the enemy turned their attack on these, and in the fierce fight that followed, the noble sons of Virata were slain. Bhishma followed up the victory by leading an attack on the Pandava army and routing it completely.

On the second day, however, the Pandavas recovered their strength because of the brave leadership and the determination of Arjuna, Dhrishtadyumna and Bhima. On this second day, Arjuna met the unconquerable Bhishma in a battle; but so well matched were they that neither could win or lose. Besides, though he had steeled himself to destroy Bhishma, at the sight of that brave veteran, his great-uncle whom he loved and venerated, the head of his family who had been more than a father to him, Arjuna could not bring himself to put forth his best effort. The battle thus ended in a draw. But that same day, on another front, the Pandavas fighting under Dhrishtadyumna and Bhima won a great victory.

116

BHISHMA'S FALL

Day after day the warriors fought. Sometimes it seemed that one side won and sometimes the other. Mighty deeds were done on both sides. But it was Bhishma who, time and again, carried the day; there was no one like him, for he had had many decades of experience and was unconquerable. Wherever Bhishma went, he brought death and terror and destruction, and made the enemy fly as from a raging fire. It was all the Pandavas could do to keep up their courage before his onslaughts, for surely they would have been defeated and totally destroyed, if Arjuna's deeds of valour had not repeatedly saved the day and allowed them breathing space. No less remarkable were the deeds of Arjuna's valiant son, Abhimanyu. Time and again the gallant boy was put to the test; time and again he emerged victorious. His courage never once failed him as he led many attacks upon the enemy. Arjuna's heart swelled with pride as he saw how, when surrounded upon all sides by fierce Kaurava warriors, Abhimanyu fought back, like a young lion, single-handed, never once turning back, never despairing. Bhima was there too, fighting with great courage, cutting down the brothers of Duryodhana, one after another, for he had sworn to destroy them. And beside Bhima stood his son, Ghatotkacha, whose mother was Hidimbi. But even their combined efforts were of no avail against the mighty Bhishma, who attacked them like the God of Death himself.

117

Again and again Krishna spoke to Arjuna, urging him to conquer Bhishma. Krishna knew that victory would never be won while Bhishma was still alive. But Arjuna, in spite of all his resolutions, shrank from the terrible deed. He loved Bhishma too deeply. Every day the battle raged, and great numbers of men fell on the battlefield; but Arjuna's heart cried out against the slaying of Bhishma; he could not bring himself to do it. On the ninth day of the war, Bhishma was still alive and strong as ever and Krishna, seeing how he pushed back the Pandavas with his might, lost his patience with Arjuna for the half-hearted manner in which he fought. Jumping from the chariot, he took his discus in his hand, crying out that if Arjuna would not slay Bhishma, he would do the deed himself. But Arjuna held him back in distress. He did not wish Krishna to go back on his promise to Duryodhana that he would not bear arms or fight in the war. He did not wish Krishna to be false. "Tomorrow I will kill Bhishma," promised Arjuna. "Wait until tomorrow." And Krishna was pleased.

Arjuna kept his word. On the tenth day he brought Bhishma down, but only by adopting means that were blatantly unfair. For Arjuna, even Arjuna, as Krishna reminded him, was no match against the mighty son of Ganga. Man to man, if Bhishma fought back, Arjuna stood no chance against him, so strong was Bhishma's arm, so deadly his aim. It was, therefore, for them to see that Arjuna did not confront Bhishma in a straight encounter. It was only thus that he could be rendered powerless.

"Bhishma scrupulously obeys the Kshatriya code," Krishna reminded Arjuna. "Come what may, he will not raise his hand against a woman or one born as a woman. Therefore bring Shikhandin, and place him before you in your chariot; then from behind Shikhandin take aim and shoot your darts. Bhishma will never fight Shikhandin, for all the world knows he was born as a woman!"

Arjuna heard these words with a grieving heart. Where was this dreadful war leading them? Into what morass of wrongdoing and unrighteousness? Yet now that they were in war, victory must be won. Arjuna steeled his heart and made his decision. Bhishma would die.

On the tenth day, men saw Arjuna's shining chariot moving swiftly through the army formations. Shikhandin of Panchala stood in it where

Arjuna should have stood, his bow poised for action. Arjuna himself crouched behind him, hidden from view. From this vantage point, Arjuna shot his arrows. So fast did they fly and so sure was their aim that men knew at once they were not shot by the prince of Panchala, but by one far mightier and more skilled than he could ever be.

From his own chariot Bhishma looked up and smiled, for he understood everything. Now was the hour of his fall. He had been true all his life, but was to be brought down by untruth! Bhishma did not mind. Death, he knew, must come to all men, and he who had lived a life of honour and goodness did not flinch from it.

He saw Shikhandin and remembered the vow that Amba had taken long years ago to destroy him—Amba whom he had unintentionally wronged had been reborn for this and blessed by Shiva, the God of Destruction. Bhishma laid down his arms. He would never fight one who had been born a woman. Even in the face of death, Bhishma scorned to do something which he considered ignoble and unchivalrous. So he stood waiting for his death while the arrows came swift and thick and struck him on every side. They struck at his shield and shattered it. They struck him through his armour, and pierced his flesh in so many places that there was not a needle-point of space left anywhere upon his body. But he would neither strike back nor turn and run. He stood there like a gallant old lion in his strength, until there came at last from the bow of Arjuna, one final deadly arrow, with the speed of lightning, that pierced his heroic heart.

Bhishma laughed when he saw it, for he knew it was Arjuna's arrow, and the knowledge pleased him as he fell, mortally wounded.

A loud cry went up from the people. Then a hush fell upon the battlefield. The two warring parties called a truce as they gathered around to pay Bhishma homage. They knew his greatness and recognised him for a hero such as the world had never seen. Friend and foe alike came and honoured him as a soldier, strong of arm and stout of heart; honest and true to his beliefs; open and outspoken, hating everything that was mean and ignoble, and of a courage unflinching and unfaltering in the hour of danger. When they came to his side, they saw how his body did not touch the ground, but was held up on the arrows that had pierced it.

"Look!" they whispered, "The warrior lies upon a bed of arrows. What bed could be more fitting for such a soldier?"

But he was tormented by pain. His head hung down as he lay gasping for breath. "A support for my head," he gasped. But when they brought him cushions and pillows he smiled gently and whispered, "These are not the pillows that I would use." He turned his eyes upon Arjuna, who nodded, for he alone, of all of them there, understood the old warrior's meaning.

Then Arjuna took three arrows from his quiver and shot them one after another in quick succession, so that they struck the earth near Bhishma's head. The warriors who had gathered there gently propped the dying man's head against the arrows. Then Bhishma was happy, for

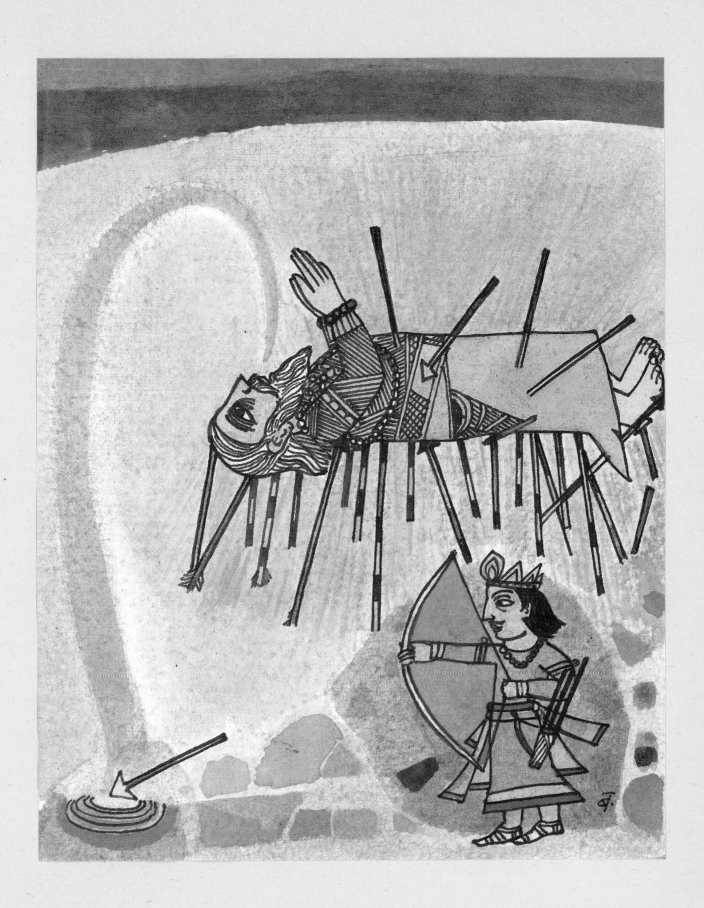

now there was no part of him that had not been touched by the arrows of the enemy.

Now, when all the warriors had paid their respects, Karna came to Bhishma's side. During Bhishma's life, Karna had hated him bitterly. The two men, both so brave and honourable, had never seen eye to eye on any subject. Karna had stayed out of the fight because Bhishma had been chosen commander. He had always doubted Bhishma's loyalty to the Kaurava cause, but now, as Bhishma lay upon the battlefield pierced by Arjuna's arrows, Karna knew that Bhishma had been true. Kneeling at Bhishma's side, he asked for forgiveness, which Bhishma gave readily. Duryodhana came too, and Bhishma, fixing his dying gaze upon him, begged him again to make peace with his cousins even at this stage. Peace was infinitely better than war, Bhishma told him, and the Pandava cause was just. But Duryodhana hardened his heart against the old warrior's advice.

"That I cannot do!" he said. "I will fight till the end." Bhishma grieved sorely for the misguided prince.

Presently his mouth and lips grew parched with thirst and he gasped for water. But when they brought him water in gold and silver vessels he would not take it. He fixed his eyes on Arjuna, who alone understood his meaning. Arjuna shot an arrow into the earth, causing a spring of cool, clear water to bubble out and reach the dying warrior's lips. Then he drank this sweet water and it refreshed him as he lay there. And yet, it was not time for him to go.

"The sun is in the southern regions of the earth," he whispered to them. "Until he begins his northward journey, death must keep away from me."

For many years ago, when Bhishma was young, his father had given him this blessing: that death itself would not conquer him unless he wished it to do so.

"I will lie here upon the field of battle," said Bhishma, "until the sun makes his return journey and lights up the northern part of the world."

One by one, at his bidding, the warriors left him, and went to their places to continue the fight. But Bhishma lay upon his bed of arrows while the days passed. Around him the war raged with the wild cries of frenzied men and the throb of drums, the twanging of bowstrings, the trumpeting of elephants and the neighing of horses. The arrows sped over his head and fell around him like golden rain, but Bhishma's mind remained clear and unclouded to the end, and his heart was at peace.

120

ABHIMANYU

On Bhishma's fall, Duryodhana chose Karna, as commander-in-chief of the Kaurava army. But Karna stepped aside and yielded place to Drona, who was older and more experienced.

On the eleventh day of the war, Duryodhana, planning the operations, commanded Drona to bend his efforts to the capture of Yudhishthira. If Yudhishthira was captured alive, Duryodhana reasoned secretly to himself, he could be enticed into yet another game of dice and defeated. Such a defeat would be so much easier to accomplish than a defeat upon the battlefield.

Drona, reluctant at heart, nevertheless had to agree. Duryodhana was his master, and obedience, he knew, was the first duty of a soldier.

So Drona went into battle, thrusting through the Pandava lines with fierce determination, making his way to the heart of the formation, where he knew Yudhishthira would be. It was no mean or easy task for even so great a soldier as Drona. Arjuna, alerted by what was happening and guessing Drona's objective, sprang to the defence of his brother and king. Arjuna was fighting now on two fronts; his attention was divided between the savage attacks of Susharma's sons on the one side and of Drona on the other. Susharma's sons, the Samsaptakas, were reckless in their daring. Seeing that the war had gone badly for their side, they had come together and sworn to go into the thick of the fight and never retreat. Only death was to stop their advance; and in the event of the death of one brother, another was to step into his place and go steadily on.

121

Never was such desperate courage seen. It seemed to Arjuna that they fought more like demons than human beings. It was all he could do to withstand their impetuous and determined onslaughts.

Seizing a moment's respite when the Samsaptakas had been thrown off their guard, and making hurried arrangements for checking their advance, Arjuna rushed to his brother's help.

Backwards and forwards went Arjuna on that eleventh day of the battle. On the twelfth day the position worsened, for on that day Drona broke through the Pandava army and would surely have captured Yudhishthira during Arjuna's absence, had Bhima not rescued him at the very last moment.

The thirteenth day of the battle dawned. The fighting was growing more desperate and fearful. Neither side could yet claim victory; neither side would give in. On the thirteenth day, however, Arjuna determined to bring the battle with the Samsaptakas to an end, for it had gone on too long and sapped the energy of the Pandava army. For a while Drona's advance had been checked. Arjuna did not doubt that Yudhishthira would be safe. So he begged Krishna to drive his chariot to the scene of the Samsaptaka attack.

When Arjuna was gone, Yudhishthira found himself face to face with Drona. He noted that Drona had arranged his army in the shape of wheel. For a while his attack had been repulsed, but Yudhishthira knew that Drona was awaiting the first opportunity to advance and take him prisoner. It seemed to Yudhishthira that the best way to prevent this would be to wrest the advantage from their hands by launching an offensive and attacking the enemy boldly. But the enemy who had pierced the Pandava phalanx had planted themselves in a tight ring. Yudhishthira knew that the formation was a complicated one, and few people knew how to break it up. Among the Pandavas, there were only four who had knowledge of it: Arjuna, Krishna, Pradyumna and Abhimanyu, Arjuna's young son. Arjuna, Krishna and Pradyumna were

away. Yudhishthira therefore sent for Abhimanyu and spoke to him of his plan.

"Would you be willing to lead the attack on Drona's units?" he asked, "You, my child, are the only one who has any knowledge of the army's wheel formation."

The boy gladly accepted the leadership of the army, proud that so great a task had been entrusted to him. In his eagerness, he did not stop to consider that he did not know how to make his way out of the formation, should he need to retreat.

Abhimanyu ordered his charioteer to make straight for the Kaurava army. As he sped away, Yudhishthira was beset by doubts. What if Abhimanyu failed? He was little more than a child, and Yudhishthira had sent this raw youth into the heart of the battle.

122

But Abhimanyu felt no doubts. His heart soared with hope, for he did not know what fear was. Yudhishthira had promised to send others to help him. Abhimanyu did not doubt that they would come. But the attack, he knew, had to be made by one individual. He had to break his way through, and only then could the others in his unit follow him.

Abhimanyu rushed at the enemy lines. So great was the fury of his attack that the rings broke before him, and he pierced them one after another. The enemy was taken completely by surprise. Abhimanyu's chariot entered the enemy formation. The boy gave a cry of triumph. He had achieved what few had been able to do. But now came the tragedy; for as soon as he entered, the Kaurava soldiers, recovering

from their initial surprise, came together again and the circles closed on him. Abhimanyu was trapped.

Fighting the enemy on every side as he advanced, Abhimanyu never looked back. He did not know he had walked into a fatal trap and if he had known, he would not have cared. Single-handed he fought on, cutting down all who stood against him, using his weapons with such skill and courage that the enemy was astounded. The Kauravas would have been completely routed if Jayadratha, king of the Sindhus, had not rallied them together and checked their flight. He engaged Yudhishthira and the Pandavas, so that they could not advance to help Abhimanyu. Drona and five other warriors in chariots surrounded the boy, but still he fought bravely. Then, Dushahsana cut off his arm with his great sword. Abhimanyu continued to fight. Dushahsana then cut off his other limbs, one by one. But Abhimanyu's eyes remained proud and defiant, eager for combat, even while he lay helpless upon the earth. At this moment, Jayadratha, king of the Sindhus, charged up to Abhimanyu and dealt the final blow that killed him. The deed done, the Kauravas returned to their camp at the sounding of the truce at sunset, rejoicing in the victory they had won.

For the Pandavas it was a black day. When Abhimanyu did not return, Yudhishthira knew that the worst had happened. His heart grew heavy as he sat waiting; what would he say to Arjuna when that warrior returned? How would he break to him the news of his child's death?

But Arjuna did not need to be told in words. As he and Krishna drove back in the chariot after having defeated the Samsaptakas, Arjuna felt strange forebodings in his heart. In the gathering darkness he seemed to see evil omens; shrouds of death, owls hooting and corpses and blood. His hands grew cold and his mouth grew dry as, approaching the camp, he heard no joyful sounds of welcome, no music, no laughter. Trembling in every limb, Arjuna entered and saw his brothers before him, silent, with faces downcast. Cold fear gripped him and he knew the truth in his heart, even before Yudhishthira told him. Then Arjuna sank upon the floor and wept bitterly. He looked at them standing around him helplessly, and reproached them angrily for having sent his beloved son to his death. It was hard and bitter for him to bear the thought that the boy had ventured out alone and that help had not reached him, when he had most needed it. Bitter were the tears that Arjuna shed as he cursed himself and his brothers that night; and no one could console him save his friend Krishna, with his words of deep and gentle wisdom. All night long Arjuna lay prostrate with grief. They brought Abhimanyu's mother Subhadra to him, and the sweet Uttara, Abhimanyu's bride. The sorrowing parents clasped the young girl to them and wept over her for her fate. But Uttara looked at them with strange calm eyes. "Build me a pyre," she said, "I will enter the flames and join my beloved Abhimanyu." At that, Arjuna roused himself and restrained her.

"No!" he cried, holding her. "No, dear one—this you will not do. You are still young and you must live." For he knew that she carried in her womb the unborn child of Abhimanyu. One day the child would grow up and carry on the name of their clan.

The night wore on. The Pandavas sat huddled in their camp and the only sounds to be heard were the lamentations of Arjuna. As morning broke and the first bugle sounded, announcing the beginning of hostilities, Arjuna arose. His face was grim and set, his fists clenched tight. He looked at the weeping women and swore aloud the terrible oath, that before sunset that day he would destroy Jayadratha or would himself be destroyed. Thus determined, Arjuna mounted his chariot and leaving Satyaki to defend Yudhishthira he went to battle.

Spies had carried to the Kauravas the news of Arjuna's great oath, and Jayadratha, terror-stricken, had wished to fly from the field of battle. But Duryodhana persuaded him to remain, promising him that the Kaurava forces would that day be dedicated solely to the task of protecting him. Onward sped Arjuna's chariot driven by Krishna, piercing through the Kaurava army, through the lines of their elephants, putting the animals to rout, trampling upon men and causing panic and confusion. But Arjuna paid no heed to this. Consumed with the single thought of Jayadratha's destruction, he fought his way onward. But as he went on he came face to face with Drona, who barred his way and would not let him pass. Arjuna fought hard to overcome him. But Drona proved too strong and in the end Arjuna had to evade him, only to meet fiercer and more determined opponents at each step, so that it seemed to him for a while, as he fell back fainting and exhausted, that he would be vanquished before his aim could be accomplished. But seeking strength from his resolve, he advanced grimly upon the enemy.

When he pierced through to the very heart of the army, Duryodhana sprang up and faced him, challenging him to a duel. They fought fiercely like a pair of lions and their war cries resounded on all sides. Repeatedly Arjuna attacked Duryodhana, but his shafts seemed to have lost their power. Then he understood that Duryodhana was protected by the magic armour that Drona had given him. Arjuna was desperate and it was desperately that he fought, vowing to himself again and again that he would never give up. Duryodhana, meanwhile, was growing exhausted. But already the afternoon was darkening into evening. Soon the sun would set; the truce would sound and the fighting would cease. Once the sun set, Duryodhana knew that he and Jayadratha were safe. Arjuna too looked at the western sky, flooded with the glowing colours of sunset, and knew that truce was perilously near. Would Arjuna's great oath remain unfulfilled? Would the death of Abhimanyu remain unavenged? Would Jayadratha escape his punishment at the hands of the sorrowing father?

Krishna was watching. He knew that today Jayadratha must die at the hands of Arjuna. The sun must not set until Jayadratha had been killed. As the hour of sunset drew near, Krishna by his power caused the sun to be shrouded in a mist so heavy that no man could tell when it set that day. The fighting went on, for no truce was sounded. The shining arrows sped like shafts of lightning through the darkness.

Arjuna, who had all but given up hope, saw he had acquired a fresh lease of time. Gathering new courage and strength he went into the fray once again and, overpowering Duryodhana with arrows carefully aimed at those parts of his body that were not covered with armour, he came at last to the centre of the army formation where Jayadratha hid, full of terror. Then seeing him, Arjuna cried out for vengeance in a terrible voice and let his arrows fly. They went whistling through the air and slashed Jayadratha's head from his body, and the mighty warrior fell dying to the earth.

Even after this, the fighting continued, savage and relentless, far into that terrible night, while the fearful sounds of war shook the earth and the sky. Terrible were the duels that took place between Satyaki and Drona, Drona and Bhima, Nakula and Karna, and Karna and Bhima. Bhima destroyed seven of Duryodhana's brothers, including the good and righteous Vikarna, and would himself have been slain by Karna, had the latter not remembered his promise to Kunti and spared his life. Last of all, came the duel between Karna and Ghatotkacha, Bhima's son. In the darkness these two advanced upon each other, Ghatotkacha fought with such great skill and savage fury that Karna would surely have been killed, had he not used the mighty weapon which long ago he had acquired from Indra in exchange for his armour and earrings. In a moment of desperation, forgetting Indra's words of caution, Karna let the thunderbolt fly. It struck the valiant Ghatotkacha in the chest. He staggered for a moment, then fell dead upon the ground.

Ghatotkacha was slain. The Pandavas mourned for him and Bhima tore his hair and wept.

Karna had triumphed, but even as he turned away from the scene, he realised his folly. What had he done in his moment of desperation? Had not Indra warned him that the thunderbolt would be useful only once and against one single enemy? Had he not resolved that he would use it against Arjuna and Arjuna only? Now he had expended that one perfect weapon in a careless, unthinking, desperate moment. He had destroyed Ghatotkacha...but what of Arjuna? Karna turned away. Around him a dark fate seemed to be drawing a web; on all sides the threads were tightening around him.

THE DEATH OF DRONA

The slaying of Ghatotkacha fuelled the battle afresh. Through the night and into the pale morning the battle continued with unabated rage. It was now the fifteenth day of the war; it was upon this day that Drona was slain by Dhrishtadyumna.

Krishna saw that the battle was going against the Pandavas. He saw that their forces were scattered like driven rain before Drona's powerful and deadly attacks, and he knew that Drona must die if the Pandavas were to live. But he knew too that once more trickery must come into play, for Drona was too strong for the Pandavas. Krishna leaned over and spoke to Arjuna: "Cry out, Arjuna, cry out aloud that Ashwatthama, Drona's son, has been killed! Let the news reach Drona. When he hears it, he will be so overpowered by sorrow, he will have no more heart to fight. He will sink in dejection, and his hands will lose their grip, his mind its clarity. Thus weakened, Drona might be slain." But Arjuna refused indignantly to stoop to such an unworthy act. Bhima, however, had no such scruples. Knowing that Drona must be destroyed if victory was to be won, he cut down and killed an elephant named Ashwatthama, and then cried out, "Ashwatthama is slain!" Now when Drona heard this cry, he was in the midst of battle. He refused to believe it.

"It is not true!" wailed the old man, who loved his only son more than his life. "It is a trick they are playing upon me." But Bhima's voice resounded again, "Ashwatthama is dead! Ashwatthama, Ashwatthama is dead!" Drona turned pale and began to tremble. Yet he could not believe what he had heard. Steadying his fainting heart, he cried out, "I will not believe it until I hear it from Yudhishthira, for Yudhishthira is a man of truth and has never been known to utter a falsehood!" And now Yudhishthira had to repeat the lie and cry out that Ashwatthama was dead, or be vanquished by Drona, who was already drawing his bow. Hating himself and full of grief and shame, Yudhishthira had now to tell a falsehood. He raised his voice and repeated "Yes, Ashwatthama is dead!" and then muttered softly and inaudibly, "Either the man or the elephant!"

At Yudhishthira's first words, Drona felt the blood drain from his

126

body and the strength from his limbs. His son had been the centre of his life; every action of Drona's had been inspired by love of his son. Now when he heard that Ashwatthama had died, Drona's heart failed him. Letting his bow fall, he stood dazed on the battlefield. "What does life hold for me now?" he cried to himself. "What is the use of living?" Then he sat down where he was and gave himself up to the meditation on God, for he no longer cared for the world or victory or even his own safety.

127

As he sat there, defenceless, his mind upon God, there came before him Dhrishtadyumna, the Panchala prince, whose father was Drona's bitter enemy. He seized Drona by his white hair and with a mighty cry of revenge, cut off his venerable head.

At this savage action the warriors around stood aghast, and many men raised their voices against Dhrishtadyumna's foul deed. Murder, it was, no less; and a very grave sin to slay a man without defence who was engaged in prayer. When the truth about the elephant came to light, they looked with reproachful eyes at Yudhishthira, who lowered his gaze and was silent. He who had been above untruth had come down to the level of ordinary, sinning human creatures. Nor was it any consolation to Yudhishthira that his lie had been disguised as truth. He did not try to defend himself, for he knew he had acted wrongly. It was a dark day indeed for Yudhishthira. Dhrishtadyumna, however, cared nothing for the qualms that Yudhishthira, Arjuna and Satyaki felt. For he had achieved the death of Drona and now victory was almost certain.

Upon Drona's death the Kaurava forces broke up and fled in wild disorder. But Ashwatthama, the son of Drona, rushed upon the scene and, rallying them, checked the rout. When he heard of the dastardly manner in which his beloved father had been done to death, all his anger came surging up and he flung himself into the fight, determined once and for all to make an end of Dhrishtadyumna and his friends, the Pandavas. In his wild fury, he released shafts of explosives and fumes and fires. The Pandavas crouched weaponless upon the earth till the danger had passed. But the dreadful carnage continued, as the desperate and vengeful Ashwatthama rode among them in his chariot, like the God of Death himself.

It was only the coming of night that gave the Pandavas some respite, for Ashwatthama went from the battlefield, exhausted in body and sick of heart and spent the rest of that night mourning his father.

KARNA

Upon the death of Drona, the Kauravas chose Karna as commander of their army. But the Pandavas' victory now was almost assured. The Kauravas, it seemed, were fighting with their backs to the wall. Yet they did not give up hope, for a true Kshatriya fights to the last and falls bravely upon the battlefield. And so the Kauravas rallied again under the valiant Karna and went into battle. Nor did they allow their spirits to wane; for they were determined to win, even at the edge of defeat.

And yet, though they would not acknowledge it, theirs was a rapidly and effort as his opponent's. Then came the final moment, when Karna's chariot-wheel stuck in the mire. Shalya informed Karna of this, but would not budge from the charioteer's seat to help. He had not forgotten the morning's quarrel and he now sat sulky and vengeful, determined to make things difficult for Karna. Karna cried to Shalya, begging his help, but Shalya shrugged his shoulders and taunted, "Prove your valour now, Karna! Now is the time to show us your much vaunted skill in war." Karna jumped down. "Wait, Arjuna!" he begged. "Stop shooting your arrows for a while until I free the wheel of my chariot. You are a man of chivalry and righteousness and law; surely you will not hit when your opponent is unable to fight back!"

At this, Arjuna was about to lower his bow when Krishna gave a laugh and spoke to Karna sharply, reminding him of the many times when he, Karna, had acted unjustly and unchivalrously. Karna had sided with the evil Duryodhana and aided him in his wicked ways, said Krishna. Had he forgotten the day of the gambling match? Had he forgotten the shaming of Draupadi? Why had Karna not remembered the rules of chivalry on that day? Or again, when the young Abhimanyu had fought alone and single-handed? Had Karna forgotten? "If you had acted rightly then, Karna," called out Krishna bitterly, "things would never have come to this pass! But why do you expect others to play fair when you did not?"

At Krishna's words, Karna threw back his head angrily. "Very well!" he said, "I will fight and kill you, even though I do so at a disadvantage." Shalya continued to sit, sulky and unhelpful, in Karna's chariot. From where he stood on the ground, Karna took aim and shot an arrow at his foe. While Arjuna was engaged in warding it off, he bent quickly and put his shoulder to the wheel. But the wheel had stuck fast in the blood and mire and would not move. Karna left it for a moment and aimed his very best weapons against his foe. So swift and unexpected was this attack that Arjuna staggered back for a moment.

In the respite, Karna again made an attempt to move the chariot wheel. But the web of fate was closing all around him. Luck, fickle, inconstant luck had deserted him always when he most needed it, and on this last day it was no different. The chariot-wheel stuck fast. Karna evaded Arjuna's attacks and lifted his bow to shoot. But as he aimed his arrow Karna felt his hand tremble and his confidence suddenly ebb away. The knowledge of the use of weapons, acquired after years of effort, seemed to slip away from him, and his mind became a blank. It was the curse of Parashurama taking effect. As his hand shook and slipped, two swift arrows came speeding through the air; one struck the standard of Karna and brought it to the ground, while the other cut his head and put an end to the life of the great warrior.

As life left him, it is said that a radiance came from his body which, ascending into heaven, mingled with the light of the sun. Arjuna looked on, dazed by the sight that met his eye, and his mind was filled with thoughts at the same time profound and sad.

Wrongdoing had produced more wrongdoing. Hatred had given

130

birth to hatred. Evil thoughts of revenge had begun a never-ending chain of evil thoughts. All round him upon that blood-soaked field were the horrors of a wicked war in which the nobler qualities of love, truth, justice and mercy had been thrown to the winds.

As Arjuna made his way back to the camp, he was silent and heavy-hearted. He knew that in all that had happened, no man had escaped from sin. The Pandavas had been as guilty as the Kauravas.

THE DEATH OF DURYODHANA

Long and loud did Duryodhana mourn the death of his friend Karna, weeping inconsolably over his lifeless body, while his few remaining generals stood mutely around him. All, all were gone. Most of his brothers had been slain by the bloodthirsty Bhima. Bhishma had been treacherously cut down, and Drona foully murdered. And now Karna—killed as they too had been killed, at a moment when he stood defenceless and unarmed! Bitterly did Duryodhana weep, cursing the cruelty of fate.

Then Kripa spoke, reminding him quietly that perhaps he himself was to blame, and not fate. For it was he, Duryodhana, who had from the first turned his back upon righteousness and set these terrible events in motion through his jealous, hate-filled thoughts. "You must now cease this terrible war, Duryodhana!" Kripa begged. "Now, at least, make your peace with your cousins. Let us not destroy everything." But Duryodhana shook his head. "It is too late now," he said, wearily. "I cannot go back. What hope of peace is left to me now? It is far better to fight bravely and die bravely than to give up in the face of difficulty and danger." Duryodhana's words were as noble and dignified as they were tragic. Defeat and death, he knew, were certain, but having come so far he would not surrender.

On the eighteenth day, Duryodhana appointed Shalya commander and they went into battle again. But it was a lost game. Yudhishthira met Shalya and after a brave fight killed him, while, on another front, Sahadeva made short work of Shakuni, Duryodhana's evil genius with the crafty, poisonous mind. And, on a third front, Bhima took his toll of the surviving brothers of Duryodhana, so that, at the end of the day, only four warriors remained alive on the Kaurava side—Kripa, Ashwatthama, Kirtivarman and Duryodhana.

Then Duryodhana, sick and exhausted, refusing all encouragement, fled at last and took refuge from his enemies among the water weeds, where moorhens and wild ducks nested. And there the Pandavas pursued him, crying out, "Come, Duryodhana, come and do battle or yield! Why, after all these days do you fly like a weakling and try to escape death?"

From his shelter, Duryodhana answered them wearily, "My friends, my brothers and all whom I held in esteem are dead, killed upon the battlefield. What do I want with an empire now, alone and desolate as I am? Go, Yudhishthira, take my kingdom, take the world and rule it. I give it to you: a kingdom of dead and dying men, of weeping widows

and orphaned children. Take this accursed kingdom and rule it."

But Yudhishthira laughed. "We have come this far," he said. "The struggle is nearly over. I do not need you to make me a gift of what I can easily seize from you. Come then and fight us or be forever branded a coward!"

Then Duryodhana reminded them that he was alone against five of them, and Yudhishthira retorted. "You did not think of this, did you, nor your other brave warriors, when Abhimanyu faced you alone and you surrounded him and attacked him on all sides? Still we will show mercy, Duryodhana. Come out of hiding and we will fight you one after another, according to Kshatriya rules."

"I have neither weapons nor armour," Duryodhana said. "How can I fight?"

"We will give you both," answered Yudhishthira. "You may choose your weapon and your opponent and fight him."

Duryodhana came out of his hiding place, holding his head high. For his opponent he singled out his enemy and rival, Bhima. For his weapon he chose the mace.

Then they fought a mighty duel with their maces, and Duryodhana was a formidable opponent for Bhima, aiming his own blows with skill and evading his adversary with dexterity. It seemed as if the victory that the Pandavas had been so sure of winning was slipping from their hands at this last moment, for even Bhima was no match for the desperate Duryodhana.

132

But as they fought, Krishna made a sign to Bhima, touching his own thigh, and suddenly Bhima remembered the vow he had made that he would break Duryodhana's thighs. He remembered in a flash the assembly hall, the game of dice and the shaming of Draupadi. Anger, red-hot anger, filled Bhima, and disregarding the rule of war, that the enemy may not be struck below the navel, Bhima lifted up his mighty mace and struck at Duryodhana's thighs and broke them. With a cry of reproach and pain Duryodhana fell bleeding to the ground. Then Bhima in a savage, mad frenzy put his foot upon the fallen man's head and danced triumphantly, so that all around stood horror-struck. Yudhishthira rebuked him, saying, "Do not trample upon him, Bhima, for Duryodhana is your cousin and a prince. Whatever his faults, whatever our suffering, your conduct is not worthy of a Kshatriya!"

But Duryodhana, lying upon the ground waiting for his death, laughed at Yudhishthira's words.

"Let him trample upon my head, Yudhishthira. This is not the only unworthy, low act he, you and the other Pandavas have committed. Why, you have won the war, but you cannot deny that you have done so only through unfair means and unrighteous conduct. Bhishma, Drona and Karna were slain through foul dishonesty. Jayadratha was destroyed by trickery, deceit and cunning. And do you think I did not see Krishna making a sign to Bhima, urging him to hit me upon my thighs? When have you acted in accordance with the Kshatriya code,

133

that you rebuke Bhima now? Let him stamp then upon my crowned head and complete the cycle of wickedness. His action cannot hurt me. It only hurts him. I am beyond pain or shame. I have been a king and an emperor and have ruled the world and tasted the joy and the power of empire. Kings have bowed before me and done me homage. I have adhered to truth in my own fashion. I have known the loyalty of steadfast friends and of brothers. My life has been full and now I welcome death as a friend. There is nothing left for me to wish for. For I will go to the warrior's heaven, where dwell those who died bravely in battle. But you, Yudhishthira, you will live and inherit this earth that has been devastated by this war. The curses of the wives you left widowed and the mothers you left childless and the children you have orphaned will be upon your head. Go, take your empire. What will it bring you but sorrow and tears?"

Fierce were the emotions that the dying Duryodhana voiced, and to the end he remained implacable and unbending. Yet, though much of what he said was true, he forgot his own part in the great tragedy. He did not see that his jealousy and hatred, as much as the Pandavas' wrongdoing, had been at the root of the evil that had befallen everyone—the death of brave warriors, the crumbling of a mighty empire. Yudhishthira bent his head in shame and grief. He was a man of peace, and would not have hurt a fly if he could have helped it. Arjuna's heart wept within him. The Pandavas turned away and left Duryodhana while he writhed in agony. Kirtivarman and the wise Kripa sat beside him in his final moments.

ASHWATTHAMA

Now the terrible Kurukshetra war was nearly over. But as fire flames up suddenly before it finally dies away, there occurred one further terrible incident that forever closed that tragic chapter.

Ashwatthama, bending over the dying Duryodhana, felt his heart sear to see how he had been treacherously done to death. The memory of his father, Drona, murdered by Dhrishtadyumna while he was at prayer, also came to him, and the memory of Bhishma and Karna and all who had fallen. "I will avenge you, Duryodhana!" whispered Ashwatthama fiercely. "I will slay every one of these men!"

Duryodhana smiled and with his dying breath named him commander.

134

Upon that dark and sordid night, when all lay sleeping, Ashwatthama entered the Pandava camp and with his sword cut the throats of all who slept there—Dhrishtadyumna, his chief enemy, the five sons of Draupadi and all whom he found—except the five Pandavas and Satyaki and Krishna, who were absent from the camp.

Having done this, he fled from the vengeance he knew would be taken. Nor was he mistaken. For when the news of the slaughter of her sons was brought to Draupadi, she cried aloud and swore to kill herself if Ashwatthama were not slain. And so the Pandavas pursued him over the wastes of the earth into his secret hiding-places. But even now they could not subdue him, for his power was so great that out of a blade of grass, he made a weapon of death and sent it against them. When they evaded it, it went like a curse and struck at the womb of Abhimanyu's wife Uttara and the baby within. But Krishna stretched out his hand and protected the unborn child. In course of time Uttara gave birth to a son, Pariksheet, who eventually ascended the throne of Hastinapura and claimed the empire of the Kurus. But Ashwatthama went wandering over the deserted earth for many years, bitter, lonely and unhappy, till death released him at last.

THE END OF THE WAR

Thus ended the war of Kurukshetra and the bitter rivalry between the sons of the Kuru clan. It was indeed as Duryodhana had cried out: the blood of the innocent, the brave and the good mingled with that of the wicked and the guilty.

There was no descendant of Kuru who survived, save the blind king Dhritarashtra and Gandhari, and the five Pandavas and their mother Kunti. Victory had fallen to the Pandavas, but it had a bitter taste.

All had been destroyed in that wicked war, and Yudhishthira felt no joy as he and his brothers made their way slowly to Hastinapura to their uncle, Dhritarashtra.

Broken in spirit and weeping, the blind king gathered Yudhishthira in his arms. He knew only too well that Yudhishthira had been less to blame in this war than anyone else. Duryodhana had brought it upon himself by his blind stupidity, his unreasoning obstinacy, his jealousy and his hatred. It was meaningless to blame anyone now. But as the blind man heard Bhima approach, his anger rose white-hot within him. He smiled sweetly, "Come, Bhima! Come! Let me embrace you." Krishna saw the look of anger and cunning steal into the old man's face as the slayer of his sons stood before him. In an instant he pushed Bhima aside and thrust into the old king's hands a life-sized image of iron. Dhritarashtra crushed it in his arms, and so powerful was his embrace that the image shattered into a thousand pieces.

The brothers came then before the weeping Gandhari, noble and dignified even in her grief. They knelt before her, craving her forgiveness humbly. Though her sorrow and anger were so great that they could have scorched the earth, she steadied herself and serenely forgave them the wrongs they had done her.

Gandhari reproached only Krishna, knowing that if he had wished it, he could have prevented the carnage.

"You know all things, Lord," she cried passionately, "yet you remained indifferent while they murdered one another without thought or mercy." Krishna looked at her with compassion. What could he say to this great and noble lady in her grief? What comfort could he give her? He made no answer at all. In his heart he knew, as she would sooner or later know too, when the first anguish had subsided, that man makes his own fate, and not even the gods can intervene if he is intent on his own destruction.

Then the king and the queen descended the steps of the palace, the Pandavas following, and made their way weeping towards the banks of the river Ganga. As they walked, they were joined by hundreds of mourners: widows, orphans and bereaved old parents. Slowly the sad procession moved through the deserted streets and arrived at the river, breaking into mournful chants of prayer. It was then that Kunti revealed to her sons that Karna was their brother and it was they who must perform for him the religious ceremonies that bring tranquillity to the souls of the dead. As the full meaning of her words dawned upon him, it seemed to Yudhishthira that the final blow had been struck, and he broke down and wept inconsolably.

One more man was still alive at the end of the war. The son of Ganga, the valiant Bhishma, still lay upon his bed of arrows awaiting the final hour. Day after day this mighty hero had lain thus, while the war had raged around him. He had seen with compassionate eyes the carnage around him, the useless anger and killings, the passions and the heroism of the men who fought.

At the end of the war, when the funeral ceremonies were over, and the Pandavas had cleansed themselves of their sins by penance and by bathing in the waters of the Ganga, it was time for Yudhishthira to be installed once again as the king. Then, along with Krishna, he went to Bhishma and knelt before him in homage and reverence. At Krishna's request, Bhishma spoke to Yudhishthira, instructing him at length upon his duties as king, upon virtue and upon life and death and the many, many problems that man must face during his stay upon the earth.

Day after day he spoke to him, while the sun moved steadily northwards. Then, at last, came the day of the summer solstice. Bhishma had wished to see the full glory of the sun before he died. When that happened, he smiled and called to death to come and take him, and death obeyed his word.

Yudhishthira ruled with wisdom and goodness over the domains he had won. As the days passed, men began to forget the sorrows of the war, and the wounds in their hearts healed, so that whatever they might have suffered, they began to love Yudhishthira and the Pandavas, who worked tirelessly for their good. As for Dhritarashtra and Gandhari, who had been bereaved of their hundred sons, Yudhishthira treated them with love and kindness and honour as if they were his own parents, and when they died, the Pandavas performed their funeral ceremonies.

Yudhishthira and his brothers lived for many years, until the time came for them to leave the earth, in their turn, and travel to the heavenly regions beyond. Then, led by Yudhishthira, the four brothers and Draupadi went where death took them.

As they went on their very last journey, they found themselves followed by a stray dog. The rigours of the journey were immense and, one by one, Draupadi, Nakula, Sahadeva, Arjuna and Bhima fell by the

wayside. Yudhishthira, still followed by the dog, finally reached the gates of heaven. There he was confronted by the gatekeeper who declared that the dog, being a lowly, unclean animal, was barred from entering heaven's gates.

When Yudhishthira heard this, he turned away, and would not go in, saying that he would not forsake the dog who had sought his protection and had followed him so faithfully. He would rather be in hell with the dog than be comfortable in heaven without him. His virtuous answer pleased the gods, and they allowed Yudhishthira to enter heaven in his mortal form. The dog was now revealed to be Dharma, Yudhishthira's heavenly father. But this was not the end of Yudhishthira's trials.

As he entered heaven, he looked in vain for Draupadi and his brothers, and finally found them racked with unbearable torments, in a foul and terrifying place. Yudhishthira's heart nearly burst with grief. He declared to the gods that he would live eternally in that place of torture, giving his wife and brothers what comfort he could.

It was Yudhishthira's final test. The scenes of torment vanished as if blown away, and his wife and brothers stood revealed before him whole and joyous, while the gods welcomed them all. Draupadi and the Pandavas lived a long time in heaven enjoying the good things of those regions, until at last they ascended to the final level of happiness in which man becomes one with the eternal, and is free from the mortal cycle of birth, death and rebirth.

138

The Principal Characters in the Mahabharata

Shantanu: King of Hastinapura; great-grandfather of the Kaurava and Pandava princes.

Ganga: The first wife of Shantanu; goddess of the river Ganga. Mother of Devavrata, who was afterwards known as Bhishma.

Satyavati: The second wife of Shantanu; mother of Chitrangada and Vichitraveerya.

Devavrata: The eldest son of King Shantanu by Ganga; heir-apparent to Hastinapura's throne. He gave up his claim to the throne in favour of his step-brothers, Satyavati's sons. He also remained unmarried, so that his family ended with him. He had no children to challenge the claim of Satyavati's descendants to Hastinapura's throne. He lived at the palace in Hastinapura, and was respected by all as a wise statesman. He was a powerful warrior. He lived to a great old age, and though an old man at the time, he took part in the Kurukshetra war.

Chitrangada: Elder son of Shantanu and Satyavati. He ruled Hastinapura for a few years, but died young and childless.

Vichitraveerya: Second son of Shantanu and Satyavati. He came to the throne of Hastinapura on the death of his brother Chitrangada. He had two wives, Ambika and Ambalika.

Ambika and Ambalika: Daughters of the king of Kashi. They were married to Vichitraveerya. Ambika was the mother of Dhritarashtra, and Ambalika was the mother of Pandu. Vichitraveerya also secretly married a humble serving girl in the palace, and her son was Vidura.

Amba: The sister of Ambika and Ambalika. Vichitraveerya refused to marry her, because she had loved Shalva, and had been engaged to him. Shalva, however, also refused to marry her. Amba then tried to persuade Bhishma to marry her, but he too would not. Angry at being thus humiliated she killed herself. She was reborn as Shikhandini.

Vidura: A son of Vichitraveerya. His mother was a humble serving woman in the palace.

Shikhandini: Daughter of King Drupada of Panchala. Though born as a woman she changed her sex and became a man. Many years later she joined the Pandavas in their war against the Kauravas, and helped to kill Bhishma.

Dhritarashtra: Blind son of Vichitraveerya and Ambika. He became king of Hastinapura on Vichitraveerya's death. He was the father of the hundred Kaurava brothers, of whom Duryodhana was the eldest.

Gandhari: Wife of Dhritarashtra; daughter of the king of Gandhara. Mother of Duryodhana and the other Kaurava princes.

Shakuni: Brother of Gandhari.

Duryodhana: The eldest son of Dhritarashtra and Gandhari.

Dushahsana: One of the Kaurava princes, son of Dhritarashtra and Gandhari.

Jayadratha: Also called Saindhava. He was king of the Sindhus, and a son-in-law of Dhritarashtra. In the Kurukshetra war he fought on the side of the Kauravas.

Pandu: Son of Vichitraveerya by Ambalika. He was a sick man, frail in health. He spent his days in a forest hermitage with his two wives, Kunti and Madri. He was the father of the Pandava princes.

Kunti: Daughter of the Sura chieftain of the Yadava clan. She was adopted by a king called Kuntibhoja. Kunti's brother, Sura's son, was Vasudeva who was the father of Krishna. When she was still a young, unmarried girl, she had fallen in love with Surya, the sun god, by whom she had had a baby boy. She kept his birth a secret and abandoned the child. Nobody knew Kunti's secret. When she was older she was married to Pandu, and she became the mother of the Pandava princes.

Madri: The second wife of King Pandu. She was the mother of Nakula and Sahadeva. When Pandu died in his forest home, Madri killed herself. Kunti brought up her two boys with her own sons.

The Pandava Princes: The sons of Kunti and Madri and cousins of the Kauravas. Pandu was their earthly father, but they were gifts from the gods to Kunti and Madri.

Yudhishthira: The eldest of the Pandava princes. He was a gift to Kunti of Dharma, the god of justice.

Bhima: The second Pandava prince, gift to Kunti of Vayu, the god of the wind.

Arjuna: The third Pandava prince, gift of Indra, god of the heavenly regions.

Nakula and Sahadeva: Twin sons of Madri, gifts of the

Ashwins, gods who accompany the storms and tempests.

Karna: A son born to Kunti before she was married. His father was Surya, the god of the sun. He was thus a brother of the Pandavas, though they did not know it.

Adiratha: A humble charioteer, in the service of the king of Hastinapura. He found Karna who had been abandoned by Kunti and left to die, and he brought up the boy.

Radha: Wife of Adiratha, and foster mother of Karna.

Drupada: King of Panchala. Father of Shikhandin and of the twins, Draupadi and Dhrishtadyumna.

Draupadi: The wife of the five Pandava princes.

Drishtadyumna: Twin brother of Draupadi.

Drona: Teacher of the Kaurava and Pandava princes. He lived at the palace in Hastinapura. He was the most renowned teacher of the day. He and Drupada had been students together.

Kripa: Drona's brother-in-law. (His wife's brother.) He was also a teacher at the palace.

Ashwatthama: Son of Drona.

Ekalavya: Son of a tribal chieftain, who wished to be Drona's pupil.

Abhimanyu: Arjuna's son. Besides Draupadi, who was the wife of all the Pandava princes, Arjuna was married to Subhadra. Abhimanyu was Subhadra's and Arjuna's son.

Subhadra: Arjuna's wife. She was the sister of Krishna, and Abhimanyu's mother.

Krishna: Grandson of Sura; son of Vasudeva. Kunti was Sura's daughter and Vasudeva's sister. Hence Krishna was Kunti's nephew. Krishna was a respected and powerful statesman of the time.

Ghatotkacha: Son of Bhima. His mother was Hidimbi, a tribal queen.

Hidimbi: A tribal queen whom Bhima married. Her son was Ghatotkacha.

Hidimba: Brother of Hidimbi, whom Bhima had to fight and kill before he married Hidimbi.

Virata: King of Matsya, in whose palace the Pandava princes stayed in disguise and in hiding, during the last year of their exile.

Uttara: Virata's daughter, who was given in marriage to Abhimanyu.

Uttara Kumar: King Virata's son, and brother of Uttara.

Kichaka: Brother-in-law of Virata (the brother of Virata's wife). He was a powerful noble at Virata's court. He was killed by Bhima.

Shalya: The brother of Madri; maternal uncle of Nakula and Sahadeva.

Special Notes on some Colour Plates

No. 3 (facing page 14): *Surya, the sun god, Kunti and Karna*

The lotus flower shown at the foot of the painting symbolises the life-force of the sun. It often figures in Indian literature as a flower that opens only at the touch of the sun's rays, and closes at sunset.

No. 5 (facing page 34): *Karna and Arjuna at the Tournament*

Notice the figure of the charioteer Adiratha embracing Karna, his foster-son.

No. 6 (facing page 42): *The Five Pandava Princes*

Although all five brothers look closely alike, there are subtle distinctions. Yudhishthira carries a royal pennant and his bearing and expression are sombre and dignified. Bhima, the fearless, carries his mace, and his sturdy features, his direct gaze, and even the flourish of his moustache symbolise his invincible strength. Arjuna, recognised as the perfect man, combines delicacy of feature with martial courage as symbolised by his bow, the divine *Gandiva*. Nakula and Sahadeva, the inseparable twins, clasp hands. Their smaller size reflects the supportive role they play to their three elder brothers.

No. 7 (facing page 48): *Draupadi's Swayamvara*

Notice the locked gazes of Arjuna and Draupadi before Arjuna begins to shoot at his target. See also his shaven head, bare torso and simple clothes: his disguise as a Brahmin.

No. 9 (facing page 62): *Yudhishthira Enthroned*

In this painting are shown several traditional symbols of kingship. Apart from the royal crown, the main one is the royal *chhatri*, or umbrella-like shade, always held above royalty; the others include the royal pennant, the female attendant with a fly-whisk, the carved lions on which the throne rests, the ritual sacrificial fire, and the array of offerings promising a reign of plenty.

The lotus held in Yudhishthira's hand signifies that he is a man of peace; it is also the symbol of the goddess Shree (or Lakshmi) who bestows prosperity.

No. 10 (facing page 72): *The Disrobing of Draupadi*

In this dramatic scene, usually referred to as *Vastraharana*, the painter has used the symbols of the god Vishnu—the discus, the mace and the conch—to signify the miracle by which Krishna, who is an incarnation of Vishnu, protects Draupadi. Notice also Draupadi's attempt to cling to the royal *chhatri* for the protection she does not get, and her reaching out to a helpless Yudhishthira.

No. 11 (facing page 86): *Bhima and Kichaka*

To depict the fake assignation, the painter has used the symbols of a love-tryst: the darkened chamber, the single lamp, the burning incense, and the pair of parrots—the parrot being the bird that carries Manmatha, the god of love. Also shown are dancer's anklets and a drum to denote the dancing-hall where the assignation takes place.

No. 12 (facing page 92): *Prince Uttara Kumar and Arjuna*

The sinister presence of the owl in the tree is a reminder of the grim setting of this episode.

No. 13 (facing page 102): *Duryodhana, Shakuni and Dushahsana*

The dark tones of the picture overtly convey conspiracy and evil. More subtle, however, are Duryodhana's cold eyes and talon-like hands.

No. 14 (facing page 114): *Krishna reveals the Bhagavad Gita*

The scene depicted here is the philosophic core of the epic. Appropriately, the painter has used images that express the oneness of creation, and the divinity that pervades all things: bird, fish, man, tree, sky and planet. Krishna's halo both emphasises his divinity and, with the other suns in the picture, heralds the revelation of his cosmic form, "brighter than a thousand suns". The name Krishna means literally "the dark one" and his darkness is always depicted as a dark blue.

No. 16 (facing page 136): *The Golden City*

The serenity of this picture symbolises the restoration of *dharma* (harmony, peace and the perfect world order) to the Kuru kingdom under Yudhishthira, who is *dharma* incarnate.

Notes on Chapter Symbols

Title page and introduction: The sage Vyasa, the composer of the original *Mahabharata,* is said to have dictated the entire epic, without a pause, to the elephant-headed god Ganesha, who had made this a condition to his writing it down at one sitting.

Chapter 1: The river-goddess, Ganga, is shown riding the *makara* or crocodile, who is traditionally associated with her. In one hand she holds the *kalasha:* the symbolic vessel of prosperity.

Chapter 2: The *rudraksha* (lit. eye of Shiva) are prayer beads that symbolise the ascetic.

Chapter 3: Surya, the sun god, is shown in his chariot drawn by seven horses.

Chapter 4: The five Pandava princes are here represented by the implements of their excellence: Yudhishthira's royal pennant, Bhima's mace, Arjuna's bow and arrow, and Nakula's and Sahadeva's horse-whips.

Chapter 5: The bird in this symbol represents the peak of skill in archery.

Chapter 6: This symbol shows the Nagas, spirits of the river, half human and half serpent.

Chapter 7: Ekalavya is here shown idolising the clay image of his chosen *guru,* Drona.

Chapter 8: This picture shows Indra disguised as an old man to trick Karna into giving away his protective armour and earrings.

Chapter 9: Varnavata in flames.

Chapter 10: The cart of food meant for the demon, Bakasura.

Chapter 11: The decorated elephant which carries Draupadi to her *swayamvara.*

Chapter 12: The caparisoned horse symbolises imperial power.

Chapter 13: The evil Shakuni casts his net of intrigue through the gambling match to trap Yudhishthira and, through him, to destroy Duryodhana.

Chapter 14: The trees represent the Pandavas' years of exile in the forest.

Chapter 15: The stand laden with fruit and wine symbolises the luxury of the palace where the Pandavas spend their year in hiding.

Chapter 16: Duryodhana's attack on Matsya is presaged here by the spy scouting the city.

Chapter 17: The drum denotes the joy and festivity depicted in this chapter.

Chapter 18: An envoy presents a missive to a king to signify the many negotiations that take place in this chapter.

Chapter 19: A soldier dressed for battle.

Chapter 20: The symbol that runs through the chapter shows the havoc wrought by war.
The concluding symbol is the pennant of the god Vishnu, the preserver, which bears a picture of the monkey god Hanuman, Vishnu's perfect devotee. This is the pennant which flies over Arjuna's chariot.

Kongō-Class Battleships

In the Imperial Japanese Navy in World War II

LARS AHLBERG

HANS LENGERER

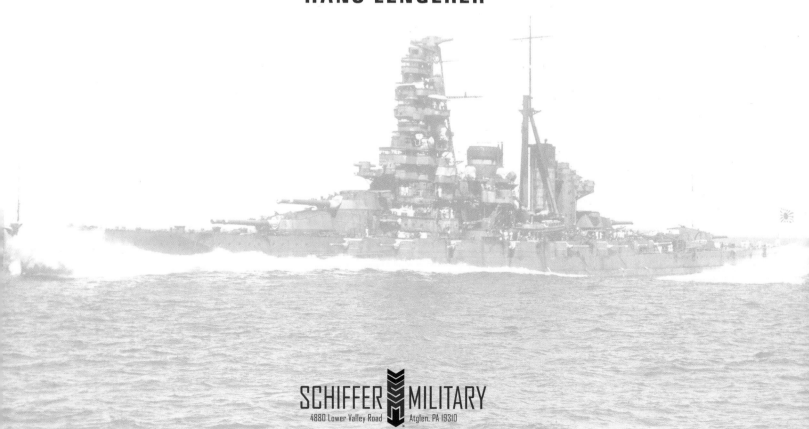

SCHIFFER MILITARY

4880 Lower Valley Road   Atglen, PA 19310

Cover design by Justin Watkinson
Type set in Impact/Minion Pro/Univers LT Std

ISBN: 978-0-7643-6167-8
Printed in China

Published by Schiffer Publishing, Ltd.
4880 Lower Valley Road
Atglen, PA 19310
Phone: (610) 593-1777; Fax: (610) 593-2002
E-mail: Info@schifferbooks.com
Web: www.schifferbooks.com

For our complete selection of fine books on this and related subjects, please visit our website at www.schifferbooks.com. You may also write for a free catalog.

Schiffer Publishing's titles are available at special discounts for bulk purchases for sales promotions or premiums. Special editions, including personalized covers, corporate imprints, and excerpts, can be created in large quantities for special needs. For more information, contact the publisher.

We are always looking for people to write books on new and related subjects. If you have an idea for a book, please contact us at proposals@schifferbooks.com.

Acknowledgments

In compiling this brief history of the Kongō-class battleships we are indebted to the following individuals who over a long time have given invaluable help in our research of the Imperial Japanese Navy: Messrs. Endō Akira, Fujita Takashi, Hayashi Yoshikazu, Ishibashi Takao, Itani Jirō, Iwasaki Yutaka, Izumi Kōzō, Kamakura Takumi, Kimata Jirō, Kitagawa Ken'ichi, Kitamura Kunio, Koike Naohiko, Kuroyama Kazuo, Maejima Hajime, Mizutani Kiyotaka, Morino Tetsuo, Naitō Hatsuho (via Itani), Nakagawa Tsutomu, Takagi Hiroshi, Takahashi Shigeo, Takasu Kōichi, Tamura Toshio, Todaka Kazushige, Tsuda Fumio, and Tsukamoto Hideki.

Special thanks go to Mr. Michael Wünschmann for the drawings.

All photos are from the authors' collections unless otherwise stated.

Contents

CHAPTER 1

Introduction and Summary

The battle cruiser *Kongō* was the last of a series of nine capital ships built in British shipyards, and the last one built abroad. With the conclusion of the building contract with the Vickers Co., the Imperial Japanese Navy (IJN) intended and achieved (1) release from outdated domestic constructions, (2) introduction to the most-modern hull, machinery, and weapon designs and construction techniques of capital ships, and (3) the involvement of the two largest private Japanese shipyards in the building process of large ships. The design was a joint venture of British and Japanese naval architects, and the result caused the Royal Navy to alter the design of the fourth ship of the battle cruisers of the Lion class, *Tiger*, by taking *Kongō* as type ship for the arrangement of the main gun turrets.

After the start of construction, the caliber of the main gun was changed from 30.48 to 35.56 cm. The initiative was then Cmdr. Katō Hiroharu's[1], and this was the most important characteristic together with the improved arrangement of the four twin main gun turrets.

Three sister ships were built in Japan—two in civilian shipyards and one in a naval shipyard. The yards had been prepared for this task by previous construction of smaller warships and the dispatch of many employees to Vickers when *Kongō* was under construction.

After the conclusion of the Washington Arms Limitation Treaty in 1922, the horizontal protection, which during World War I had proved to be a fatal weakness of battle cruisers, was reinforced within the scope of the permitted tonnage increase. In response to longer battle ranges, the elevation angle of the main guns was increased, and fire control and spotting gears, already fitted, were improved. Jointly with this, the former tripod mast was changed into the characteristic "pagoda type" mast. The change

from coal- to oil-burning boilers resulted in a remarkable decrease in the number of boilers and the reduction of the funnels from three to two. The engines remained the same as before so that speed was reduced owing to the considerable increase of the displacement. As a consequence the ships were reclassified as battleships.

The IJN's numerical inferiority stipulated in the aforementioned treaty and accentuated by the London Treaty in 1930, which forced the IJN to reconstruct *Hiei* into a training battleship, caused a modification of the Japanese strategy against the United States. The prestage (interception/attrition) prior to the decisive gun battle of the capital ships was emphasized, and the "defense ring" (composed mainly of heavy cruisers) around the American battle fleet was to be penetrated and destroyed by heavier-caliber guns. For the execution of this new role by the Kongō class, high speed was the most important presupposition. Therefore, the installation of new turbines, with more than doubled output, and the lengthening of the hull were the primary items of the second reconstruction, carried out in preparation for the termination of the treaties mentioned above. Only *Hiei* was reconstructed after the end of the treaty system, and, with regard to the foremast, fire control systems, etc., it was used as a model for the battleship *Yamato*. With a speed of 30 knots, the classification was unofficially changed into high-speed battleship, and the Kongō-class battleships, even though the oldest, were the most-active Japanese battleships in the Pacific War.

The tragic loss of *Hiei* in November 1942, due to a jammed rudder caused by the hit of a 20.32 cm shell in the steering compartment, is well known (and resembles closely that of the German battleship *Bismarck*), and this was the IJN's first battleship loss in the war. Two days later, *Kirishima* was sunk by gunfire from the new 40.6 cm gunned US battleships *Washington* and *South Dakota*. Her loss, similar to that of *Hiei*, proved that the fatal weakness of the battle cruiser—insufficient protection—was still existent despite the reconstructions.

The remaining two ships were modified on the basis of war lessons. Specifically, the high-angle guns and antiaircraft machine gun outfit were improved. Radar was also fitted during the war. The number of secondary guns was further reduced and an emergency steering gear was fitted, beside the reinforcement of the protection of the steering compartment.

During the Battle of Leyte Gulf in October 1944, *Kongō* and *Haruna* for the first time fired their main guns on enemy surface ships. On her way back to Japan from Brunei Bay in November, *Kongō* was sunk by submarine torpedoes, proving that the underwater protection was insufficient. *Haruna* was sunk at her moorings as a result of the US carrier air raid on July 28, 1945. The damages caused by the three previous large air attacks on March 19, June 22, and July 24 had not been serious.

CHAPTER 2
Requirement and Design

Among the thirty-six Japanese capital ships, ten (including the armor-clad *Kongō* [I]) were built in Britain. The majority (eight) were ordered shortly before and after the Sino-Japanese War (1894–95) in preparation for the Russo-Japanese War (1904–05). Six were completed before the beginning of that war, and two shortly afterward.

During the building, numerous Japanese naval architects, foremen, and skilled workers were dispatched to the builders to learn British design and construction methods, in order to pave the way for domestic building of large warships. These ships corresponded to successive types of the then British standard battleship types, differing primarily in the progress of armor, gunnery, and engine techniques. With the knowledge obtained in this process and others, the Navy Technical Department (NTD) not only designed conventional battleships but also made the pioneering design of a hermaphrodite type, aiming for a combination of the battleship's gun power and the speed of the cruiser. The result was the four prototype battle cruisers of the Tsukuba and Kurama classes. However, these domestic-built and officially classified first-class cruisers were not without rather grave defects both in design and practice, and when the Royal Navy, also referring to the lessons of the Russo-Japanese War, completed the battleship *Dreadnought* and the battle cruiser *Invincible*, the era of the pre-*Dreadnought* type ended.

After the Russo-Japanese War the IJN used the greater part of its tight budget for the repair and reconstruction of the captured Russian war prizes and the completion of outdated capital ships then under construction and budgeted—all of pre-*Dreadnought* types. The laying down of the *Dreadnought*-type battleships *Kawachi* and *Settsu* may be regarded as an attempt to keep pace with the development abroad, but their completion was greatly delayed. Until the end of 1910, the IJN was engaged in repairing the ships of the Russo-Japanese War, and the number of new warships was very small compared with the armament expenses of the other world naval powers. Japan's position dropped remarkably because almost all powers had started to build *Dreadnought*-type ships, and the Japanese "*Dreadnoughts*" had the fatal error that they mounted big guns of both 50- and 45-caliber length. This because of the mistaken thought that the fore and after guns should be more powerful than the side guns. In addition, there was a rumor that the main gun caliber of dreadnoughts was about to increase to more than 12 inches (30.48 cm). This improved type was later called super-dreadnought or, as Japanese authors prefer, ultra-dreadnought.

In the course of the deliberations about new naval expansion planning, the new vice chief of the Navy General Staff (NGS), VAdm. Fujii Kōichi (served December 1, 1909–March 24, 1914), among the *Dreadnought*-type capital ships, preferred the battle cruiser. When deciding the building order of the new ships, he managed to persuade the members to accept his opinion of the battle cruiser's superiority. In order to overcome the then-current technological backwardness, the type ship should be ordered from the British Vickers Sons & Co.[1], whose technique, since the building of the battleship *Mikasa*, was regarded as being superior to Armstrong, Whitworth & Co., Elswick. Navy minister Adm. Saitō Makoto (served January 7, 1906–April 15, 1914) signaled agreement with the order of one ship from Britain, and after a comparatively short preparatory phase, within which negotiations about the construction proceeded very well, the contract with Vickers Co. was concluded on October 17, 1910.

One more reason for selecting Vickers was the Royal Navy's order for the construction of the battle cruiser *Princess Royal*, a sister of the type ship *Lion*.[2]

The most-important stipulations whose effect was not limited to the construction of a vessel whose properties were to surpass those of the Lion class but were aimed for upgrading Japanese warship-building technology to the latest British practice, were the following:

> The IJN should be permitted to send naval architects, engine and weapon production technicians, engineers, assistant engineers, and skilled workers to supervise construction and study production processes.
>
> The IJN should obtain all the drawings of the hull, armor, guns, main engines, and auxiliary machinery and be permitted to utilize them for the building of sister ships in Japan.

With the order from abroad, the IJN:

> Intended an all-around upgrade of domestic shipbuilding and engine and weapon production technology to the latest conditions of a leading British shipyard.
>
> Relied on the technology transfer and used the same methods already successfully adopted at the end of the Bakumatsu period (i.e., after the opening of the country by Commodore Matthew C. Perry in 1853–54) and practiced all through the Meiji era—the dispatch of selected persons abroad to study their respective topics and the invitation of foreigners to Japan to teach their specialties.

Domestic designs had centered on vessels displacing about 18,000–19,000 tons, with a speed of 25–26 knots and armed with eight to ten 12-inch guns, arranged by taking British, American, and German capital ships as models. The adoption of a 27,000-ton ship meant a radical departure from existing designs. Even if the draft of Vickers formed the basis, the NGS required that other characteristics, based on the different strategic considerations and particular Japanese conditions (often varying widely from British tradition), should be incorporated into the design. However, it may be sufficient to state that Japanese and British technicians worked closely together and found acceptable solutions, and Sir George Thurston, who was the chief of the Warship Design Division of Vickers Co., introduced many improvements compared with the Lion class. In other words:

> The fundamental design of the battle cruiser *Kongō* was worked out in the Basic Design Section of the Shipbuilding Division of the NTD, on the basis of the detailed investigation of the proposed design and in cooperation with British technicians.
>
> The detailed design was made by the Warship Design Division of Vickers Co., which also ordered the execution of the working drawings to the Drawing Section.

Therefore, it might be correct to characterize the design of the battle cruiser *Kongō* as a joint venture of Japan and Britain, with chief importance laid on the former, and more so than had been the case when building the battleships ordered before the Russo-Japanese War.

CHAPTER 3
Revision from the Dreadnought Type to the Super-Dreadnought Type

As stated above, as long as the construction of an approximately 18,000-ton armored cruiser had been considered, the main gun caliber was within the standard adopted in the early 1890s and, during the previously mentioned design phase discussions, centered on the length of the barrel; namely, 45 caliber or 50 caliber. The latter length was eventually adopted because this gun was already under construction. Of course, the adoption of a larger caliber than that of the Lion class was also proposed but rejected after heated discussions, because Vickers Co. had no ready-made design. The contract therefore stipulated the mounting of eight 50-caliber, 304.8 mm guns in four twin turrets.

However, Cmdr. Katō Hiroharu, then naval attaché in London, investigated the armament of British capital ships and obtained confidential information about the result of comparative firings of the 50-caliber, 12-inch (304.8 mm) and the 45-caliber, 13.5-inch (342.9 mm) guns, the latter scheduled for future British capital ships. According to these data, the former was inferior to the latter in essential properties; namely, barrel life (i.e., number of rounds to be fired before the barrel was unserviceable), dispersion (i.e., the distance from the point of impact of a particular projectile to the mean point of impact of the salvo), and hit probability. In the end, this meant a no-less-than-remarkable inferiority of the Japanese counterpart of the Lion class if the decided design would remain unchanged.

Katō's reaction caused a request to navy minister Saitō to change the caliber to 356.6 mm (14 inches), and he supported his arguments by the addition of the confidential British data. When he did not receive an answer, he dispatched one of the supervisors of the construction of *Kongō* to Japan, via Siberia. Via him Katō obtained permission to unofficially deal with the adoption of this gun caliber because the official adoption had of course to depend on the results of the trial firings. The design and trial construction of the new 356.6 mm gun were ordered from Vickers Co. by the expenses of the IJN, and the company executed it in a comparatively short time. In view of the urgency, the firing trials were made on the Royal Navy's proving ground at Shoeburyness[1] because the firing range of Vickers Co. was not suited for this caliber. The trials were performed starting on March 8, 1911, and were finished near the end of the month, with the expected satisfactory result, whereupon, on November 29, 1911, the formal decision was made to adopt the larger-caliber gun. It must be added that representatives of the IJN and the Royal Navy were present at the trials, and the results were shared between both navies.

The decision to change from the 12-inch (304.8 mm) to the 14-inch (355.6 mm) caliber was not a simple one; it required numerous alterations, such as for barbettes, roller path diameter, turntables, turrets, projectile and propellant hoists, ammunition magazines, and adjacent rooms, as well as structural reinforcement to absorb the stronger forces generated by firing of the larger-caliber gun. Protective measures against the stronger blast were also necessary. It was also unavoidable that the displacement of the ship would increase.

However, Vickers Detailed Design Division was a very efficient organization, and even though the keel of *Kongō* had been laid down on January 17, 1911, all alterations were introduced in time, so neither was the construction process delayed nor did already-built parts have to be broken up.

A comparison of the principal particulars of the 50-caliber, 12-inch and the 45-caliber, 14-inch guns is presented in table 1 shown opposite.

Table 1
Principal particulars of the 50-caliber, 12-inch and 45-caliber, 14-inch guns

Item/Type	50 cal. 12-inch gun (Kawachi class)	45 cal. 14-inch (Kongō class)
Caliber (mm)	304.8	355.6
Length of barrel (m)	15.659 (51.4 cal.)	16.469 (46.3 cal.)
Weight of the barrel (tons)	69	84.689
Weight of shell (AP) (kg)	400	635.03
Weight of propellant (kg)	95.38 (common); 139.95 (strong)	136.5 (common); 150 (strong)
Barrel pressure (tons/cm²)	27.6 (common); 29.33 (strong)	?; 30.5 (strong)
Muzzle velocity (m/s)	820 (common); 865 (strong)	800 (common); 845 (strong)
Volume of chamber (liters)	?	283.5*
Life of barrel (rounds)	200–250	250–280
Number of grooves	72 (1 turn in 28 cal.)	84 (1 turn in 28 cal.); depth 3.05 mm

Note:
*This volume is valid for *Kongō*'s *Bi* (Vickers)–type model I guns. *Hiei* had *Bi*-type model II (volume of powder chamber increased to 303.2 liters). *Haruna* and *Kirishima* had type 41 model III guns (breech changed from *Bi*-type to type 41).

CHAPTER 4
Construction

The most significant item was the dispatch of technicians to perform the technology transfer to the utmost degree.[1] Thus, specialists of each field were sent to Vickers Co., and beside officers belonging to the shipbuilding, engine, and weapon production branches, engineers, assistant engineers, foremen, and workers (scheduled to be promoted) arrived in Britain. These men studied all the technical processes related to warship construction, particularly those executed in the hull, engine, and weapon production factories. In addition, the number of superintendents and assistant superintendents (superior workmen class) was remarkably increased in Britain. The fitting-out committee also consisted of many more members than was common.[2] The stay in Britain usually lasted eighteen months for the study of the actual work, and after that period the personnel were changed. Among the personnel were, for example, the later chief of Kure Navy Yard (in 1924), then Cmdr. Godō Takuo[3]; Cmdr. Noda Tsuruo; naval engineers Hata Chiyokichi, Yokota Eikichi, and Uruno Shihei; and the shipbuilding commanders Shinjo Suekurō, Fukui Jumpei, and Yoshida Yasushi.[4] All these people were later in charge of building the capital and other ships of the so-called 8-8 Fleet.

It deserves particular attention that the dispatch was not limited to naval officers and navy officials. A considerable number of civilians from Mitsubishi Company, Nagasaki Shipyard, and Kawasaki Company, Kōbe Shipyard, were also dispatched to Vickers for the same purpose.[5] Among them were the chief of the Shipbuilding Division of the Nagasaki Shipyard, Shiba Kōshirō, and engineers Abe, Tamai, Ogawa, et al.,[6] while Kawasaki Kōbe sent engineers Yoshikunimera, Katayama, and others. The personnel from these private shipyards also studied gantry crane and building-berth techniques and launching technology, and Kawasaki's excellent launching technology originated from these studies.

More than 100 selected men were dispatched for study missions to Britain during that time, and if the "regular" supervisors, superintendents, and fitting-out and trial committee members are added, the total becomes about 200. These were the men who upgraded the level of the IJN and the private shipyards, and who at about the middle of World War I ascertained real independence from abroad and enabled a gradual shift to the phase of creativity.

The dispatch of engineers and others from Japan's largest civilian shipyards was part of a program to involve selected private facilities in the construction of large warships and to expand this heavy branch of industry. Until the Shipbuilding Encouragement Law of 1896,[7] the civilian shipyards did not develop to a notable level, but afterward various aids were given to develop some enterprises, among them Mitsubishi Nagasaki and Kawasaki Kōbe, which developed to become the most-eminent ones. The IJN started with the order of torpedo boats, destroyers, gunboats, and submarines (at that time a specialty of Kawasaki), followed by small (light) cruisers, which gave them an opportunity to study and learn the technologically more sophisticated warship design and construction procedures.[8] With the order to Mitsubishi and Kawasaki to construct one sister ship each to the battle cruiser *Kongō*, the IJN wanted to "kill two birds with one stone"; namely,

- to establish a system that four capital ships could be built at the same time
- to aid these and other private shipyards in enduring the post–Russo-Japanese War recession

With the completion of the battle cruisers *Kirishima* and *Haruna* in Mitsubishi Nagasaki and Kawasaki Kōbe, respectively, these shipyards had upgraded their facilities, design, and construction techniques and management system to the world's standard and successively received the orders for battleships *Ise* and *Hyūga*, then battleships *Tosa* and *Kaga*, and were also selected for building the battle cruisers *Takao* and *Atago* before the Washington Arms Limitation Conference ended the construction of Japan's "dream fleet."

Other, smaller shipyards were also encouraged by the IJN and followed the great progress of these two shipyards, although at a much-smaller scale. However, they also upgraded their techniques, facilities, and management to be able to build smaller warships up to the class of light cruisers, thus taking the former position of the "big two." Therefore, it may be right to state that with the construction of the battle cruisers of the Kongō class, not only were warship design and construction techniques upgraded to the latest level, but it also paved the way for the building of the 8-8 Fleet, both in terms of software and hardware.

Table 2
Construction data and fates

Name	Builder	Laid Down	Launched	Completed	Fate
Kongō	Vickers Co.	1/17/1911	5/18/1912	8/16/1913	11/21/1944: sunk by USS *Sealion* (SS-315) near Keelung
Hiei	Yokosuka Navy Yard	11/4/1911	11/21/1912	8/4/1914	11/13/1942: heavily damaged by US naval artillery and aircraft near Savo Island; scuttled
Haruna	Kawasaki Kōbe	3/16/1912	12/14/1913	4/19/1915	Heavily damaged by air raids 3/19 and 7/28/1945; sitting on bottom near Kure
Kirishima	Mitsubishi Nagasaki	3/17/1912	12/1/1913	4/19/1915	11/15/1942: sunk by USS *South Dakota* (BB-57) and USS *Washington* (BB-56) near Savo Island

Note:
Haruna was named on December 14, 1913; other ships, on June 5, 1911.

View looking forward of the *Kongō* on the slipway at Vickers in 1911. It shows the extension of the double bottom up to the armor belt shelf. The floors, longitudinals, and frames are partly in place. *Vickers, courtesy of the authors*

The forward part of *Kongō* on the slipway in 1911. The photo shows the framing and the deck beams for the protective deck. *Vickers, courtesy of the authors*

The after part of the *Kongō* in 1911. The hull is complete to the level of the protective deck. *Vickers, courtesy of the authors*

Kongō's stern section on May 18, 1912, showing the twin rudders. Note the wood backing for the armor belt. The backing consisted of planks of hardwood, approximately 9 inches wide, fixed longitudinally to the inner planking. The armor, secured by heavy bolts (3 inches in diameter), will be fitted after launching. *Vickers, courtesy of the authors*

金剛の尻

Kongō's stern on May 18, 1912,
showing its four propellers, the
twin inclined rudders, and the
stern walk

Kongō's bow section on May 18, 1912, just prior to launching. Note the launching cradle. *Vickers, courtesy of the authors*

The launching of *Kongō* on May 18, 1912. It was attended by the shipyard workers and the management of Vickers. The Japanese supervisors were also present. *Vickers, courtesy of the authors*

H.I.J.M.S. KONGO
PHOTO-NEWS-MAIL -

Kongō fitting-out on April 17, 1913. This is a photo taken from the steamer *Atsuta Maru*, which had just arrived from Yokohama with 550 Japanese officers, warrant officers, petty officers, and ratings. They boarded *Kongō* the next day for the trials that started on April 20, after a short introduction of the would-be crew to their duties. Fitting-out officer was Capt. Nakano Naoe.

Kongō afloat after launching on May 18, 1912. Note how little water she draws at this stage of the process. All the heavy items of equipment have yet to be embarked and fitted. *Vickers, courtesy of the authors*

Portside photo of *Kongō* in April 1913. The ship was completed on August 16 and left Britain under the command of Capt. Nakano Naoe for Japan the same day, and she arrived at Yokosuka on November 5. She was transferred to the 1st Kantai (Fleet), 1st Sentai (Squadron), on December 1 as the fleet flagship of VAdm. Katō Tomosaburō, and her commanding officer became Capt. Yamanaka Shibakichi. *Sekai no Kansen*

Kongō leaves Barrow for Belfast on April 20, 1913. Note the 40-caliber, 8 cm single guns on the turret tops. Only *Kongō* was fitted with such guns. *Vickers, courtesy of the authors*

The hull of the *Hiei* on November 5, 1912, just sixteen days before launching at Yokosuka Navy Yard. Construction of the ship went smoothly partly thanks to a big gantry crane that had been extended and reinforced. This crane was completed at the end of March 1905 and had been used for the first time for the construction of the armored cruiser *Kurama* (in 1912 battle cruiser). *Kure Maritime Museum*

Hiei during fitting-out on September 20, 1913. The masts and the base of the superstructure are in place, but not the three funnels. Behind the ship is the large 200-ton crane. Her fitting-out officer was Capt. Takagi Shichitarō.

Not yet completed and with construction personnel onboard, *Hiei* departs Yokosuka for Kure, where she will be docked in no. 3 and be prepared for trials on March 23, 1914.

Hiei soon after commissioning in 1914. The ship had been completed on August 4, 1914, and her first commanding officer was Capt. Takagi Shichitarō. *Hiei* was the second Kongō-class battle cruiser and was the first to be built in Japan. The drawings were purchased from Vickers, and the main gun turrets and machinery were delivered from Britain. Unlike on *Kongō*, the first funnel was moved slightly toward the stern and raised in order to prevent smoke from entering the bridge. All three Japanese-built ships had this feature. *Sekai no Kansen*

View of Battle-Cruiser "HARUNA" under Construction. （シーレクリトンガ所船造﨑川）　景光上陸の中造製なるは艦洋巡

A colorized commemoration postcard of the launching of *Haruna* at no. 4 slip at Kawasaki Shipyard (*Zōsensho*), Kōbe. The ship was named after a volcano in the Gumma Prefecture and had been laid down on March 16, 1912. She was the third ship of the Kongō class and was built within a period of thirty-seven months

Haruna was launched at Kawasaki Shipyard, Kôbe, on December 14, 1914, and the ceremony was attended by Prince Fushimi Sadanaru, Lord Keeper of the Privy Seal of Japan. Private and public parties also attended the ceremony, and about ten ships, including the armored cruiser *Yakumo*, took part in the celebrations. *Kure Maritime Museum*

Another colorized postcard of the *Haruna* showing her being fitted-out at the shipyard. It is estimated that the photo was taken in late October–early November 1914. Here turret no. 2 is receiving a gun barrel lifted by a 150-ton crane, and smoke is seen rising from the third funnel. Her fitting-out officer was Capt. Funakoshi Kajishirō.

Construction of *Kirishima*'s middle deck in 1913. Note the slopes at the sides of the flat center part and the rivet construction. The plate thickness was 19 mm.

A colorized postcard of *Haruna* from April 25, 1915. The ship left Kōbe the same day, commanded by Capt. Funakoshi Kajishirō, and headed for Yokosuka. Note the immense volume of smoke from her funnels and the torpedo nets along its side.

The laying-down ceremony of *Kirishima* at Mitsubishi Nagasaki Shipyard on March 17, 1912. *Kirishima* was the fourth and last of the Kongō-class battle cruisers and was laid down as no. 225 ship. *Sekai no Kansen*

Construction of *Kirishima*'s upper deck, probably at the beginning of 1913. The deck is almost complete. The large hole in the deck on the right is the port hawsepipe, through which the anchor chain was passed. There should be two on the starboard side, but a plate is placed over them to prevent workers from falling into them. The two holes forward are for the fairleads.

Another photo of *Kirishima* from the beginning of 1913. We're looking toward the stern, and this picture shows the 19 mm thick deck. The square openings are leading down to the boilers. *Sekai no Kansen*

Scene from the construction of *Kirishima*'s upper, middle, and lower decks, looking forward, in April 1913. The spaces on both sides of the lower deck were used as coal bunkers and were also part of the protection. The protection of this class was similar to British battleships, such as *Erin* and the King George V class. *Sekai no Kansen*

A view of *Kirishima*'s bow section in mid-1913. The hawsepipes and outer plating are being attached to the frame of the hull. The 76 mm thick armor plates are not in position. *Sekai no Kansen*

Kirishima shortly before launching on December 1, 1913. Although the gantry crane blocks the view, the hull is fully decorated. Note that the bow crest, the chrysanthemum, is placed higher than on *Kongō*. Ships present during the ceremony were the battleship *Hizen*, the destroyer *Shiratsuyu* (perhaps visible to the left on the photo), and the Austro-Hungarian protective cruiser *Kaiserin Elisabeth*.

Kirishima due to be launched, photographed on December 1, 1913. Note the twin rudders and the stern walk. Many spectators, including craftsmen with families and students, visited the ceremony. *Sekai no Kansen*

Kirishima being launched on December 1, 1913. The Imperial Gun fired at 1021, and sixteen minutes later the *Kan'in-no-miya* and navy minister Adm. Saitō Makoto entered the stand and read the launching order. The rope was cut by the head of the Mitsubishi Nagasaki Shipyard, and the Sasebo Navy Band played while the ship slid gently into the water. *Sekai no Kansen*

Kirishima moments after being launched on December 1, 1913. Note the extremely shallow draft caused by the main gun turrets, funnels, side armor, etc. not yet being installed. It is interesting that both the Sun Flags (*Nisshōki*) and Rising Sun Flags (*Kyokujitsuki*) are displayed together. The ship was later moved to the fitting-out pier. *Sekai no Kansen*

A 150-ton crane lifts the revolving part of *Kirishima*'s no. 3 main gun turret. *Sekai no Kansen*

Kirishima on April 9, 1915, ten days prior to her official completion, in a commercial photograph taken by Mitsubishi Nagasaki Shipyard. Her first commanding officer, and previous fitting-out officer, was Capt. Kamaya Rokurō.

CHAPTER 5
General Arrangement

The copies of the original drawings of *Kongō* convey a complete general view and require no further explanations. However, they may be supplemented by a few self-explanatory tables.

Table 3
Principal particulars

Item/Ship	Haruna		Hiei
Condition	As Completed	After Second Reconstruction	After Second Reconstruction
Length at waterline (m)	211.963	219.456	219.456
Length between perpendiculars (m)	199.187	199.187	199.187
Length over all (m)	214.579	222.047	222.047
Beam at waterline (m)	28.042	28.895	29.870
Beam, maximum (m)	28.042	30.906	31.968
Depth (m)	15.526	15.54	15.52*
Draft, mean (m)	8.218	9.174	9.373
Displacement, normal (tons)	27,384	35,594.7	37,000
Speed (knots)	27.78	30	29.7
Shaft horsepower	64,000	136,000	136,000
Fuel (coal/oil) (tons)	4,200/1,000	—/6,320	—/6,240
Radius (knots/miles)	14/8,000	18/10,000	18/9,800
Armament (elevation)	45 cal., 36 cm × 8 (20°)	45 cal., 36 cm × 8 (43°)	same
	50 cal., 15 cm × 16 (15°)	50 cal., 15 cm × 14 (30°)	same
	40 cal., 8 cm × 4	40 cal., 12.7 cm × 8 (HAG)	same
		25 mm machine guns × 20	
Torpedo tubes (underwater)	53 cm × 8	—	—

Sources:
Fukuda Keiji, *Gunkan Kihon Keikaku Shiryō* ("Outline of the fundamental design of warships," Tokyo: Konnichi no Wadai-sha, 1989), pp. 1–2. However: *according to *Kaigun Zōsen Gijutsu Gaiyō* ("Outline of naval shipbuilding technique," Makino Shigeru et al., handwritten 1948–1954), p. 946.
Fukuda, *Gunkan Kihon Keikaku Shiryō*, p. 2, states 13.183 m; in the "Weight and center-of-gravity data . . ." section, p. 5, 13.164 m is given; and p. 7, 14.9 m, but without noting the measuring points.

Table 4
Coefficients and ratios

Ship	Haruna		Hiei
Item/Condition	As Completed	After Second Reconstruction	After Second Reconstruction
Block coefficient (Cb)	0.547	0.543	0.545
Prismatic coefficient (Cv)	0.556	0.565	0.567
Midship coefficient (C⊗)	0.984	0.9615	0.961
Waterline coefficient (Cwl)	0.654	0.6565	0.611
Length/beam ratio (L/B)	7.559	7.10	
Draft/length ratio (d/L)	0.39	0.418	
Beam/draft ratio (B/d)	3.412	3.15	
Length/depth ratio (L/D)	13.6	14.1	
Depth/draft ratio (D/d)	1.89	1.695	

Note:
Wetted surface 7,286.926 m². Increase of draft 1 cm by 40.5 tons (*Haruna* as completed).

Table 5
Freeboard

Ship	Haruna	Hiei	Kirishima
Item/Condition	As Completed	After Second Reconstruction	After Second Reconstruction
Length, waterline (m)	211.963	219.456	
Draft, mean (m)	8.218	9.373	
Speed (knots)	27.78	29.7	
Freeboard forward (m)	8.902	7.747	7.305
Freeboard amidships (m)	7.308	3.790 (?)	3.437 (?)
Freeboard aft (m)	5.841	4,800	4.558

Source:
Fukuda, *Gunkan Kihon Keikaku Shiryō*, p. 32. The data for freeboard amidships after the second reconstruction are supposed to be mistakes in writing and must have been about 6.15 and 6 m, respectively.

Table 6
Weight distribution as built

Item/Ship	Kongō		Haruna		Kirishima	
Normal displacement	26,624.4	100	26,951.1	100	26,739.54	100
Hull	8,083.4	30.37	8,098.45	30.05	7,972.48	29.82
Fittings	1,365.64	5.13	1,408.46	5.23	1,451.92	5.43
Protection	6.343	23.84	6,548.76	24.3	6,502.22	24.32
Machinery	4,459.6	16.76	3,994.44 + 414.75	16.36	4,438.45	16.6
Armament	4,332.04	16.27	4,282.99	15.89	4,159.25	15.55
Equipment	940.92	3.53	1,103.56	4.09	976.31	3.65
Coal	1,100	4.08	1,100	4.08	1,100	4.11
Margin	0	0	0	0	138.91	0.52

Source:
Fukuda, *Gunkan Kihon Keikaku Shiryō*, p. 58.

Note:
In the case of *Haruna*, the second figure is the weight of water in the machinery.

Table 7
Legend of weight (mainly after reconstruction)

Ship	Hiei		Kongō			Haruna	Kirishima
Item/Condition	As Completed	%	After Second Reconstruction	After Second Reconstruction	%	After Second Reconstruction	After Second Reconstruction
Hull	7,930	26.4	10,207	10.385	28.6	10,122	10,169
Fittings	1,273.5	4.7	1,680.9	1,558	4.4	1,568	1,640
Armor	4,511.7	15.0	10,749.4	6,309	17.3	10,904	10,604
Protective deck	1,989.6	6.6		4,002	11.0		
Equipment, permanent	478.2	1.6	360	438	1.2	427	351
Equipment, consumables	488.1	1.6	546.8	523	1.4	488	561
Guns	3,812.4	12.7	5,146	5,443*	15.0	4,776	5,002
Torpedo	225.6	0.8	39	105	0.3	40	45
Electric	470.7	1.6	547	505	1.4	522	543
Aircraft	—	—	56.8	—	(56)	10	46
Nautical instruments	?		17.7	?		?	?

Machinery	4,738.3	15.8	3,005**	2.737	7.5	3,439†	2,975††
Oil	657	2.2	4,160	4,200	11.5	4.452	4.269
Coal	2,824.5	9.4	—	—	—	—	—
Light oil	—	—	21	26		23	21
Lubricating oil	47.4	0.2	63	69		44	63
Reserve feed water	345.4	1.2	200	211		61	94
Margin	195.9	2.7	—	-189		109	75
Total	29,988		37,000	36,314		37,189	36,669

Notes:

* Weight of guns 3,639.1 tons, ammunition 1,416.6 tons, total 5,055.7 tons. Therefore, this group includes nearly 400 tons of other groups such as aircraft, nautical instruments, etc.

** Engine 2,705 tons, water 300 tons

† Engine 3,141 tons, water 298 tons

†† Engine 2,682 tons, water 293 tons

Displacement is official trial displacement (according to "Weight and center-of-gravity data," p. 5, the conditions of *Hiei* were as follows: full load 32,074 tons, trial 29,988.3 tons, normal 27,209.5 tons, light load 24.661.4 tons).

Note the remarkable increase of the weight of protection to about 10,750 tons, from about 6,500 tons in the case of *Hiei*. The weight of armament (guns) also increased, but the main reason was the increase in the protection of barbettes etc. belonging to this weight group.

When the weight of the machinery of *Hiei* as completed is compared with that of *Kongō* after the second reconstruction, roughly 4,750 tons vs. 2,700 tons, the output was more than doubled (64,000 shp vs. 136,000 shp = 212.5%), with only 58 percent of the original weight. This is evidence of remarkable progress in warship machinery within twenty years.

Table 8
Stability

Ship	Haruna (as completed)			Hiei (after second reconstruction)			Kirishima (after second reconstruction)		
Condition	Normal	Full	Light	Standard	Full	Light	Standard	Full	Light
Displacement	27,384	32,306	24,668	37,000	39,441.8	30,443.8	36,668	39,141	29,996
Draft	8.218	9.419	7.541	9.373	9.889	7.849	9.726	10.292	8.166
KG (m)	9.464	9.028	9.854	9.06	8.67	10.15	9.025	8.690	10.076
GM (m)	1.753	1.871	1.649	2.35	2.63	2.29	1.867	2.130	1.184
OG (m)	1.245	- 0.391	2.313	- 0.31	- 1.22	2.31	- 0.700	- 1.602	1.910
Range	?	?	?	72	78	62.6	73.5	79	62
Maximum GZ	?	?	?	1.455	1.462	1.195	1.220	1.26	1.25

Source:
Fukuda, *Gunkan Kihon Keikaku Shiryō*, p. 76.

Profile and plan of *Kongō* as built.
Michael Wünschmann

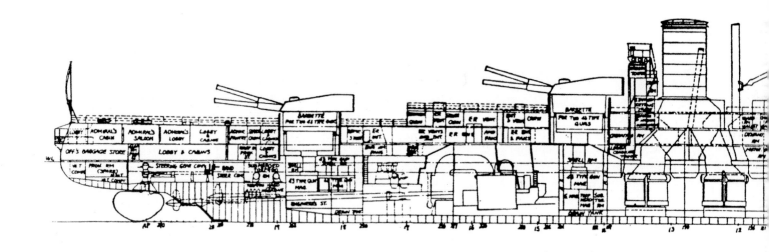

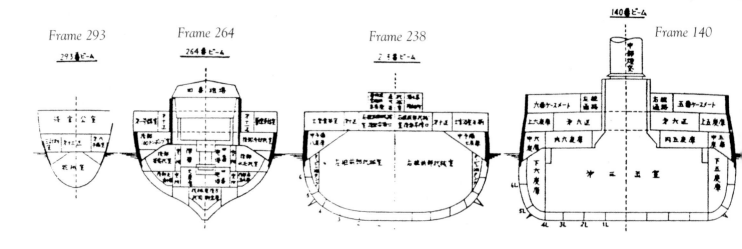

Frame 293   *Frame 264*   *Frame 238*   *Frame 140*

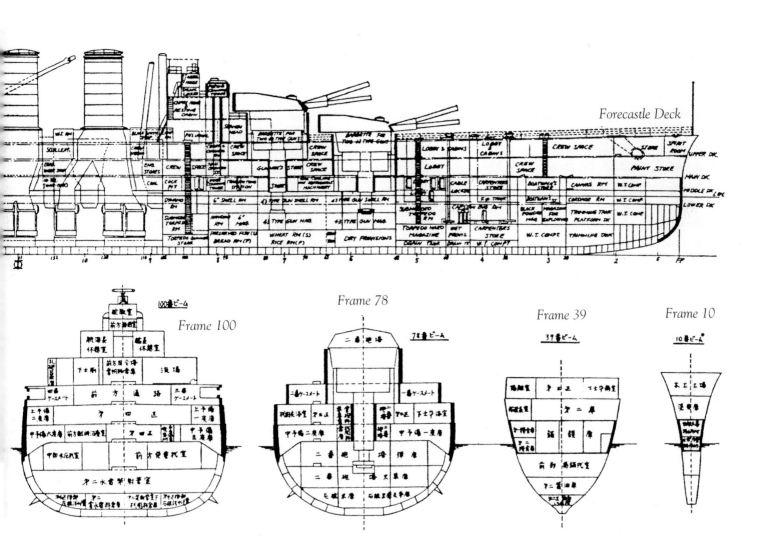

Forecastle Deck

Frame 100

Frame 78

Frame 39

Frame 10

The battle cruiser *Kongō* on July 23–29, 1914, when she was the fleet flagship of the 1st Kantai, flying the flag of VAdm. Katō Tomosaburō. It belonged to the 1st Sentai together with the *Satsuma*, *Settsu*, *Tsukuba*, *Iwami*, and *Suō* (RAdm. Tsuchiyama Tetsuzō). *Sekai no Kansen*

Stern view of *Kongō* anchored off Shinagawa on February 9, 1922. Note that her name is written in *hiragana* on the stern. It is a mourning ship following the death of former field marshal and prime minister Yamagata Aritomo. At this time, *Kongō* belonged to the 2nd Kantai, flying the flag of VAdm. Nakano Naoe. At this time, *Kongō* was commanded by Capt. Takemitsu Kazu. *Sekai no Kansen*

Kongō followed by *Hiei* at low speed in 1923. *Kongō* (fleet flagship) and *Hiei* formed the 4th Sentai of the 2nd Kantai, commanded by VAdm. Katō Hiroharu. *Sekai no Kansen*

Hiei as completed at Yokosuka on August 24, 1914. The day before, Japan had broken off diplomatic relations with Germany, and on the twenty-fourth, *Hiei* sailed to Sasebo. On the tenth, *Hiei* had been incorporated into the 3rd Sentai together with *Kongō*, *Kurama* (flagship of VAdm. Yamaya Tanin), and *Tsukuba*. The ship on the right is probably the battleship *Kawachi*.

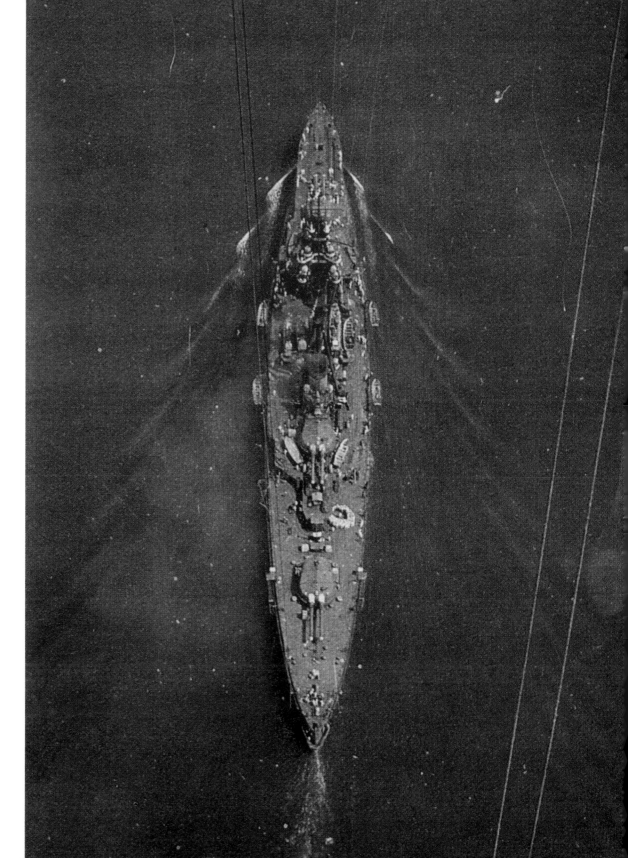

Hiei photographed from an observation balloon in 1922 at an unknown location. At this time, the 2nd Kantai was not set up due to budget restrictions after the disarmament agreement, and *Hiei* belonged to the 1st Kantai, 2nd Sentai, at this time. It is possible that the photo was taken late in 1922, when a balloon for a short time was assigned to the 1st Kantai for training purposes. *Kure Maritime Museum*

Haruna is prepared to leave Kawasaki, Kōbe, on April 24, 1915, where the ship had been completed only five days earlier. *Kure Maritime Museum*

Haruna at Yokosuka in 1920, while flagship of the 2nd Kantai, led by VAdm. Prince Fushimi Hiroyasu. To the left is the battleship *Yamashiro*. *Kure Maritime Museum*

Kirishima (Capt. Shima Takeshi) at Sasebo on December 21, 1915, soon after completion. The ship is shown immediately after the grand maneuvers of that year. Note the 4.5-meter rangefinders on turrets 2 and 3.

CHAPTER 6
Protection

The waterline belt had a thickness of 203 mm over the vital parts and tapered to 76 mm at the ends. Above it, two layers of a shorter belt of 152 mm thickness extended up to the uppermost deck, the upper one protecting the secondary guns.

The barbettes of the main guns were protected by 229 mm (some sources state 254 mm) of thick armor above the uppermost deck and 76 mm below, because here the protection by the belt armor was effective. The gunhouse sides were protected by a thickness of 229 mm, the front shield was 254 mm thick, the roof was 76 mm, and according to Ishibashi Takao[1] the rear was 254 mm.

At the time of design and construction, horizontal protection was largely neglected, and protection by 19 mm (lower deck extending over machinery spaces and magazines) and 38 mm (uppermost deck) thick plates proved to be very weak against bombs and shells fired from large distances. Therefore, reinforcement of the horizontal protection was permitted by the Washington Treaty and executed as part of the first reconstruction (for details, refer to that item).

The steering compartment was also only very lightly protected (19 mm and 25.4 mm), and this brought about the loss of *Hiei*, as stated in the summary.

CHAPTER 7
Machinery

Improved Parsons Turbines of *Kongō*, *Hiei*, and *Kirishima*

The engines of *Kongō* and *Hiei* were ordered from the builder of *Kongō*: Vickers Ltd., Naval Construction Works, Barrow-in-Furness. The builder of the hull produced those of *Kirishima*: Mitsubishi Nagasaki.

The design resulted in 290 rpm, 64,000 hp, and a ship speed of 27.5 knots, and the propelling machinery consisted of two sets of so-called double-expansion improved Parsons turbines, arranged in two compartments separated by a longitudinal bulkhead at centerline. Each set of turbines was composed of one high-pressure turbine (HPT) and one low-pressure turbine (LPT). The former rotated the outer shaft, and the latter was coupled to the inner one. The high-pressure (HP) and low-pressure (LP) astern turbines were attached to the after end of the casings of the corresponding ahead turbines, and by this arrangement all four shafts were working when going astern.

The principle of the so-called improved Parsons turbine (i.e., the combination of impulse and reaction type turbines) was adopted only for the HP ahead and astern turbines. The two LP turbines were of the reaction principle throughout.

By the combination of the impulse and reaction systems, the disadvantage of the former Parsons turbine (which was forced to reduce the steam pressure by passing through the control valve when low speed was required) was removed by placing one Curtis impulse wheel at the HP end. Each wheel carried a single stage of impulse blading consisting of four rows of rotating blades with their corresponding guide vanes. The nozzles (Curtis stage nozzles) were arranged in groups, and great care was bestowed upon the maintenance of high initial pressure by shutting off the supply of steam from one or more of these nozzle groups when the turbines were working at reduced power.

Following to the impulse wheels there were a two-stage cruising element and seven stages of reaction blades in the case of the ahead turbines, and two short stages of reaction blading in the astern turbines.

The design of the impulse blades and the method of their attachment were particularly cared for, and this principle was also applied using the best selection of material: special nickel-coated mild steel (MS) except for the last row of moving blades, which were made of brass. The blades were welded on to sectional function rings of MS, and the latter were dovetailed into grooves on the wheel rim, to which they were fixed by brass packing caulked into one side of the groove.

Generally, the object kept in view when designing these turbines was the maintenance of high economy in all service conditions, and to keep uniformity of the turbine load; the power of the LPT was increased by 10 percent compared with the HPT. It must also be pointed out that the combination of HP ahead and astern arrangement, together with the introduction of impulse wheels and a two-stage cruising element in one casing, necessitated exceptionally large dimensions and was a departure from the usual practice in high-powered marine turbines, and, therefore, great care was also given to the detailed design of the rotors and casings, using forged steel in most elements, such as rotor drum, spindles, impulse wheels, casing, and shafting, to ensure sufficient strength and freedom of distortion under all steam conditions.

It is also noteworthy that the entire arrangement, including steam and exhaust pipes, feed, drain, and oil-lubricating systems, was such as to preserve the independence of the port and starboard turbine sets and to allow either set to be worked when the other was disabled in case of, for example, damage. Particular attention was paid to the fixing of steam and other pipes with regard to expansion. The fixing was limited to the lowest-possible grade, and provisions were also taken in case of valves, for instance, to permit free expansion.

As for the condensers, two units were provided to each turbine set (i.e., one condenser per turbine) and two each were fitted in one condenser compartment. The diameter of the exhaust pipe was 2.13 meters. The arrangement, method of fixing to the hull, and penetration of the after bulkhead between the engine rooms and condenser compartments were paid considerable attention. The condensers were of the "Uniflux" type, with different pitches of the tubes between 24.6 and 38.1 mm (upper part 24.6 mm, middle part 26.2 mm, lower part 38.1 mm), thus avoiding the staying of air exhaust and condensed water passing through the cooling tubes, and improving efficiency by the rapid movement.[1] This resulted in a considerable reduction of the cooling area. The tube casings were made up of steel plates and angles, and the end covers were made of cast iron to prevent galvanic action of the tubes, among other features. The number of tubes amounted to 9,065, the cooling area was 1,347 m², and the flow volume was 6,595 tons/h. The treated steam volume amounted to 101.6 tons/h.

In the past, the vacuum pump and circulation (water) pump had commonly been used, since with the adoption of the turbine it became evident that the increase of vacuum would produce a big effect, but the vacuum pump had an unsatisfactory effect and was replaced by the Weir dual-type air pump, having one air and one water barrel. In these ships, one independent air pump of Weir type for each condenser were fitted. However, *Hiei* was fitted with the single-expansion type instead of the dual type.

The four circulating pumps for the main condensers were of the centrifugal type driven by two-crank engines fitted with forced lubrication.

There was also one auxiliary condenser in each condenser compartment to take the exhaust steam from the auxiliary machinery. For these, two air and two circulating pumps were also provided.

Table 9
Engine trials of *Kongō* and *Hiei*

Item/Ship	Kongō	Hiei	Steam Consumption (kg/hp/h)	Kongō	Hiei
hp, designed	64,000	64,000	Designed: main machinery	5.21	5.21
hp, closed ventilation, 10/10	78,275	76,127	Designed: auxiliary machinery	0.91	0.91
hp, open ventilation, 10/10	?	69,973	At 10/10 (full speed)	5.16	5.38
hp, astern full, designed	32,000	32,000	At 8/10	5.67	5.83
hp, astern full, actual	24,712	26,790	At 6/10	5.70	5.99
rpm, designed	290	290	At 4/10	6.20	6.71
rpm, actual	300.6	295.95	At 2/10	7.28	7.67
Speed, closed ventilation	27,537	27,724	At 1/10	9.23	9.58
Speed, open ventilation	?	27,028	At 10 knots	13.54	12.57

Source:
Nihon Hakuyō Kikan-shi, *Teikoku Kaigun Kikan-shi* (Tokyo: Hara Shobō, 1975), vol. II, p. 464ff, particularly pp. 470–471.

Note:
The high steam consumption at low speeds signifies a relative uneconomical working of the direct-coupled turbines.

Table 10
Power-to-weight ratios

	Haruna	Kongō	Hiei	Kirishima
shp	80,476	78,275	76,127	79,680
Weight (kg)	4,376.8	4,459.6	4,524.8	4,438.5
shp/weight	18.27	17.6	16.8	17.95

Source:
Fukuda, *Gunkan Kihon Keikaku Shiryō*, p. 151.

Brown-Curtis Turbines of *Haruna*

Haruna was the first ship of the IJN fitted with this type of turbine. The principal differences between the Brown-Curtis turbine and the conventional Curtis turbine were that (1) the rotor (*shadō-bu*) was placed next to several wheels (*yoku-sha*), the rotor had neither diaphragm (*shikiri*) nor nozzles (*funkō*) but impulse blades (*shōdō-yoku*), and pairs of static blades (*seidō-yoku*) formed one unit of impulse stage and the static blades functioned as nozzles against the moving blades (*dō-yoku*); and (2) the astern turbine (*kō-shin*) also consisted of wheels (*yoku-sha*) and rotor (*dō-sha*).

The principal arrangement of the turbines in the engine rooms was the same as in the sisters, as was the use of one HPT and one LPT ahead turbine per side. The astern turbine was incorporated into the casings at the after end to bring about the same effect as described earlier.

The HPT ahead had six stages, of which the first one had four rows of blades and all the others three; the rotor had fifteen rows. The LPT ahead had no stages but only a rotor with thirty-eight rows of blades. The HPT (LPT) astern consisted of one stage with four (14) rows of blades, and the rotor had ten (12) rows.

Boilers

All ships except *Hiei* were fitted with thirty-six Yarrow water-tube boilers, with large tubes, in eight boiler rooms, four on each side of the centerline bulkhead, which extended over the whole length of the machinery spaces. Steam pressure was 19.2 bar in the boilers and 14.3 bar at the turbine inlet.

The boilers were arranged to work under forced draft with closed stokeholds. In order to burn oil fuel as well as coal, a complete installation of pumps, heaters, filters, and collectors with all connections was provided. Electrical indicators for regulating the firing of the boilers were fitted in the boiler rooms, the furnaces being numbered to correspond to the numbers that were periodically displayed on the indicator dials.

Five steam-driven air compressors were fitted for cleaning the boiler tubes externally by air jet.

Thirty-four fans, of which two were of the double-breasted type while the others all belonged to the single-breasted type, supplied forced draft. The fans were driven by compound steam engines fitted with forced lubrication.

The steam and exhaust piping arrangement was constructed so that the turbines could be supplied by steam from any of the eight boiler rooms.

Because *Kongō* was the model for the sisters, this arrangement was repeated in *Haruna* and *Kirishima*, but in their cases steam pressure on the turbine inlet was 17.1 bar, though the boilers still had the same pressure.

Hiei was fitted with thirty-six Kampon water-tube boilers made in Yokosuka Navy Yard, and these had the same working pressure as the Yarrow boilers. By the way, the influence of open and closed stokeholds (or natural and forced draft) can very well be illustrated in the case of *Hiei*, which developed 69,973 and 76,127 ihp, respectively.

Further data about the main machinery in the original condition and after the reconstruction are provided in the tables, and some more data may be found in the summarized descriptions of the first and second reconstruction.

Table 11
Weight of machinery

Ship	Haruna			Kongō		Hiei		Kirishima
Condition	As Completed	First Reconstruction	Second Reconstruction	As Completed	First Reconstruction	As Completed	Second Reconstruction	As Completed
shp	80,476	75,806.9	141,211	78,275	73,855	76,127.3	136,000	79,679.7
Weight	4,376.8	3,942.5	3,384.7	4,459.6	3,701.8	4,524.8	3,005	4,438.5
shp/weight	18.27	19.2	41.7	17.6	19.95	16.8	45.2	17.95

Source:
Fukuda, *Gunkan Kihon Keikaku Shiryō*, p. 151.

Table 12
Change of space and weight of machinery

Item	shp	Area (m²)	shp/Area	Weight[1]	Weight[2]	Shp/w 1	Shp/w 2[3]
Condition/Name	*Haruna*						
As completed	64,000	1,685	38.0	4,586	4,760	13.9	13.4
First reconstruction	75,000	1,240	60.5	3,742	3,918	20.1	19.2
Second reconstruction	136,000	1,335	101.7	3,299	3,439	41.2	39.6
Condition/Name	*Kirishima*						
As completed	64,000	1,685	38.0	4,576	4,763	14.0	13.4
First reconstruction	75,000	1,175	66.2	3,449	3,625	21.8	20.6
Second reconstruction	144,000	1,219	118.2	2,890	3,030	49.6	47.5

Source:
Fukuda, *Gunkan Kihon Keikaku Shiryō*, p. 153.

Notes:
[1] W 1 = Weight without capstan etc.; W 2 = Weight with capstan etc.
[2] shp = Designed values except for the *Kirishima*, which is after its second reconstruction.
[3] Note the big differences in weight after the first and, particularly, after the second reconstruction.

Table 13
Machinery spaces

Ship	Hiei	Kongō		Haruna	
Condition	As Completed	First Reconstruction	Second Reconstruction	First Reconstruction	Second Reconstruction
shp	73,000	73,000	136,000	73,000	136,338/141,211
Engine room, length (m)	29.871	29.871	29.871	29.871	29.871
Width (m)	20.12	20.12	20.12	20.12	20.12
Height (m)	10.21	10.21	10.21	10.21	10.21
Area (m²)	594.6	594.6	594.6	594.6	594.6
shp per m² / engine room	122.8	122.8	228.7	122.8	229.29/237.49
Number of boilers	36 mixed	8 oil	8 oil	6 oil, 10 mixed	11 oil
Boiler room length	51.205	35.356	39.014	46.94	46.94
		1st to 3rd 13.71		1st + 2nd 13.71	
Width	21.335	4th 21.33	16.056	3rd 12.50	14.17
				4th 21.33	
Height	8.077	8.077	8.077	8.077	8.077
Area	1.092	594.6	624.22	649.4	740.2
shp per m² / boiler room	66.9	122.8	217.9	112.4	184.19/190.77
shp / total area			112		102.14/105.79

Source:
Fukuda, *Gunkan Kihon Keikaku Shiryō*, p. 147; Fukui Shizuo, *Kaigun Kantei-shi* (*Japanese Naval Vessels Illustrated, 1869–1945*, vol. 1, *Battleships & Battle Cruisers*) (Tokyo: Kabushiki Kaisha Bestsellers, 1974), p. 243, for *Haruna* 10/10 and 10.5/10 trial after second reconstruction (i.e., the smaller value refers to 10/10 trial).

Kongō during trials in the Irish Sea at 0930 on April 20, 1913. Note the measuring tank for water consumption trials forward of the after turret. A similar tank was placed on the starboard side. This method of measuring the circulation of boiler water was discontinued after the Ise class battleships. Note also the flow of discharged water at the hull side.

Kongō during trials on May 8, 1913, in the Firth of Clyde. On this occasion the displacement was 27,580 tons, and *Kongō* attained a speed of 27.54 knots. This photo was actually the first one published.

Hiei on 10/10 trials off Tateyama on April 26, 1914. All boilers are in action, and at 27,390 tons the ship attained 27.725 knots with 76,127.3 shp. Note the large measuring tanks for water consumption trials aft of turret 3.

A photo from about 1914 showing the loading of a high-pressure turbine casing. It is said that *Kirishima*'s Parsons turbines weighed more than 200 tons, so they had to be disassembled in order to be handled by the 150-ton crane. *Sekai no Kansen*

Installation of one of *Kirishima*'s thirty-six Yarrow-type, mixed-fired water-tube boilers in mid-1913. These boilers were necessary to generate steam for the operation of the main turbines, and they were fitted in eight boiler rooms.

CHAPTER 8
Armament

Main and Secondary Guns

The most prominent characteristic of the battle cruisers of the Kongō class was the mounting of 45-caliber, 355.6 mm guns instead of the earlier-decided 50-caliber, 304.8 mm guns. The guns were of various types:

Kongō was equipped with eight 45-caliber type Bi (Vickers) 36 cm guns, model I, with 283.5-liter volume in the chamber, produced by Vickers in Britain (and naturally mounted during the fitting-out stage).

Hiei was equipped with the same type of gun but model II, differing from K I by the increase of the chamber volume to 303.2 liters. According to the "Annual Report" of the Navy Ministry (*Kaigunshō Nenpō*), four guns were produced in the Gunnery Division of the Kure Navy Yard and the Japan Steel Works, the latter working raw material imported from Vickers.

Haruna and *Kirishima* had 45-caliber type 41 36 cm guns, model III, with the same chamber volume as model II, but the breech bush and breech were changed to type 41, derived from the Vickers ones.

Seven guns for *Haruna* were produced by Japan Steel Works, using imported raw material from Vickers, and one gun was imported from that company, together with all eight guns for *Kirishima*.

Table 14

Principal technical data of the 36 cm (main) and 15 cm (secondary) guns

Item/Type	45 cal. type 41 36 cm	50 cal. type 41 15 cm
Caliber, nominal/actual	36 cm / 355.6 mm	15 cm / 152.5 mm
Barrel length, breech face to muzzle	16.002 m	7.6199 m
Barrel length, overall / in calibers	16,469 m / 46.31	7.8756 m / 51.677
Weight including breech mechanism	84.689 tons	8.36 tons
Construction	wire-wound, liner radially expanded, four layers at muzzle and breech	three layers (tubes), liner radially expanded but older guns wire-wound*
Breech	In contrast to the cylindrical interrupted screw breech of Vickers type, the fore and aft parts of the type 41 were inclined 5 degrees to facilitate opening and closing. Seen from the side, the middle part appeared like a bulge. Invented by the later vice admiral (weapon production) Dr. Arisaka Shōzō, the adoption of this breech was officially announced on August 21, 1908, and used on 8 cm guns and upward for nearly all Japanese naval guns as type 41 (1908) breech.	
Number of grooves / depth and width	84 / 3.048 mm × 8.865 mm	72 / 1.27 mm × 7.62 mm
Twist	uniform (1 in 28 cal.)	uniform (1 in 30 cal.)
Length of rifling	13.737 m	6.584 m
Bore cross section	1,015 cm²	168 cm²
Chamber, length	2.007 m	0.949 m
Chamber, volume	283.5 to 302.16 liters**	26.14 liters
Powder container	4 bags (1/4 charges) 132 kg	1 bag (1/1 charge) ? kg
Muzzle velocity, designed/actual	770 m/s/805 m/s***	850 m/s
Maximum bore pressure	30 bar	28.8 bar
Muzzle pressure	5.1 bar	4.9 bar
Projectile weight	673.5 kg (type 91 AP, TS)†	
	625.0 kg (CS, IS)	45.36 kg (CS)
Charge weight	95.38 kg to 139.95 kg††	12.76 kg
Ignition weight	0.9 kg	0.06 kg
Projectile travel	13.994 m (type 91 AP shell)	6.6705 m
Point of complete combustion	18 cal. from muzzle	19 cal. from muzzle
Maximum range, horizontal/vertical	35,478 m/9,757 m	21,000 m/10,000 m
Approximate life	250 to 280†††	500 to 600

Notes:

* It is supposed that the guns of the Kongō class belonged to the wire-wound type.

** In report O-54 (N) of the US Naval Technical Mission to Japan, p. 11, 294.9 liters are given for barrel models II and III, using type 91 AP (boat-tailed) shells, but as long as the type 88 AP shell was used, the length of the chamber was 2.0997 in. and the volume was 303.16 liters. The chamber length of model III2 and III4 barrels was 2.1009 m but had the same volume, and the length of rifling was 13,733.9 m. The model IV was an experimental "inner-tube-changed gun" with only seventy-two grooves. According to the late RAdm. Takasu Kōichi, there was another experimental model of a Krupp breech, but the designation, if any, is unknown.

*** The muzzle velocity depended on the weight of shell and also charge. Also, V0 changed considerably toward the end of its life, and according to the historian Kunimoto Yasufumi it was reduced to 348 m/s after firing 280 rounds.

† AP = armor piercing; TS = target practice shell; CS = common shell; IC = incendiary shell. The weight of the type 88 AP shell was 635.03 kg.

†† Three types of charges were used; namely, full (4/4), reduced (3/4), and weak (2/4). There was also a strong charge (full + up to 20 percent), but it was used only for trial purposes.

††† Calculated by equivalent full charges (the IJN did not use this term); that is, strong charge was calculated as two shells fired, reduced charge as ½ shell fired, and weak as 1/16 shell fired.

Table 15
Principal ballistic data of the 36 cm main gun

Elevation/Range	Elevation / Angle of Fall	Striking Velocity	Penetrative Power (AP shell) in mm	
			Vertical (VC)	Horizontal (NVC)
			15,000 m = 417/302	124
20° = 22,500 m	20° = 31°48′	20,000 m = 396 m/s	20,000 m = 358/193	135
25° = 25,800 m	25° = 39°06′	25,000 m = 403 m/s	25,000 m = 272/163	157
30° = 28,300 m	30° = 45°40′	30,000 m = 418 m/s	30,000 m = 229/?	208

Notes:
VC = Vickers Cemented
NVC = New Vickers Cemented
Note the decrease in penetration power against vertical armor and the increase against horizontal armor, depending on the range.
Note also the slight increase of the remaining velocity due to the large angle of fall.
Maximum range with 43° elevation angle was 35,478 m; maximum altitude of the trajectory was 9,757 m.
In the column "Penetrative Power," the higher value refers to the type 91 AP shell as given in *Umi to Sora* ("Sea and Sky") 5 (1958): 94; the lower values are stated by Fukuda, *Gunkan Kihon Keikaku Shiryō*, p. 159, without specification of the shell. However, even if the lower values are considered correct, they prove that the armor of the Kongō class was insufficient to secure the planned immunity zone from 20,000 to 25,000 m.

The secondary guns were 50 cal. type 41 15 cm guns whose particulars and ballistic data can be found in tables 14 and 16. Sixteen guns were mounted in casemates, divided evenly between both sides of the ship. The original Vickers gun was adapted by a change in the beech and breech block to the Japanese type 41.

Table 16
Principal ballistic data of the 15 cm gun

Elevation/Range	Elevation / Angle of Fall	Remaining Velocity	Penetrative Power
15° = 14,200 m	?	?	48.2 mm (vertical)
20° = 16,300 m	20° = 36°53′	324 m/s	negligible
25° = 18,000 m	25° = 43°23′	334 m/s	?
30° = 19,500 m	30° = 49°38′	349 m/s	?

Source:
Fukuda, *Gunkan Kihon Keikaku Shiryō*, p. 159, and *Umi to Sora* 5 (1958).

A 45-caliber, 36 cm gun for *Kongō* being tested in 1913 at Eskmeals Gun Range. Eskmeals Gun Range is located on the western coast of England, about 10 kilometers north of the Vickers Barrow-in-Furness. The loading arm behind the breech is clearly visible. *Gakken*

Kongō photographed during gunnery practice between April 1925 and July 1926, and turret 1 is trained to port. It is now twelve years since her commissioning, and her appearance is much changed. Note the funnel cap.

Hiei (Capt. Yoshikawa Yasuhira) south of Tokyo Bay on October 24, 1919. This is a "battle scene" from an exercise conducted off Miyake-jima, and both main and secondary guns are in use. The photo was taken from *Kongō*, and behind *Hiei* is *Kirishima*. *Kure Maritime Museum*

Haruna conducted gunnery tests on February 7, 1915, on the south of the Kii Channel, and two guns received minor damage to the breech blocks. The photo shows the no. 1 turret's right gun firing. *Kure Maritime Museum*

Another photo from *Haruna*'s gunnery test on February 7, 1915. The left gun of the no. 1 turret is firing. *Kure Maritime Museum*

A third photo from the gunnery test of *Haruna* on February 7, 1915. *Kure Maritime Museum*

Kirishima firing a full salvo from her eight 36 cm main guns during gunnery tests west of Amakusa on February 10, 1915. Despite the use of smokeless powder, the starboard side of the ship is almost totally enveloped in smoke.

A 50-caliber, 15 cm gun as mounted on *Kongō*. The projectiles were identical to those used for the 45-caliber guns on the battleship *Kashima* and others. The Vickers-type (*Bi Shiki*) breech was lighter and simpler than the Armstrong type (*An Shiki*). *Gakken*

Main Gun Mounts

In the report O-47 (N)-1 of the US Naval Technical Mission to Japan, titled *Japanese Naval Guns and Mounts: Article I Mounts under 18*, the authors pointed out, as generalization, "that all Japanese naval turrets and mounts are of sound and practical design and construction, but have no really outstanding features" and "are all old-fashioned when compared with US and British standards." They explain that the only major-caliber Japanese turrets were for 14-inch and 16-inch guns, and "all of these turrets were built either before, during, or just after" World War I, more or less as copies of the British-built turrets for the battle cruiser *Kongō*, and state that "they are similar in principle, and in most details to the . . . turrets built for *Kongō*, which in turn are, with the exceptions mentioned later, similar to the 15-inch turrets of Queen Elizabeth and Royal Sovereign classes."

Japanese authors agree with this opinion and grant that the Vickers turret of *Kongō* was the fundamental type, but if details such as (1) structure of the barrel, (2) type of breech, (3) diameter of the barbette, (4) loading system (i.e., free or fixed), (5) elevation angle, (6) shape of the turret (gunhouse), and (7) type and mounting of rangefinder are analyzed, the IJN used fourteen types in the forty twin gun mounts of the four ships of the Kongō class (sixteen units), two ships of the Fusō class (twelve units), and two ships of the Ise class (also twelve units). However, no particular designation was made, but all were known as the type 43 14-inch twin turret.

The principal differences of the turrets of the Kongō class were that (1) they were angle shaped in *Kongō* and *Hiei*, but round shaped in *Haruna* and *Kirishima* and (2) the elevation angle was −5° to +25° in *Kongō* and −5° to +20° in the sisters. Because of the free loading system, the diameter of the barbette was 9 m.[1] The number of gunners in the gunhouse was twenty-one, and all told for one main gun turret was over ninety.

The image below shows the general arrangement of the main gun mount of the Kongō class. Readers who want to know details should refer to the fine book *The Big Gun: Battleship Main Armament, 1860–1945*,[2] by Peter Hodges, who describes the British 15-inch mounts (of Queen Elizabeth and other classes) on pp. 70ff., and very detailed in appendix 3, pp. 128ff.[3]

Like the guns, the mounts were also manufactured in the Gunnery Division of Kure Navy Yard and Nippon Steel Works, and it deserves special attention that the later VAdm. Godō Takuo, once a supervisor of the construction of battle cruiser *Kongō*, was responsible for the mounts.

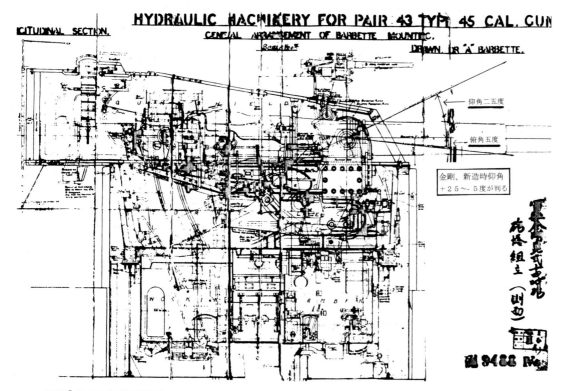

"A" turret (turret 1) of the *Kongō* from an original Vickers blueprint. Note the maximum elevation (+25 degrees) and depression (−5 degrees). *Senzen Senpaku*

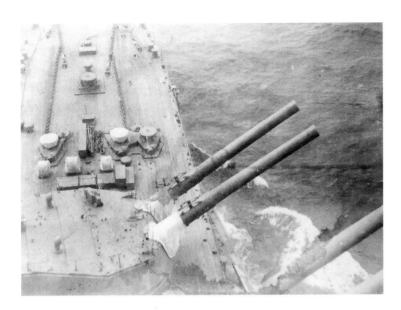

The forward 36 cm main gun turrets of *Kongō* trained to starboard. The time of this photo is unknown but is believed to have been between 1913 and 1929. *Private collection, previously unpublished*

Hiei during a gunnery exercise off Sasebo in June 1925. All guns are trained to port, and at the time of this photo the maximum elevation was still 20 degrees. Note the changed foremast, the fitting of a cap on the first funnel, and the arrangement of searchlights around the first and third funnels. The troublesome and almost useless torpedo defense nets are still fitted.

Another photo of *Hiei* taken from a balloon, this time around 1925. Note that *Hiei* had angular-shaped main gun turret houses, just like *Kongō*. *Haruna* and *Kirishima* had rounded turret houses.

A picture of *Hiei* during the grand maneuvers east of Honshū in late October 1927. This was the second large maneuver after the disarmament treaty, and several new ships participated, particularly large submarines and the aircraft carrier *Akagi*. This photo was taken from *Kongō*, the flagship of the 4th Sentai, 2nd Kantai (commanded by VAdm. Yoshikawa Yasuhira), and *Hiei* was commanded by Capt. Okamoto Ikuo. Note how difficult it was to operate the secondary guns in this sea state.

The forward half of the barrel fell into the sea, and the breech fell down into the barbette. *Kure Maritime Museum*

During gunnery exercises off Cape Motsuta, Shimamaki (Hokkaidō), on September 12, 1920, the right barrel of the no. 1 turret of *Haruna* (Capt. Ōishi Shōkichi) was torn apart by a detonation. The armored roof was blown off, and seven men in the turret were killed and eight wounded. *Kure Maritime Museum*

As can be seen, the forward part of the turret shield also was blasted out and fell overboard. On this photo the roof has been covered by a tarpaulin. After the accident, *Haruna* proceeded to Yokosuka for repairs. *Kure Maritime Museum*

CHAPTER 9
Reconstructions and Modifications

General

Before the outbreak of the Pacific War, the Kongō class was reconstructed twice to keep pace with the technological progress, and to be adapted to the new strategical concepts that the IJN was forced to work out due to the quantitative inferiority determined by the Washington Arms Limitation Treaty. The reconstruction was as thorough as was permitted, or as was practicable. During each reconstruction the ships' characteristics changed, and after the first reconstruction, the vessels were reclassified as battleships, and after the second reconstruction, unofficially, as high-speed battleships. These changes do sufficiently express the character of each reconstruction, which may be summarized as such: (1) reinforcement of horizontal and underwater protection, (2) increase of the maximum firing range of the main guns, and (3) modification of the boiler rooms during the first reconstruction, while the second reconstruction aimed for (1) an increase in speed by replacing the main engines and boilers, (2) modification of the fire-directing systems and other command installations, and (3) fitting of a damage control system.

Reconstruction under the Terms of the Washington Arms Limitation Treaty

The Washington Arms Limitation Treaty of 1922 determined the relative possession of capital ships (battleships, battle cruisers, and aircraft carriers) of five countries to 5:5:3:1.75:1.75 and the so-called naval holidays (i.e., the prohibition of building new capital ships for ten years, with the exception of aircraft carriers).[2] However, replacement was admitted if the age of the capital ship exceeded twenty years since completion. In other words, the

ship's age was determined as twenty years, at least. This was a long period of time, within which a remarkable progress of weapon and engine technology was forecasted, so that at the end of this period, only obsolete ships would exist. Before the conclusion of this treaty, warships had been the subject of frequent conversion, reconstruction, or refitting work in order to keep pace with technological progress, or to adapt them to strategic changes. The Kongō class was designed in 1909–10, with minor changes in 1911, and in the decade before the treaty negotiations, the development of submarines and aircraft—still in their infancy when these battle cruisers were designed—was particularly rapid. In addition, lessons learned from the Battle of Jutland produced such an effect on capital ship design that it was divided between pre- and post-Jutland ships. All countries saw the need to protect the capital ships against the new threats. Thus, in order to dampen these feelings, the treaty allowed reconstruction with a determined content and within a limited increase of tonnage.[3] The reconstruction influenced not only the structure of the ships; technical progress in other fields and changes in the strategic concept also demanded modifications not specified in the treaty. Therefore, they were not excluded and were carried out in response to the situation. As a consequence, the content of the reconstruction of the capital ships became extensive, particularly in the case of Japan and the United States.

The first reconstruction began with the battle cruiser *Haruna*, which had suffered an explosion accident of the first main gun turret during an exercise on September 12, 1920, and was followed by the *Kirishima*. Then both *Kongō* and *Hiei* were begun at the Yokosuka and Kure Navy Yards, respectively, in September and October 1929, but as a result of the London Treaty, the latter had to be converted into a training battleship, thus reducing the strength of Japanese capital ships to nine.

Table 17
The first reconstruction

Ship	Yard	1924	1925	1926	1927	1928	1929	1930	1931	1932
Haruna	Yokosuka Navy Yard	3				31.7				(4)
Kirishima	Kure Navy Yard	(1)		(2)	3			31.3		(4)
Kongō	Yokosuka Navy Yard	(1)		(2)	(3)		9		31.3	(4)
Hiei	Kure Navy Yard—Conv. Training BB	(1)		(2)	(3)		15.10			31.12

Notes:
1. Conversion of the foremast (fire-directing gear, rangefinder, searchlight control, etc.).
2. Increase of 8 cm high-angle guns from four to seven single mounts.
3. Conversion of the foremast into a tower (pagoda) type.
4. Improved antiaircraft defense by mounting four 12.7 cm twin high-angle guns.
5. The first reconstruction of the *Hiei* stopped on April 24, 1930. Moved to Yokosuka Navy Yard on November 7, where conversion into a training battleship started. One month before its conversion was finished, it was classified *renshū* (training) *senkan* (battleship), on December 1, 1932.
6. All ships except the *Hiei* were reclassified battleships on June 1, 1931.

Reconstruction in Preparation for the Expiration of the Naval Arms Limitation Treaties

Because of the prolongation of the naval holidays and the extension of the unfavorable ratio of possession to most auxiliary craft in the London Arms Limitation Treaty of 1930, the strategic conception for war against the primary hypothetical enemy, the US Navy (USN), was modified. The concept of reducing the superior enemy battle fleet on its advance across the Pacific, in order to obtain approximate parity between the forces, was supplemented by the addition of one more phase: the further reduction of the enemy's strength by a night engagement prior to the decisive battle. In this concept, light surface forces, such as destroyers and light and heavy cruisers, were to be the main actors. In order to penetrate the outer defense of the enemy's, as it was supposed, circular formation formed by heavy cruisers and to enable close-range torpedo attacks on the confused formation of the main force, the Kongō class was to destroy the outer defense ring by using their superior gun power and then retire from the battlefield in order to fight in the successive decisive battle, as part of the main force. However, in their current configuration, with reduced speed, the ships were not suited for this role, and unless their speed could approach that of the night torpedo attack forces, the execution of this strategic concept was not possible. Therefore, the primary goal of the second reconstruction was to make the ships faster and, hence, fit to accomplish their new role.

The second reconstruction was carried out in the same order as the first one, beginning with the *Haruna* in August 1933 and ending with the *Kongō* in January 1937. However, at the end of 1936 the system of the naval arms limitation treaties expired, and the reconstruction of the *Hiei* to a "full sister" of the already modernized ones had begun the previous month. Its reconstruction differed from that of the sisters because it was used as a quasi trial ship for some features planned for the super-battleships *Yamato* and *Musashi*, whose construction began about one year later, so it seems more convenient to deal with its reconstruction separately.

Table 18
The second reconstruction

Ship	Yard	1933	1934	1935	1936	1937	1938	1939	1940
Haruna	Kure Navy Yard	1.8	30.9					(1)	(2)
Kirishima	Sasebo Navy Yard		1.6		8.6	(1)			(2)
Kongō	Yokosuka Navy Yard			1.6		8.1			
Hiei	Kure Navy Yard				26.11				31.1

Notes:
1. Strengthening of light antiaircraft armament by mounting twenty 25 mm machine guns in ten twin mounts.
2. Fitting of emergency damage control equipment.

Principal Items of the Reconstructions

Before stating details, it might be useful to give a short survey of the principal items of the first and second reconstruction works, generally valid for the modernization of all Japanese capital ships in the period between World War I and World War II. The principal items of the first reconstruction were the following:

Owing to the increased battle range and, hence, angle of fall of the shells of the major-caliber guns, the horizontal protection over the vital parts was strengthened. At that time the effect of armor-piercing (AP) shells fired from great ranges was considered more dangerous than that of bombs, and by this measure the protection against bomb hits was of course also strengthened.

The submarine had proven its fighting power in World War I, and protection against torpedo hits was an urgent necessity. Therefore, bulges were added as antitorpedo protection, and in addition, longitudinal torpedo bulkheads were fitted in order to improve protection of the vital parts.

The strengthening of the protection below the waterline was against the effect not only of the torpedo, but also the so-called underwater trajectory shell, which was accidentally discovered at that time during the experiments with the incomplete battleship *Tosa*. From that time, the method to obtain hits with AP shells below the waterline belt of the enemy's capital ships was considered important, and since it was rumored that the USN was also developing a particular shell, this measure also aimed for defense against this shell.

The torpedo net was removed since its inefficiency had been recognized.

By the addition of bulges, the beam on the waterline was widened, and this was necessary in order to maintain stability, to avoid the reduction of the reserve buoyancy, and to approximately maintain the draft. The latter was also very important for the position of the upper edge of the belt armor above the waterline.

The maximum elevation angle of the main guns was increased from 33° to 43° in order to obtain a firing range nearly equal to the 410 mm guns of the battleships of the Nagato class, with which they were to form a battle line.

In company with this, the foremast was altered, the fire-directing instruments were modified, and numerous other modifications were executed, with the primary goal of completing the ships' ability to take part in long-range gunnery engagements.

Reduction of the number of boilers and the use of oil-burning and mixed-burning boilers. Conversion of coal bunkers to heavy oil tanks to increase the radius of action.

Fitting of aircraft (seaplanes) facilities.

Modification and improvement of the wireless communication equipment.

Modification and improvement of other electrical equipment.

Removal of one part of the torpedo tubes.

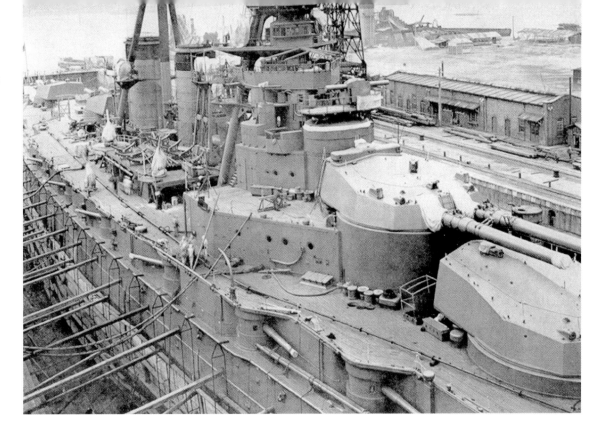

A photo of *Kongō* on December 24, 1928, in dock no. 5 at Yokosuka Navy Yard. The first reconstruction has started and the forward funnel has been landed. It can be seen to the right of the bridge structure. Her commanding officer was Capt. Ikenaka Kenichi.

Kongō on October 21, 1929. The first reconstruction is underway, and the ship is being fitted with bulges. The reconstruction proceeded while the crew was still aboard, and laundry is being dried. The reconstruction started on December 1, 1928, and was finished on September 15, 1931. Note that the censor has been at work.

Another photo of *Kongō* on October 21, 1929. The funnels are down, and the ship has been stripped of a lot of topside equipment. *Kure Maritime Museum*

Kongō still in drydock at Yokosuka—here, on November 29, 1930, with bulges fitted and improved underwater protection. Paintwork appears to be finished.

On February 20, 1931, the reconstruction of *Kongō* (Capt. Ikeda Keinosuke) is 86 percent complete. The two funnels are in place, and the boiler arrangement was similar to *Kirishima*'s. The thick top parts of the funnels are for rainwater protection. *Kure Maritime Museum*

A photo of *Kongō* from August 30, 1932, almost a year after having finished the first reconstruction. The ship is leaving Yokosuka and is the fleet flagship of the 1st Kantai, flying the flag of VAdm. Kobayashi Seizō, and is commanded by Capt. Higurashi Toshiu. No 12.7 cm high-angle guns are yet fitted. *Sekai no Kansen*

Kongō (Capt. Kondō Nobutake) in October 1933, probably at Kōbe. The mainmast is now significantly shorter, and on its top is VAdm. Suetsugu Nobumasa's flag. He was in command of the 1st Kantai.

Kongō pictured in 1932, still with her 8 cm high-angle guns. Note the mantelets and the angular-shaped main gun turrets. *Private collection, previously unpublished*

Kongō in 1933. The 8 cm high-angle guns have been replaced with eight 12.7 cm high-angle guns in twin mounts. *Private collection, previously unpublished*

The training battleship *Hiei* at Kôbe in 1933. Following the London Naval Treaty concluded in April 1930, the Imperial Japanese Navy decided to disarm *Hiei*. Consequently, her first modernization at Kure, where she had been docked since October 15, 1929, had to be stopped.

On June 1, 1931, the Kongō-class battle cruisers were reclassified as battleships, but on December 1 of the following year, *Hiei* was reclassified as a training battleship. The disarmament ended on July 20, 1933, and *Hiei* is here photographed in May. A 12.7 cm twin high-angle mount is visible between the funnels, and another one is at the base of the bridge structure. These were fitted only on the starboard side. To port were four single 8 cm high-angle guns. *Sekai no Kansen*

Training battleship *Hiei* at Yokosuka in July 1933. Note that the low-angle gun director on top of the "pagoda mast" has been removed

Hiei (Capt. Sada Kenichi) on July 25, 1933. As a training battleship she was stripped of its side armor, its speed was reduced to 18 knots, main gun turret no. 4 was landed, and antiaircraft armament was changed. Note that the low-angle gun director on the foremast is in place.

Hiei at Yokohama on August 25, 1933, during the naval review. Despite the harsh international relations during the disarmament treaties, a large number of ships were added to the fleet. A large-scale maneuver was held in August and 150 planes participated—an unprecedented number. Onboard *Hiei* was the emperor, and also seen here are the light cruiser *Kinu* and the destroyer *Inazuma*.

Hiei's forward main gun turrets and foremast photographed in 1933–37. Note the angular shape of the gunhouses and the absence of portside 12.7 cm high-angle mounts. The rangefinder forward of the compass bridge has a base length of 4.5 meters. *Sekai no Kansen*

A rare photo of the rear of *Hiei*'s foremast in 1933–36. The rangefinders on both sides of the tower have a base length of 3.5 meters. To the right is one of the starboard side's twin 12.7 cm high-angle mounts and a 4.5-meter rangefinder. *Sekai no Kansen*

The foremast of *Hiei* (Capt. Ōkawachi Denshichi) in September 1935. *From the top*: main gun-firing station, main gun command station, upper lookout station, target speed and bearing-measurement station, mast command station, lower lookout station, compass bridge, 4.5-meter rangefinder, and conning tower.

Hiei pictured in Tokyo Bay in October 1935. At that time, the Imperial Japanese Navy had already given notice that they were about to cancel the Washington Naval Treaty, and they were preparing themselves for the period without restrictions. Note the tarpaulin over the barbette of the removed after main gun turret.

Hiei (Capt. Inagaki Ayao) at Kōbe at the end of October 1936. *Hiei* was frequently used by the emperor when he was reviewing the fleet. By this time, ballast had already been moved into the no. 4 turret, and on April 1, 1937, it was decided to remilitarize *Hiei*.

Haruna in 1928. *Sekai no Kansen*

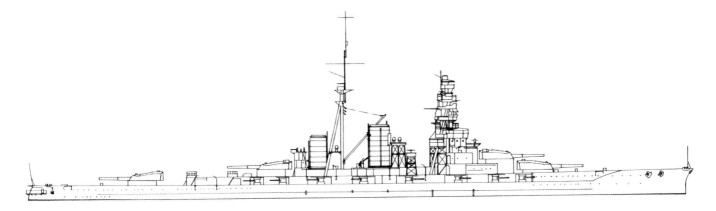

As a result of the turret explosion, *Haruna* was the first to be reconstructed. The work was carried out at Yokosuka Navy Yard (*Kōshō*) and was completed on July 31, 1928. Changes included, for example, an elevation increase of the 14-inch guns from 25 degrees to 33 degrees, upgraded fire-precaution measures of the magazines, increased protection, a pagoda-type foremast built up to three levels, and rebuilt boilers. Here *Haruna* (Capt. Isumi Kizō) is running 10/10 trials off Tateyama on May 25, 1928. At a displacement of 33,825 tons, she reached 25.861 knots with 75,807 shp.

The reconstructed *Haruna* at Yokosuka on October 25, 1928. To the left is the battleship *Hyūga*, and behind *Haruna* can be seen part of the superstructure of the battleship *Mutsu*. Note that *Haruna*'s torpedo nets have been removed, and the number of funnels has been reduced to two. *Kure Maritime Museum*

Haruna, *Hyūga*, and *Mutsu* on exercises in 1933. This photo was taken from *Kongō*, and together the four ships formed the 1st Sentai of the 1st Kantai, with *Mutsu* as Adm. Kobayashi Seizō's fleet flagship. *Private collection, previously unpublished*

Haruna with the battleship *Hyūga* beyond in 1933. Note the short mainmast of *Hyūga*, which she had only in 1933. *Private collection, previously unpublished*

Kirishima (Capt. Fujisawa Takuo) as she appeared on March 10, 1930, toward the end of her first reconstruction at Kure. She has just been undocked, and her foremast and funnels are changed. The background has been "corrected" by a censor. Two more months were required for painting and other works before the reconstruction was actually finished.

The emperor on October 26, 1930, on the bridge of *Kirishima*, when he supervised the naval maneuvers. *Private collection, previously unpublished*

A photo of *Kirishima* from 1932. On June 1, 1931, the Kongō-class battle cruisers were reclassified as battleships. At the time of the photo, *Kirishima* was assigned to 1st Kantai, 1st Sentai, together with *Kongō* (VAdm. Kobayashi Seizō), *Hyūga*, and *Ise*. Behind turret 3 is a navy type 14 EY1 reconnaissance seaplane, but a catapult is not yet fitted.

Kirishima leaving Yokosuka in September 1932. She has been "converted" into a battleship, and the number of boilers has been reduced to ten, six fewer than *Haruna*, so the first funnel is a little thinner. On turrets 2 and 3 are now 8-meter rangefinders, as a result of expected increased battle ranges. In addition, armor protection has been strengthened.

Kirishima during gunnery practice. The main guns are trained to port, and the elevation has been increased to 33 degrees. The date of the photo is unknown, but a 4.5-meter rangefinder for the secondary guns is visible (installed in 1930) on the conning tower, and there are no 12.7 cm high-angle guns (installed 1932–33). *Sekai no Kansen*

The principal items of the second reconstruction were as follows:

Change to oil-only burners (except the *Haruna*, which maintained part of the "old" boilers) of much-increased capacity, and the adoption of the principle to fit in only one boiler per one watertight boiler room. The purpose was to reduce flooding and also the effect on the machinery.

Replacement of the direct-connected Parsons steam turbines by Kampon-type all-geared turbines in order to more than double the original output.

Lengthening of the stern by more than 7 meters to reduce the hull (propulsion) resistance and to compensate the disadvantageous effect of the weight increase, as stated above (first reconstruction "b", last paragraph).

Reconstruction of the foremast into a tower bridge, and completion of the fire-directing equipment for main and secondary guns and also night battle facilities.

Increase of the elevation angle of the secondary guns from 15 degrees to 30 degrees and removal of two guns to decrease the number to fourteen.

Removal of the torpedo tubes.

Fitting of an emergency damage control system (executed after the reconstruction in the *Haruna* and *Kirishima*, but considered to be part of it).

Fitting of gas-protection installations.

Modifications

Aside from these two major reconstructions, there were some modifications before the execution of the first reconstruction, some between the first and second reconstruction, and a few more carried out in preparation for the outbreak of war.

Modifications before the First Reconstruction

Fitting of the IJN's first domestically produced fire director atop the foremast and enlargement of the platform to install the director in 1915 (*Haruna*) and 1916–17 (sisters).

Fitting of 110 cm searchlights on a platform between the first and second funnels (*Kongō*) or forward of the first funnel (sisters) in 1917–18.

Replacement of the four 8 cm high-angle guns by the same number of 40-caliber, 8 cm high-angle guns (equally distributed amidships on both sides).

Increased height of the first funnel to avoid the influence of smoke and fumes on the bridge, and, later, fitting of a cap on the forward part of the funnel since the first measure did not have the desired effect (in *Kongō* in 1920).

Modification of fire-directing and searchlight control devices and their fitting on platforms added to the foremast, whose shape approached the comparatively complicated structure so typical of the IJN's capital ships in 1924.

Increased elevation of the main guns from 20 degrees (*Hiei, Haruna,* and *Kirishima*) or 25 degrees (*Kongō*) to 33 degrees in 1922 (*Haruna*) and 1924 (*Kongō, Hiei,* and *Kirishima*) to obtain a maximum firing range of about 29,000 meters, compared with the former 25,800 meters.[4]

Addition of three 40-caliber, 8 cm high-angle guns, a total of seven in 1926 (in *Haruna*, part of the first reconstruction).

Reconstruction of the foremast into a tower (pagoda) type in 1927 (in *Haruna* and *Kirishima*, part of the first reconstruction).

Fitting of a rain cap on top of the second funnel of the *Kongō* for experimentation in 1928, since corrosion became a serious problem. After several modifications, this cap was installed in the sisters and other capital ships and heavy cruisers.

Removal of the booms of the torpedo nets in 1928 (*Kongō* and *Hiei* only).

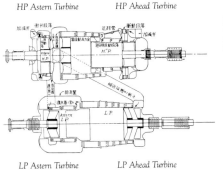

HP Astern Turbine   HP Ahead Turbine

LP Astern Turbine   LP Ahead Turbine

Improved Parsons turbines (*Kongō, Hiei, Kirishima*). Kaigun Kikan-shi

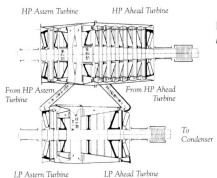

HP Astern Turbine   HP Ahead Turbine

From HP Astern Turbine   From HP Ahead Turbine

To Condenser

LP Astern Turbine   LP Ahead Turbine

Brown-Curtis turbines (*Haruna*). Kaigun Kikan-shi

Kongō (Capt. Matsushita Hajime) off Tokuyama in October 1927. The ship is being prepared for a large exercise and is fitted with mantelets (*mantoretto*) around the foremast decks. During the exercise she was the flagship of the 2nd Kantai of the Blue Force. *Kure Maritime Museum*

Midship section of *Kongō* (Capt. Yoshida Zengo) at Yokohama on December 2, 1928. At this time, she was the fleet flagship of the 2nd Kantai, commanded by VAdm. Yoshikawa Yasuhira, and immediately after this photo the first reconstruction at Yokosuka began. *Sekai no Kansen*

Hiei around 1928. The torpedo nets have been removed, the foremast has been changed, and an aircraft derrick is fitted aft. However, one year later the ship was demilitarized.

The bridge structure of *Kirishima* (Capt. Yasumura Sukeichi) on May 4, 1921. The photo shows her in the dock of Sasebo Navy Yard when the work on her foremast was almost completed. Note the open compass bridge with no fixed roof, just canvas.

Kirishima in slightly changed appearance in 1923. By this time, *Kirishima* had undergone some modifications, such as the fitting of a main gun-firing command station (previously called the firing-observation station) in the upper part of the director.

First Reconstruction

Strengthening of the Horizontal Protection

1. The thickness of the protective deck (middle deck) above the vital parts was increased, with the goal of withstanding the impact of 36 cm AP shells fired from 20,000–25,000 meters.

Table 19
Strengthening of the protective deck (middle deck)

Location	Existing Thickness	Additional Thickness	Total Thickness
Boiler rooms	19 mm nickel steel	63 mm high tensile steel	82 mm
Engine rooms	as above	82 mm to 89 mm HT	101 mm to 108 mm
Forward magazines	as above	102 mm NVNC (flat)	121 mm
		76 mm HT (slopes)	95 mm
After magazines	as above	102 mm to 114 mm NVNC	121 mm to 133 mm
Lower deck, aft	44 mm (material?)	76 mm (material?)	120 mm

Note:
HT = high tensile steel; NVNC = new Vickers, not cemented; KC = Krupp cemented

2. Because damage to the magazines resulted in an almost certain loss of the ship, even greater protection was provided to them by fitting additional armor plates to the barbette armor of the main guns.

Table 20
Strengthening of Barbette Armor

Location	Existing Thickness	Additional Thickness	Total
Ammunition hoists of nos. 1 and 2 turrets	63 mm KC	76 mm KC	139 mm
Below the superstructure deck of no. 3 turret	76 mm KC	76 mm KC	152 mm
Below the upper deck of no. 4 turret	76 mm KC	76 mm KC	152 mm

Note:
KC = Krupp cemented

3. Roofs of main gun turrets

The thickness of the roof plates of the main gun turrets was doubled by adding 76 mm armor plates to make it a total of 152 mm.

4. Front shield of main gun turrets

The thickness was increased from 254 mm to 280 mm.

5. Funnel uptakes and ventilation ducts

To avoid shells falling at a steep angle from plunging through the large openings of the funnel uptakes and ventilation ducts in the protective deck coaming, armor was used to strengthen the horizontal protection as follows:

a. funnel uptakes	165 mm
b. ventilation ducts to boiler rooms	178 mm
c. ventilation ducts to engine rooms	102–127 mm

It should be noted that armor intended for the abolished capital ships of the 8-8 Fleet was used. Of course, the plates had to be rolled again to obtain the required thickness.

By these measures, the weight increased remarkably and the work also demanded skillful execution. Immunity against 36 cm AP shells was limited to a small zone and may in no way be considered sufficient. In other words, even as battleships, the original defect of the design as battle cruisers remained. In addition, compared with the initial protection system, the horizontal protection was remarkably strengthened, while the vertical protection had to remain unchanged (forbidden by the treaty regulations), so the "balance" was totally lost.

Reinforcement of the Underwater Protection

Underwater protection was provided by (1) an increase in the thickness of hull plating, (2) the fitting of longitudinal torpedo bulkheads, and (3) the fitting of bulges to protect the vital area against the detonation of 200 kg explosives.

The reinforcement of the hull plates was made by either three (ammunition magazines) or four (machinery spaces) layers of 25.4 mm thick HT plates, fitted either some distance from the hull-side plating[5] or directly over the plating, depending on the position.

In addition, a longitudinal torpedo bulkhead of the thickness of approximately 76 mm was installed.

The bulges were newly fitted, and their purpose was mainly to provide space for the expansion of the destructive detonation gases, to attain larger buoyancy (increase of 3,000 tons) and to preserve stability by increasing the beam at the waterline. The upper part of the bulges was to be filled with watertight steel tubes 254 mm in diameter. By this measure, copied from the British battleships *Rodney* and *Nelson*,[6] it was hoped to maintain buoyancy in case of damage, and it was to be executed, therefore, just before the outbreak of war. For the same reason, the bulges were also divided into watertight compartments (WTCs) and oil-tight compartments (OTCs) in the area of the machinery spaces and WTCs in the area of the ammunition magazines. It may be added that they were extended over the major part of the double bottom in order to limit the effect of the so-called underwater diving shell. However, there is no doubt that irrespective of bulges, double bottom, strengthening of hull plating, and torpedo bulkhead, the protection was insufficient to withstand a 36 cm shell, as shown by the *Tosa* experiments.[7]

Armament

The maximum elevation of the main guns was increased from 33 degrees to 43 degrees in order to increase the firing distance to 33,000 meters. This was part of the "out-range strategy" for the gunnery engagement between the main battle forces and enabled the ships to fight in line with the more heavily armed battleships of the Nagato class. The stock of ammunition per barrel was also increased (probably from 80 to 100 shells).

Four of the eight submerged torpedo tubes were removed, and the spaces were converted into magazines to store the additional shells and powder bags.

The number of 40-caliber, 8 cm, three-year-type high-angle guns was increased from four to seven. Two guns were placed on the upper deck and one more was placed aft of the mainmast. However, no fire-directing system was fitted for these weak high-angle guns, so even their value of "scaring off" attacking airplanes was doubtful.

Haruna (Capt. Arichi Jugorō), in the foreground, together with the battleships *Yamashiro* (*left*) and *Ise* during the grand maneuver off Honshū on October 21, 1930. *Kure Maritime Museum*

Kirishima (Capt. Kitaoka Haruo) at Yokohama on August 24, 1933, during the rehearsal for the 1933 Naval Review. By raising the elevation to 43 degrees, the maximum range of the main guns increased to 35,478 meters. *Kure Maritime Museum*

A photo of *Kirishima* during gunnery practice around 1933–34. Although armament was restricted by the naval treaties, training was not, and the Imperial Japanese Navy practiced hard, perhaps particularly gunnery. "Monday, Monday, Tuesday, Wednesday, Thursday, Friday, Friday" was its slogan. *Gakken*

A photo of *Kirishima* firing her main guns, using the alternate firing method, in 1941. The smoke from the muzzles spreads forward, but the blast spreads farther behind the muzzle, generating heat.

Officers of the *Kirishima* assembled for a memorial photo in the 1930s. Note the aerial mast on the main gun turret and the unpainted teak deck. *Private collection, previously unpublished*

Conversion of the Forward Tripod Mast into a Pagoda-Type (Tower) Structure

Together with the increase of the maximum firing range, the forward tripod mast was incorporated into a towerlike pagoda structure, which remarkably altered the appearance of the ships. This mast structure provided room for the larger and more-complicated components of the fire control systems for the main and secondary guns as well as the expansion of bridges; lookout, signal, and spotting stations; operation and chart rooms; the wireless room; restrooms; toilets; and other spaces.

An unusual front view of *Haruna*'s pagoda-type foremast in 1930. Above the no. 2 main gun turret is the top of the conning tower. The rangefinder in the center of the photo has a base length of 4.5 meters. Behind this rangefinder is the compass bridge, with the lookout station above it and, on top, the upper bridge. *Sekai no Kansen*

Machinery

The aim was to produce less smoke, to increase the radius of action, and to save space and weight.

The thirty-six large-tube, Yarrow-type (in case of the *Haruna I Gō Kampon*), mixed-burning, water-tube boilers were replaced by sixteen small-tube, *Ro Gō* Kampon–type, water-tube boilers. Ten were mixed burners and six were pure heavy-oil burners.[8] Even if these boilers generated more steam than before, they needed less space and, consequently, the number of funnels could be reduced to two. The forward funnel, from which smoke and fumes had sometimes had an disturbing effect on the stations on the forward tripod mast before reconstruction, was removed.

Coal capacity was reduced from 4,200 to 2,661 tons, but heavy-oil storage was increased from 1,000 to 3,292 tons in order to obtain a remarkably larger radius of action (i.e., 9,500 miles at 14 knots compared with the former 8,000 miles at the same speed). For this purpose, part of the coal bunkers was reconstructed into heavy-oil tanks, and also part of the watertight compartments was made oil tight (OT) by sufficient caulking, to be used as tanks.

It should also be noted that some coal bunkers above the lower deck were converted into living and store compartments.

Aircraft Facilities

The space between no. 3 and no. 4 main gun turrets on the superstructure deck was used for the installation of a catapult on the centerline, and rails and turntables on both sides, for the accommodation of three to four type 14 three-seat seaplanes for reconnaissance and spotting. They were lowered into the sea and recovered by a derrick fitted on the main deck to starboard abaft the no. 3 turret. A gasoline tank was also built in the vicinity.

Kongō performing catapult tests at Yokosuka about January 26, 1933. The catapulted plane is a Nakajima navy type 90-2-2 E4N2 reconnaissance seaplane, and at this time the catapult was a Kure type no. 2, model 3. *Private collection, previously unpublished*

Kongō (*center*) in the 312-meter-long dock no. 5 at Yokosuka Navy Yard in May 1933. Behind her, in the same dock, are three Kamikaze class destroyers: *Asakaze*, *Matsukaze*, and *Hatakaze*. This was an experiment to test the working ability of the Yokosuka Navy Yard. In the 226-meter-long dock no. 4 is the heavy cruiser *Chōkai*. Note the Kure type no. 2, model 3 catapult on *Kongō*. *Sekai no Kansen*

Haruna around 1929. She has an aircraft derrick to starboard aft for handling the Yokoshō E1Y3 type 14 long-range reconnaissance floatplane and later also the Nakajima E2N1 type 15 floatplane.

Haruna in 1933. The searchlight platform at the base of the mainmast has been removed, and a Kure type no. 2, model 3 catapult has been added on the aircraft handling deck between turrets 3 and 4. *Private collection, previously unpublished*

Two Nakajima E4N2 type 90 single-seat, short-range reconnaissance seaplanes from *Haruna* are flying over *Haruna* in Ise Bay, sometime between July 28 and August 1, 1935. *Private collection, previously unpublished*

A view of *Haruna*'s aircraft-handling deck, with three Nakajima E4N2 type 90 single-float seaplanes, while in Sukumo Bay in 1935–36. In the right background is the battleship *Fusō*, and barely visible beyond is *Yamashiro*. Also visible is the 8th Sentai (light cruisers). *Kure Maritime Museum*

Second Reconstruction

General

The principal aim of the second reconstruction was, as stated above, to increase the ship speed to 30 knots. This was because high speed was the most important presupposition for the execution of their supporting role in the modified operational concept of the night battle. It was attained not only by fitting a new propulsion plant but also by the lengthening of the hull in order to reduce propulsion resistance. Lack of space does not permit us to deal with all items of this reconstruction in detail, so it is limited to the more important ones.

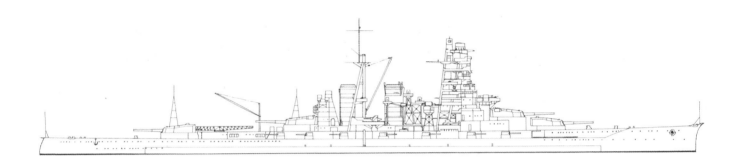

Kongō in 1937. *Sekai no Kansen*

The reconstructed *Kongō* (Capt. Matsuura Eijirō) at Yokosuka on January 13, 1937. The catapult between turrets 3 and 4 was a Kure type no. 2, model 3, but it was replaced prior to the Pacific War with the new Kure type no. 2, model 5.

Another view of *Kongō* at Yokosuka on January 13, 1937. The two forward secondary guns have been landed, and the total number was thereby reduced to fourteen. From December 1, 1937, *Kongō* and *Kirishima* formed the 3rd Sentai in the 1st Kantai; *Kongō* was flying the flag of VAdm. Katagiri Eikichi.

Kongō during the grand maneuver in September 1940. *Kure Maritime Museum*

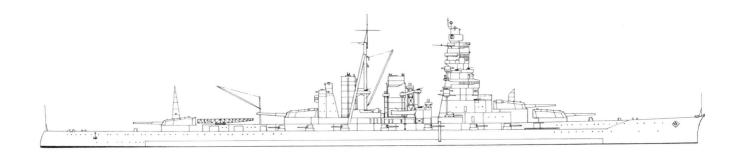

Hiei in 1940. *Sekai no Kansen*

Installing an armor plate on *Hiei*'s side on December 14, 1937. The plate was suspended from the top, pulled from the inside, and pressed from the outside. Not only was the side armor reinstalled, but a new damage control system was also installed, and a pipe system with pumps and holes for flooding and discharging was installed (see page 109). *Gakken*

Kirishima photographed from *Haruna* during high-speed navigation in 1937. They are here proceeding at battle speed 5, making about 29 knots. *Kure Maritime Museum*

Another view of *Kirishima* as seen from *Haruna* during high-speed maneuvers in 1937. The speed cones on the signal yards seem to indicate battle speed 5, and a speed increase from 28 to 30 knots has probably been ordered. *Sekai no Kansen*

Kirishima (Capt. Makita Kakusaburō) at Sukumo Bay on May 10, 1937. The ship's second reconstruction had started at Sasebo Navy Yard on November 18, 1934, and it was completed on June 8, 1936. After this reconstruction, her speed was significantly raised by replacing engines and boilers. Note the elevated gun barrel of turret 2.

During the second reconstruction, *Kirishima*'s mainmast was reduced in height, as can be seen on this photo taken on May 10, 1937, in Sukumo Bay. Note that the number of secondary guns has been reduced to fourteen, by landing secondary guns 1 and 2, and that the ship is fitted with eight 12.7 cm twin high-angle guns.

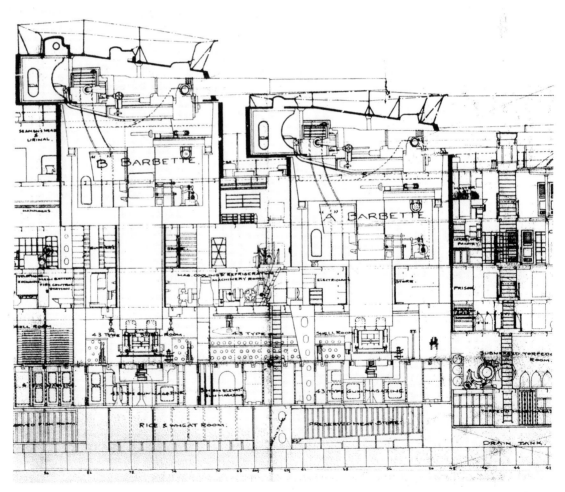

Original blueprint showing *Kirishima*'s "A" & "B" turrets. Note the positioning of the storerooms beneath the forward magazines, effectively forming a triple bottom. Note also the submerged torpedo room forward of "A" magazine.

Kirishima (Capt. Tada Takeo) and the aircraft carrier *Akagi* in Sukumo Bay on April 27, 1939. The fleet had entered two days earlier, and this photo was taken by SLt. Fukui Shizuo from the light cruiser *Mikuma's* starboard side. In the distance between *Kirishima* and *Akagi* can be seen the destroyer *Harusame*, and to the left, probably, the destroyer *Murasame*.

Increased Engine Power

The first reconstruction was limited to changing of the boilers and the related auxiliary machines, and the main engines were left as they were so that the speed decreased. However, for the reason stated above, the speed had to be increased to 30 knots. This meant a complete revision of the propulsion system. The main engines and the reduction gears were changed to the same type as fitted in the heavy cruisers of the Mogami class, but the condenser was changed to be hung below the low-pressure turbine (LPT) (in the Mogami class it was installed alongside the LPT). The cruising turbine (CT) was connected to the inside shafts, and the exhaust was introduced to the outside-shaft high-pressure turbines (HPT).

Haruna was refitted first, but because of the tight budget, not all the boilers could be changed. Therefore, six of the oil-burning boilers, fitted during the first reconstruction, and two boilers produced for the battleship *Tosa* (expended as real target due to the stipulations of the Washington Treaty) were improved by attaching air preheaters, and three new boilers were also fitted. This made a total of eleven boilers. Steam pressure was 20 kg/cm^2 and saturated steam was used. The power was decided to be 136,000 shp.

The tight budget also prevented the change of the steering gear to the electric-driven hydraulic type, so the *Haruna* retained the old type of steam-operated system. However, it had insufficient power because of the increase of speed. As a countermeasure, the maximum rudder angle was restricted to 30 degrees, instead of 35 degrees.

The *Kirishima* and *Kongō* received the same engines as the *Haruna*, but all their boilers were changed to eight oil-burning ones of the same type as fitted in the heavy cruisers *Suzuya* and *Kumano*. Instead of using saturated steam as in *Haruna*, superheated steam was adopted. Therefore, the engine power had a considerable surplus compared with the planned one, but it was decided to have 136,000 shp, just as with *Haruna*.

In contrast to these ships, which had the IJN's "ideal distribution" of four turbine sets in four engine rooms and eight boilers in eight boiler rooms, *Haruna* had an "imbalanced" system with eleven boilers, and piping was complicated compared with its sisters.

Hiei was reconstructed after the termination of the arms limitation treaties and was refitted like the *Kirishima* and *Kongō*. The steering system of these ships was changed to the electric-hydraulic system.

The reduction of the rudder angle as in *Haruna* (causing a worsening of the turning ability), the use of eleven boilers, and particularly the "reduction" of the engine power to 136,000 shp in the other three ships, mainly because *Haruna* had it, is hard to explain, since speed was the primary factor of the refitting.

The following tables summarize some principal machinery data after the second reconstruction, in addition to data already included in other tables.

Table 21
Radius of action of *Hiei* after second reconstruction

Displacement 36,700 tons, speed 18 knots, radius 18 knots—10,000 miles; ehp 9,861, shp 21,400, P.C. 0.46 (*Kirishima* 0.46.1; *Haruna* 0.47.5), fuel consumption shp/h/kg 0.207, fuel 6,000 tons.

Source:
Fukuda, *Gunkan Kihon Keikaku Shiryō*, p. 121.

Table 22
Standard of calculation of radius of *Haruna*

Speed	Hours	shp	Consumption, Designed (shp/h/kg)	Tons of Oil	Consumption, Trial (Shp/h/kg)
30.2	18	136,380	0.221	1,200	0.205
23	36	90,000	0.2237	1,600	0.2065
18	195	20,000	0.2672	2,300	0.2491

Note:
Total consumption 5,100 tons + 20%

Source:
Fukuda, *Gunkan Kihon Keikaku Shiryō*, p. 123.

Table 23
Speed, horsepower, and displacement

Item/Ship	*Haruna*	
Displacement (D) (tons)	27,384	35,595
Speed (V) (knots)	27.78	30
shp	64,000	136,000
Length waterline (Lwl)	211.963	219.5
V/VL	1.053	1.118
shp/V × D	0.079	0.1275
V/D 1/6	5.05	5.22
ehp	—	61.500
Propulsion coefficient (P.C.)	—	0.452

Source:
Fukuda, *Gunkan Kihon Keikaku Shiryō*, p. 116.

Table 24
Trial results after the second reconstruction

Item/Ship	Kongō	Hiei		Haruna	Kirishima
Displacement	37,003	36,341	36,332	35,500	36,897
Speed	30.27	30.17	29.94	30.49	29.8
shp	137,188	143,136	137,970	141,211	136,940
1/min (rpm)	317	321.9	318.8	310	316
Effective hp	65,000	68,300	65,100	67,800	59,500
P.C.	47.4	47.7	47.2	48	43.5

Source:
Fukuda, *Gunkan Kihon Keikaku Shiryō*, p. 113.

Table 25
Propulsive coefficient

Name	Haruna		Kirishima	
Item/Condition	Full Speed	Standard Speed	Full Speed	Standard Speed
Speed (V)	30.2	17.965	29.8	18.17
shp, trial	136,338	20,062	136,940	21,616
Tank ehpn	64,000	9,500	59,500	9,910
P.C. (ehpn/shp)	46.91	47.4	43.45	45.8
Percent ehp appendage	17.3	20.5	16.8	20
ehpn/ehp app.	0.852	0.83	0.856	0.833
Hull eff. (ehpn/thp)	1.047	1.134	1.048	1.134
Prop. eff. behind (thp/shp)	0.526	0.5045	0.485	0.485
Propeller efficiency, open	0.591	0.617	0.586	0.581
P behind / P open	0.890	0.818	0.827	0.835
Displacement	35,687	35,237	36,897	37,036
V/VL	1.125	—	1.112	—

Source:
Fukuda, *Gunkan Kihon Keikaku Shiryō*, pp. 109, 112.

Table 26
Turning

Name	Kongō		Haruna		Kirishima	
Item/Condition	As Built	After Conversion	As Built	After Conversion	As Built	After Conversion
Displacement		36,289	27,000	33,355	27,259	36,513
Speed (V)	25.25	29.1	25.9	29.6	25.0	29.9
Ar (rudder area)	30.51	36.28	31.38	36.05	30.70	36.6
Am/Ar	30.5	36.28	31.38	36.05	30.7	36.6
DT/L	3.15	3.6	2.85	3.8	2.69	3.73
Heel angle	7°30′	9°30′	5°08′	10°10′	7°05′	11°0′
A/L			2.74	3.70		
Ar/Am			1/31.38	1/36.05		
V/VL	0.96	1.08	0.98	1.10	0.95	1.12
Lwl			212	219.5		

Notes:
Ar = rudder area (m²), Am = lateral middle line area (m²), DT = transfer, A/L = advance
Displacement and length increased, as did speed, but the rudders were not changed. However, the rudder angle was reduced to 30° from 35° in *Haruna*, which resulted in a larger turning circle, but not so much that it caused problems.

Source:
Fukuda, *Gunkan Kihon Keikaku Shiryō*, p. 124.

The second reconstruction is almost complete, and *Kongō* (Capt. Sukigara Tamazō) performs a full-power test on November 14, 1936, off Tateyama. The second reconstruction at Yokosuka lasted from June 1, 1935, until January 8, 1937. The ship displaced 36,860 tons, and with 143,675 shp she attained 30.48 knots. It is said that during the reconstruction, her clipper bow was also changed and is a little sharper than her sisters'. *Sekai no Kansen*

Hiei (Capt. Abe Kōsō) during trials off Sukumo on December 5, 1939. After the termination of the Washington Treaty, lasting from 1922 to 1936, the reconstruction of *Hiei* into a high-speed battleship was carried out, and it was finished on January 31, 1940. This portside photo shows her running at full speed. At a displacement of 38,332 tons, she attained 29.9 knots with 137,950 shp. Note the different foremast compared with her sisters.

A postcard showing *Haruna* in 1934 immediately after the second reconstruction, which officially began on August 1, 1933, and ended on September 30. Her 8 cm high-angle guns has been landed and replaced by eight 40-caliber, 12.7 cm high-angle guns in twin mounts.

軍艦榛名

Haruna (Capt. Mito Shunzō) running trials off Sukumo Bay on August 28, 1934. *Haruna* was the first of the Kongō class to be remodeled to become a high-speed battleship. One of her planned missions was to destroy enemy cruisers during the night battle prior to the decisive battle between the opposing battle fleets.

Another view of *Haruna* from her trials on August 28, 1934. During the second reconstruction, the stern was lengthened, her machinery was replaced, and the elevation angle of her secondary guns was increased from 15 to 30 degrees. The elevation angle increase to 43 degrees of her main guns was probably done shortly before the second reconstruction.

Haruna steaming at 30 knots during battle practice south of Tosa on May 21, 1936. At this time, *Haruna* belonged to the 1st Kantai together with the battleships *Nagato*, *Fusō*, and *Yamashiro*. But *Haruna* was the only high-speed battleship in the fleet. At the time, she was commanded by Capt. Ozawa Jisaburō. *Sekai no Kansen*

Increase of the Elevation of the Secondary Guns and Other Armament Changes

In order to increase the firing range of the secondary guns from 14,200 to 19,500 meters, the maximum elevation was increased from 15 to 30 degrees by raising the ring supports in the casemates.

The guns in the foremost casemate on both sides and all torpedo tubes were removed to compensate for part of the weight increase. The newly adopted Hotchkiss-type 25 mm machine gun in twin mounts replaced the water-cooled slow-firing 40 mm Vickers machine guns. At the beginning of the Pacific War, all four ships had twenty 25 mm machine guns in ten twin mounts.

The 8 cm high-angle guns were replaced in 1932, before the second reconstruction, in *Kongō*, *Haruna*, and *Kirishima* when they received eight 40-caliber, 12.7 cm guns in twin mounts. *Hiei* received a new high-angle gun outfit during its reconstruction into a battleship.

Conversion of the Foremast

The conversion of the original tripod foremast into the pagoda-style tower mast had already been executed during the first conversion, but a further conversion aimed for the improvement of all items referring to the "out-range" (long range) gunnery tactics and a completion of the equipment for night battle.

The increase in various fighting, command, and observation stations; the fitting of new equipment; and improvement of already existing capacities, which were needed, required a large visual range. Therefore, much effort was made, and very exact plans were drawn and given to each branch for comment. In this way, many requirements were stated, and the final conclusion resulted in a remarkable increase in size and structure of the foremast, which became rather complicated, as shown in photos and the drawings. However, this had to be accepted because only the improvement of the fighting qualities counted. There were differences between the sisters, and in particular the *Hiei*'s mast differed because it was used as a model for the battleships of the Yamato class. The following enumeration (from top to bottom) refers to the levels generally valid for all ships (*Hiei*'s low-angle fire control system was different):

Type 94 10-meter double rangefinder with lightning conductor and radio direction finder antenna

Main gun and high-angle guns command (control) station with type 94 main gunfire director and a number of binoculars, with and without direction transmitter

Secondary gun command (control) and upper lockout station with secondary gun fire director, spotting sights, etc.

Target speed and course-measuring and command (control) station with type 13 and type 92 *sokutekiban*, large telescopes, etc.

Battle bridge

Lower lookout station with (outside) 1.5-meter rangefinder, 60 cm signal searchlight, and 25 mm machine gun

Navigation (compass) bridge

Upper bridge with #1 and #2 secondary gun auxiliary station command (control) station and 12 cm telescopes; in front of the bridge there was a platform with type 94 4.5-meter rangefinder and 25 mm machine guns

Lower bridge with the conning tower in the front, 25 mm machine guns on the sides, and high-angle gun command (control) station (between the supports of the 10-meter double rangefinder and the type 91 high-angle gunfire director and 4.5-meter high-angle rangefinder)

Shelter deck

Uppermost deck

There were the usual wireless and telephone rooms, rooms for orderlies, the restroom of the captain, toilets, communications center, etc.

The reserve fire control system for the main and secondary guns was fitted in the upper part of a superstructure behind the after (main) mast. The computers for the low-angle and high-angle guns were situated below the armor deck in the protected area.

The low-angle fire control system for the 36 cm main and 15 cm secondary guns was the type 94 fire director with type 92 computer; the high-angle fire control system was the type 91 fire director with type 89 computer.

In connection with these modifications, in order to improve the night-fighting capability, the grouping of six type 96 110 cm searchlights around the forward funnel must be mentioned. The searchlight command (control) and reserve stations (*shōshashikisho*) were installed in the tower mast.

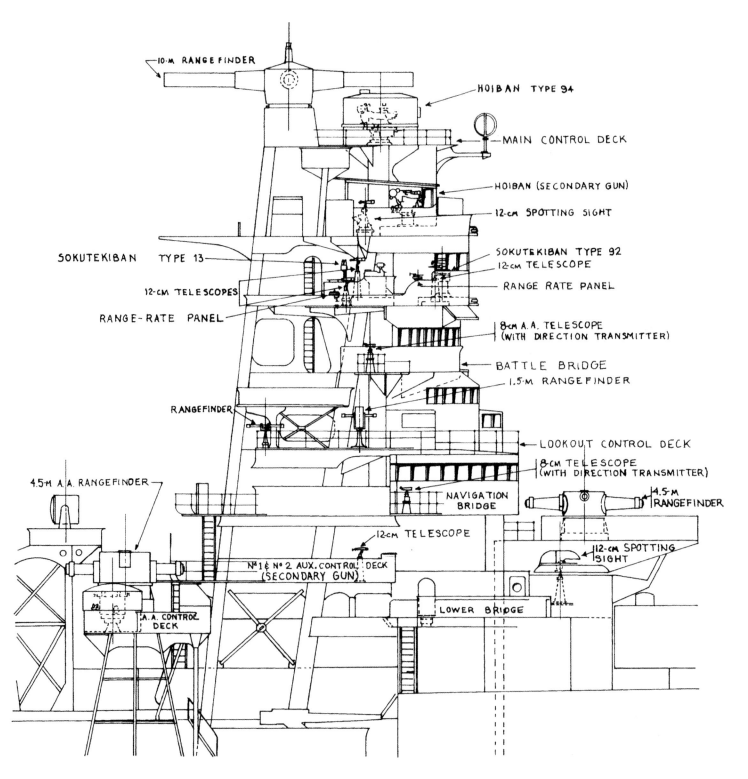

Bridge structure of *Kongō* in 1937. *US Naval Technical Mission to Japan*

Hiei performing full-power tests off Sukumo on December 5, 1939, shortly prior to her completion. On November 26, 1936, *Hiei* arrived at Kure Navy Yard for the major reconstruction. Her reconstruction was also used for some experiments with a *Yamato*-type bridge structure and fire control equipment

Hiei being prepared for the Pearl Harbor attack at Yokosuka Navy Yard on November 12–18, 1941. The degaussing cables on the hull sides have already been installed. Note the large 10-meter rangefinder on the foremast. *Sekai no Kansen*

Hiei flying the Imperial Standard at the mainmast during the Imperial Naval Review at Yokohama, on October 11, 1940. On the bridge on this occasion were the emperor and the commander in chief of the Combined Fleet (Rengō Kantai), commanded by VAdm. Yamamoto Isoroku.

Damage Control

The fitting of an emergency flooding and discharging system, as the damage control system was called in the IJN, was very late. It consisted of compartments on both sides of the hull that could be flooded quickly (each of the ten compartments with 250-ton capacity) or ordinarily (each of the thirteen compartments with 750-ton capacity). Using the quick system, a list of up to 5.5 degrees—in the second case, up to 7.7 degrees—could be corrected and the ship be brought back to an even keel. The installation of this system with its many pipes, valves, and pumps was no easy undertaking.

General Consideration of the Effect of the Reconstruction

According to the authoritative *Shōwa Zōsenshi*,[9] p. 722:

> The modernization of the ships should always be done in line with the development of the shipbuilding and weapon processes. This could lighten the national financial burden by increasing the abilities and offensive and defensive power and extend the life. Therefore, not only the IJN but other naval powers as well made efforts to maintain the ships as strong as possible.

While the general truth of this statement cannot be doubted, emphasis should be put on "could" and "as strong as possible"

in the second and third sentences, respectively. Generally speaking, the conversion of the IJN's capital ships necessitated large budgets, and while the results were impressive in certain respects, others were in fact failures despite of all investments. One example is the insufficient protection. Designed as battle cruisers, this class had a characteristic disadvantage that existed to the last, since little had been done to bring the protection, especially the vertical one, up to the standard contemporaneous battleships. Therefore, even though they were classified as high-speed battleships, their protection was insufficient[10] to resist the impact of AP shells fired from ranges even within their immunity zone, a fact well known by IJN experts. Furthermore, the second conversion of the battleships, heavy cruisers, and also aircraft carriers resulted in a delay in new construction, and this was still magnified by the measures the IJN had to execute as countermeasures following the *Tomozuru* and Fourth Fleet incidents.[11] However, one has to confess that the IJN had hardly any other choice than to try to improve their battleships by modernization, since the capacity of the shipbuilding industry did not allow Japan to replace the old battleships with new ones after the termination of the arms limitation treaties. As stated in the introduction, the IJN believed that the construction of two giant battleships of the Yamato class was sufficient for winning the decisive battle by using the "outrange" tactics, provided that the preliminary operations ended with the expected results.

CHAPTER 10

Operational Histories

General

The Kongō-class battle cruisers saw no action in World War I, although *Kongō* attempted to intercept the German light cruiser *Nürnberg*. However, at the start of the war, Britain tried to persuade Japan to send the four Kongōs to strengthen the Grand Fleet. This request was denied and the ships remained in the Pacific for such tasks as patrol duties.

Overhead view of *Kongō* sometime between November 1917 and February 1918. The photo was taken by the Yokosuka Naval Flying Corps. Note the extended forward funnel and the laundry. *Sekai no Kansen*

The "Battle of the 3rd Sentai" in Bungo Channel at 0830 on October 25, 1915. This was of course an exercise, and pictured here from flagship *Haruna* are *Hiei*, *Kirishima*, and *Kongō*. Although it cannot be seen in the picture, the bows of the ships are painted with white bow waves. *Kure Maritime Museum*

Haruna participating in the large exercise in October 1915. She was flagship of the 3rd Sentai, which also included *Kongō*, *Hiei*, and *Kirishima*. *Haruna* is painted in an experimental camouflage pattern and had left Yokosuka, passing the Uraga Channel on October 18, and in Ise Bay it met the "Blue Fleet." Over the bow can be seen the tall funnel of the transport *Manshū*. *Kure Maritime Museum*

Haruna in Ise Bay on October 21, 1915, during the grand exercises. This is a good view of her unusual camouflage pattern. The ship is taking aboard coal from *Kaga Maru* on her starboard side, and *Kaga Maru* is simultaneously supplying coal to the armored cruiser *Yakumo. Kure Maritime Museum*

A good view of *Haruna* anchored at Yokosuka on September 11, 1916, with a vice admiral's flag at the foremast. At this time *Haruna* was the flagship of 3rd Sentai, 2nd Kantai, flying the flag of VAdm. Baron Yashiro Rokurō. She was commanded by Capt. Nunome Mitsuzō. At this time, Britain had asked Japan to lend them the four Kongō class battle cruisers, a request that Japan declined. *Kure Maritime Museum*

At the start of the Pacific War, the four Kongōs were the oldest battleships in the IJN, but because of reconstructions they were also the fastest, faster than the two new super-battleships *Yamato* and *Musashi*. Their high speed made them exceptionally suitable to accompany the IJN aircraft carriers during their operations in the Pacific and the Indian Oceans.

Hiei and *Kirishima* participated in the Pearl Harbor operation, while *Kongō* and *Haruna* were involved in the invasion of the Dutch East Indies. In March 1942, all four sisters assembled in Staring Bay, Celebes, whence they participated in the Indian Ocean raid together with VAdm. Nagumo Chūichi's five carriers. This was to become the only time that the four sisters operated together.

A beautiful and powerful column of warships in November–December 1941. *Hiei* (Capt. Nishida Masao) is leading *Kirishima* (Capt. Yamaguchi Jihei) and the aircraft carriers *Shōkaku* and *Zuikaku* prior to the Pearl Harbor attack. *Sekai no Kansen*

Haruna in Staring Bay, Celebes, in February 1942. Also present in Staring Bay were the aircraft carriers *Akagi*, *Kaga*, *Sōryū*, and *Hiryū* and the battleships *Kongō*, *Hiei*, and *Kirishima*. This was the first occasion since the opening of the hostilities that the four Kongō-class battleships were together. *The Maru Special*

An image of *Haruna* (Capt. Takama Tamotsu) in Staring Bay, Celebes, from February 21, 1942. Her main gun turrets are turned to port, and three Nakajima E8N1 type 95 two-seat reconnaissance floatplanes are lined up between turrets 3 and 4. During the Pacific War, the two-seat floatplanes were used for various reconnaissance missions, including enemy strength reconnaissance and spotting during gunnery actions. *Gakken*

The 1st Kōkū Kantai (Air Fleet) leaves Staring Bay, Celebes, at low speed on February 25, 1942. *Haruna* has just finished her port turn, and *Kongō* is about to follow. *Kongō*'s main gun turrets are turned to port and elevated in anticipation of an enemy encounter. *The Maru Special*

View from *Kongō* (Capt. Koyanagi Tomiji) in February 1942. In this photo can be seen a 12.7 cm high-angle twin mount and 15 cm secondary guns. Behind the 12.7 cm mount is a 110 cm searchlight. Main gun turrets 3 and 4 are trained to starboard. The airplanes are Nakajima type 95 two-seat reconnaissance seaplanes. *Gakken*

A photograph from the aircraft carrier *Zuikaku* on March 30, 1942, with VAdm. Nagumo Chūichi's Mobile Force in line ahead. The line is led by the aircraft carriers *Akagi*, *Sōryū*, and *Hiryū*, followed by the battleships *Hiei*, *Kirishima*, *Haruna*, and *Kongō*. The fleet is heading for the Indian Ocean. *The Maru Special*

The four Kongō-class high-speed battleships maneuver with the Mobile Force south of Sumatra on April 1, 1942. They have just deployed from line ahead and are heading for the attack on Ceylon. This was the only occasion during the Pacific War when these ships operated together. From the front, the ships are *Kongō*, *Haruna*, *Kirishima*, and *Hiei*. *The Maru Special*

At the Battle of Midway, in June, the four sisters were again split, and *Haruna* and *Kirishima* operated with VAdm. Nagumo's carrier force, but *Kongō* and *Hiei* were attached to VAdm. Kondō Nobutake's Main Body.

During the Battle of the Eastern Solomons in late August, *Hiei* and *Kirishima* operated with the carriers while the two other sisters remained in home waters for overhauls and training. In mid-October, *Kongō* and *Haruna* bombarded Henderson Field (*see below*) and *Hiei* and *Kirishima* provided distant cover. Two months later, at the Battle of Santa Cruz, all ships again saw action.

Hiei in the Pacific on June 7, 1942, immediately after the Battle of Midway. The ship is refueling from the oiler *Kyokutō Maru*, and an often-used practice was the astern method, depicted here. Note that the receiving ship, *Hiei*, is ahead of the oiler. *Kure Maritime Museum*

Hiei photographed from an airplane by Lt. Cmdr. Furukawa Akira on July 11, 1942, while in Tokyo Bay heading for Yokosuka. Note the white-painted main gunfire director tower on the top of the foremast. This practice was discontinued in the summer of 1943. *Kure Maritime Museum*

Another photo of the *Hiei* in Tokyo Bay on July 11, 1942, steaming at about 24 knots. Note the Japanese flag on main gun turrets 2 and 4.

Bombardment of Henderson Field by *Kongō* and *Haruna* on October 13–14, 1942[1]

This action was the second[2] of a series of night bombardments by battleships and heavy cruisers, combined with day air raids in preparation for the transport and landing of army forces on Guadalcanal.[3] Lunga airfield was to be destroyed, since American aircraft would obstruct the operation. Previous attempts to eliminate the airfield by land and air attacks had been unsuccessful. Therefore, heavy air raids by day and bombardments by night should render the field inoperable.

The headquarters (HQ) of the Combined Fleet (CF) had planned a bombardment by battleships of Henderson Field since about early September "because the land-based air forces were unable to control the enemy aircraft," and serious planning started on October 3. RAdm. Kurita Takeo, commanding officer (CO) of the 3rd Sentai, opposed the plan because it was "too great of a danger" for the battleships and because the effects of a bombardment would very limited. However, Adm. Yamamoto Isoroku decided that it should be executed.

Type 3 and type 0 projectiles should be used, together with type 1 AP shells. The range was to be 20,000 m, and the projectiles were fired with "weak" charges in order to obtain a large angle of fall. Other reasons for choosing this range were the lack of precision of the trajectory of type 3 projectiles at comparatively short ranges, and the necessity of keeping the screening destroyers outside the range of enemy guns stationed on Guadalcanal.

For its execution of the bombardment, the 3rd Sentai asked the forces on Guadalcanal to construct necessary facilities for measuring the distances. Indirect-firing training was carried out in order to check the effects of the type 3 projectile and to study distance measuring. The position of the ships was to be measured by means of "burning methods." The "A method" used woodpiles,[4] and the "B method" used old clothes soaked with petroleum. The B method proved superior. By using a *shinkōki* (astigmatizer), the error was reduced to ±300 meters at a distance of 20,000 meters, and it was considered negligible. The type 3 projectile would almost certainly detonate 50–150 meters above ground at an angle of fall of 25 degrees, and it would spread its steel stays and incendiaries over a considerable area. For spotting, fire control parties were used.

It was decided that the fifteenth was X-day for the all-out attack of the land-based air forces on Guadalcanal, and the CO of the Support Force decided the composition of the Volunteer Attack Force to be the 3rd Sentai, Destroyer Squadron 2, less *Kagerō* (i.e., the light cruiser *Isuzu*), Destroyer Division 15 (*Oyashio, Kuroshio, Hayashio*), Destroyer Division 24 (*Umikaze, Kawakaze, Suzukaze*), and Destroyer Division 31 (*Takanami, Makinami, Naganami*).

Table 27
Volunteer Attack Force (Bombardment Group), RAdm. Kurita Takeo (Commander Battleship Division 3 [3rd Sentai])

3rd Sentai battleships *Kongō* and *Haruna*

Guard Force / Direct Escort Group

Light cruiser *Isuzu*; destroyers *Umikaze, Kawakaze, Suzukaze, Takanami, Makinami,* and *Naganami*

Sweeping Unit (Guard Unit)

Destroyers *Oyashio, Kuroshio,* and *Hayashio*

Patrol Unit (between Guadalcanal and Russel)

Destroyer Division 19 destroyers *Isonami, Uranami, Shikinami,* and *Ayanami*

Note:
The composition of the Patrol Unit is uncertain. According to *Senshi Sōsho*, the "expanded Dai 19 Kuchikutai," but the authors do not know the name(s) of the added destroyers.

The Attack Force separated from the Support Force at 0330 on the thirteenth and advanced toward Guadalcanal. At 0945 an enemy flying boat was sighted, but the staff believed that the force remained undiscovered.

At 1401 a seaplane from the light cruiser *Isuzu* took off to reconnoiter the Guadalcanal and Tulagi areas. The presence of enemy units had been reported as follows:

• one force with an aircraft carrier 70 nautical miles southwest of Rennel Island

• one enemy aircraft carrier, probably *Saratoga*, at 11°58'S/162°05'E

• six enemy destroyers and two freighters off Lunga

On the basis of this information, the staff of the 3rd Sentai considered the probability of an encounter in the evening as very high, and starting at 1600 the screening destroyers prepared for action.

The Bombardment

The Attack Force advanced to a position north of Savo Island without being discovered, and at a range of 21,000 meters, *Kongō* fired the first shell. After firing 104 type 3 projectiles, *Kongō* had to change to type 1 AP shells. The enemy returned the fire from Lunga Point, but the shells fell short.

From about 2346, flames were observed on the airfield. The force turned at 0013 and prepared to reopen fire at 0018.5, but it was difficult to see the targets, and some minutes lapsed before fire was reopened. Destroyer Division 15 (less *Kagerō*) and Destroyer Division 24 accompanied the 3rd Sentai.

The battleships expended a total of 918 main-caliber projectiles, and forty-eight 15.2 cm were fired against American gun positions in the vicinity of Lunga Point.

Table 28
Ammunition expended

Ammunition	*Kongō*	*Haruna*	Total
36 cm type 1 AP projectile	331	294	625
36 cm type 0 common projectile	—	189	189
36 cm type 3 common projectile	104	—	104
Total	435	483	918
15.2 cm common projectile	27	21	48

Notes:
Nine ammunition handlers in the magazines of *Haruna* suffered from heat stroke; one died and two never did recover completely.

According to Morison, vol. 5, p. 172, there were ninety operational aircraft (forty-five fighters and forty-five dive-bombers), and these were reduced to thirty-five fighters and seven dive-bombers early on the fourteenth. Two of the eight B-17 four-engined bombers were also destroyed. Kerosene, "critical low before," was nearly all burned. Henderson Field was "out of action," and "Cactus Force" was forced to use the grass-covered fighter strip. The psychological effect on the army troops, which fought not only against the Americans but also starvation, was enormous.

Table 29
Record of the chief gunnery officer of *Kongō* (until the change from type 3 to type 1 projectiles)

Time	Event
20:30	Watching stations; first preparation (all hands to battle stations)
22:30	Light visible port 10 degrees Cape Esperance; changed bearing to 180 degrees, range 20,900 meters
22:30	Changed bearing to 130 degrees; Cape Esperance visible very well
23:12	Speed reduced to 18 knots
23:13	Recognized Cruz Point; Targeting ready!
23:15	Fight starboard firing, fire, target enemy airfield, prepare for range measuring, star 1 degree, enemy airfield observation firing
23:16	From CO 3rd Sentai: "23:35 Start of firing"
23:17	Start of range measuring
23:29	Report of the preparation of observation. Observation station ready. Condition of 10-meter rangefinder for range measuring: method A (error of ±300 meters at 20,000-meter distance)
23:27	Prepare for firing; start targeting
23:31	Changed bearing to port
23:34	Bearing steady; stop of measuring bearing
23:34.2	Bearing decided
23:36.5	From bridge: "Ready for firing"
23:37	Fire! The first salvo has gone (one projectile detonated before reaching the highest point of trajectory)
23:39	Illumination projectile fired
23:40	Second salvo fired
23:40.5	Begin salvo firing
23:43.5	Third salvo fired (no flames are sighted, but at the hitting point the sky shines a little red)
23:46	Enemy begins lighting; we are caught in the lighting zone
23:47.5	Range to enemy searchlight is measured as 15,700 meters. Report to bridge: "Enemy searchlight within the range of secondary guns"
23:48	The enemy opens fire against us
23:53	Secondary guns open fire against enemy searchlight
23:57	To bridge: "Type 3 projectiles consumed"

The Third Battle of the Solomon Sea, November 12–15, 1942[5]

Another bombardment of Henderson Field by battleships was planned when bringing in reinforcements and supplies to Guadalcanal, on the night of November 14–15. Henderson Field was to be bombarded by battleships and heavy cruisers on November 12–13, and again on November 13–14.

VAdm. Abe Hiroaki's 5th *Teishin Kōgekitai* consisted of the 11th Sentai (battleships *Hiei* and *Kirishima*) and Destroyer Squadron 10 (light cruiser *Nagara*, Destroyer Division 16 [*Amatsukaze, Yukikaze*], Destroyer Division 6 [*Akatsuki, Ikazuchi, Inazuma*], Destroyer Division 61 [*Teruzuki*], Destroyer Division 4 [*Asagumo*], Destroyer Division 2 [*Murasame, Samidare, Yūdachi, Harusame*], and Destroyer Division 27 [*Shigure, Shiratsuyu, Yūgure*]).

The bombardment was to be undertaken by the 11th Sentai, escorted by the *Nagara* and Destroyer Divisions 16, 6, and 61.

Due to a storm, Abe had to reverse course, and the bombardment was put off to 0130 on the thirteenth. At 0115 the van destroyers (*Yūdachi* and *Harusame*) closed Guadalcanal. Visibility was improving, and as the battleships prepared themselves for the bombardment, the escort prepared for action.

At 0124, the USS *Helena* sent out a warning,[6] but since the Japanese lacked radar, it was not until 0142 that *Yūdachi* sighted the US force. What followed was one of the most confused sea battles of the war.

Although surprised, VAdm. Abe's force opened fire at 0151, and since type 3 shells were already loaded, they were used. *Hiei* was soon hit on the bridge and superstructure by numerous shells of various calibers, and it became impossible to use director control. A hit in the stern damaged steering control. However, the engines were still functioning, and it was still possible to maneuver the ship at slow speed by using the screws.

Hiei withdrew northward from the battle area, and at dawn on the thirteenth, several destroyers gathered around the ship and Abe was transferred to a destroyer. Later that day, *Hiei* was attacked by US planes and hit by several torpedoes. It was ordered to be scuttled and was torpedoed by a Japanese destroyer. *Hiei* went down around midnight, with 188 crew members being lost.

Although VAdm. Abe's bombardment force had been repulsed, the Japanese on the following night succeeded in bombarding Henderson Field with two heavy cruisers.

Kirishima survived this intense battle almost intact, and the CF decided to bombard Henderson Field again on the night of November 15.

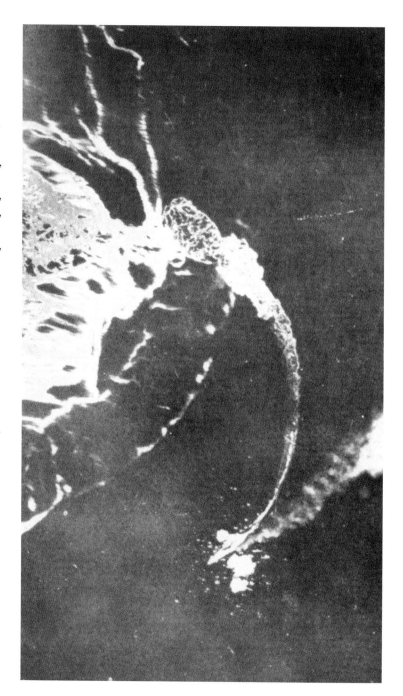

Hiei evading bombs from a US B-17 bomber on November 13, 1942. Later that day, *Hiei* was attacked by US carrier planes and torpedoed. As far as is known, this is the final photo of *Hiei*. Gakken

The Japanese force was commanded by VAdm. Kondō Nobutake, and he brought with him his own Main Body and VAdm. Abe's surviving ships. Thus, the force consisted of the 11th Sentai battleship *Kirishima*, heavy cruisers *Atago* and *Takao* of the 4th Sentai, and a screen made up of the light cruiser *Nagara*, 10th Destroyer Squadron, with destroyers *Teruzuki* (Destroyer Division 61), *Inazuma* (Destroyer Division 6), *Hatsuyuki* and *Shirayuki* (Destroyer Division 11), *Asagumo* (Destroyer Division 4), and *Samidare* (Destroyer Division 2). RAdm. Hashimoto Shintarō commanded the Sweeping Unit, composed of the 3rd Destroyer Squadron (light cruiser *Sendai* and destroyer *Ayanami* with Destroyer Division 19 [destroyers *Uranami* and *Shikinami*]).

The Sweeping Unit was sent forward and when northeast of Savo Island sighted the US force at 2210 on November 14. At 2326 the 10th Destroyer Squadron dueled with an American destroyer. The US main force, the new battleships *Washington* and *South Dakota*, was heading west into the gap between Guadalcanal and Savo Island and made radar contact at 2300. At 2333 *South Dakota* suffered a power loss but could still follow *Washington*, and at 2336 power was back.

At 2351, VAdm. Kondō headed southeast with his main force in order *Atago*, *Takao*, and *Kirishima*, and fire was opened on *South Dakota* about two minutes later. *South Dakota* was still suffering from power failure. During the following minutes, *Kirishima* fired 117 36 cm rounds (sixty-eight type 3 incendiary, twenty-two type 0 common, and twenty-seven type 1 APC shells) together with 15 cm rounds, and *South Dakota* was hit several times.

Undetected, *Washington* was then able to fire seventy-five rounds of 16-inch shells on *Kirishima* from close range. The ship was hit by about nine 16-inch shells; fires broke out and all main gun turrets were disabled. With damaged steering and hit below water, *Kirishima* listed to starboard.

Kirishima could still move but was practically unnavigable, and at 0242 most of the crew was ordered to leave the ship; at 0249, *Kirishima* was dead in the water. Towing was attempted, but at around 0320 *Kirishima* suddenly capsized to port northwest of Savo Island; 212 crew members were lost.

After the Solomons

During the successful evacuation of Guadalcanal in February 1943, the two remaining sisters covered the evacuation, and with that mission completed, they departed for Japan for much-needed overhauls, via Truk in the Caroline Islands. After the overhauls the two ships for the remainder of 1943 were based mostly at Truk, and in early 1944 they moved to Lingga, Sumatra.

Both *Kongō* and *Haruna* participated in the disastrous Battle of the Marianas in June and subsequently in the Battle of Leyte Gulf, Philippines. It can be noted that while the Japanese fleet was based at Lingga, prior to the Battle of Leyte Gulf, *Kongō* tested radar-directed gunfire and used this during the Battle of Samar at 18,000 and 19,000 meters.[7] At Samar, both ships engaged the US forces. *Kongō* at least played a role in the destroyer *Heermann*'s damage and the sinking of the destroyer escort *Samuel B. Roberts*, and *Haruna* damaged the escort carriers *Kalinin Bay* and *Gambier Bay*.[8] However, it has also recently been said that *Kongō* managed to hit the Japanese heavy cruiser *Chōkai* and thus contributed to her loss.[9]

At 0300 on November 21, 1944, *Kongō* was torpedoed and sunk by the submarine USS *Sealion* in the Formosa Strait. Probably three torpedoes hit and two boiler rooms flooded quickly, forcing *Kongō* to slow down. The ship took a 15-degree list to port and at 0520 stopped. Four minutes later she exploded. About 1,300 crew members went down with the ship, and 237 were rescued by the accompanying destroyers. *Kongō* was the only Japanese battleship sunk by a submarine.

Haruna survived the war. On December 12, 1944, she was back at Kure, where in March–July 1945, she was bombed and mined. Finally, on July 28, she sank in shallow water and was a total loss. The ship was demolished in May–July 1946.

A photo of *Haruna* (commanded by RAdm. Shigenaga Kazue) on October 25, 1944, taken by a plane from the escort carrier USS *Kadashan Bay* at the Battle of Samar. This photo was probably taken during the second half of the battle. The original photo says that it is of *Nagato*, but it is presumed, from a series of photos, to be *Haruna*. *US Navy*

Haruna under air attack from US Task Force 38 at Kure, on July 28, 1945. The ship was repeatedly hit and severely damaged. *US Navy*

Another view of *Haruna* being attacked by USN carrier planes at Kure on July 28, 1945. On this day, she was also bombed by US heavy bombers. After about thirteen bomb hits and ten near misses, *Haruna* sank in shallow water, with the loss of sixty-five crew members. *US Navy*

Haruna (Capt. Yoshimura Masatake) sank at Kure. On November 20, 1945, she was stricken from the list of warships. Salvage and dismantling started on May 2, 1946, and on July 4 the work was completed. *US Navy*

Endnotes

Chapter 1

1. Also known as Katō Kanji. He would later rise to a prominent position in the IJN and be well known for his actions in the course of and after the Washington (1921–22) and, particularly, after the London (1930) Arms Limitation Conferences.

Chapter 2

1. Besides the technological reason, economical and political considerations were also in the background: Japan had revised its import tax, and as a result the friendship between Britain and Japan had deteriorated, and it was feared that it would deteriorate further. With the order of *Kongō*, sympathies would be regained and, in addition, national finances be saved, because domestic construction would be more expensive than construction abroad. The improvement of the bilateral relations was very important also in view of the renewal of the Anglo-Japanese Alliance (in 1911).

2. That a certain Japanese technological backwardness existed had been well recognized, and perhaps this was also why, after the decision to build the armored cruisers (later battle cruisers) *Kurama* and *Ibuki*, the NTD had made more than thirty basic designs of battle cruisers, of which none had been approved and which were all considered inferior in comparison to the progress seen in Britain. One more reason was that the IJN had just begun the domestic building of capital ships in navy yards, and private shipbuilders still lacked experience.

Chapter 3

1. That this ground was made available was also a result of the Anglo-Japanese Alliance, but, on the other hand, the Royal Navy was interested in obtaining firsthand information about the results, and according to information by the late RAdm. Takasu Kōichi, "joint trial firings took place for a span of twenty days."

Chapter 4

1. Since the order from Britain of the battleships *Katori* and *Kashima*, almost seven years had passed. During that period, capital ship design had been revolutionized, and British building techniques must have progressed significantly. As stated earlier, the IJN wanted to participate and to bridge the remarkable gap in as short a time as possible.

2. When the members of the US Naval Technical Mission to Japan investigated the technical level of Japan at the end of the Pacific War, they sometimes stated in their reports that this or that was derived from Vickers technology, and a sample will be given in the section about the main guns.

3. It was quite an exceptional case for a naval architect to become the chief of a navy yard, and besides Godō there is only one more example; namely, RAdm. Yamamoto Mikinosuke, who became the chief of the Sasebo Navy Yard in 1933.

4. He belonged to Kure Navy Yard's Gunnery Division and designed most of the large guns and turrets (also the 46 cm guns of the super-battleships *Yamato* and *Musashi*). He was widely known as a high-class naval engineer, and there was a saying that "With Hata in the IJN, the battleship could be built."

5. The later VAdm. (naval architect) Niwata Shōzō in his *Do Not Forget, Yamato!* mentions that when he and his colleagues were working in Kure Navy Yard's Shipbuilding Division as lieutenant junior grades, these men always talked about their experiences in England, where they had studied the construction

techniques of the Vickers Company when building *Kongō*. He also points out that the people who were concerned with *Kongō* were in charge of the construction of the battleship *Fusō* and subsequent capital ships.

6. As pointed out earlier in chapter 1, the IJN planned to introduce these shipyards in the military-industrial complex as preparation for the domestic building of the capital ships of the 8-8 Fleet.

7. Yukiko Fukasaku, *Technology and Industrial Development in Pre-war Japan: Mitsubishi Nagasaki Shipyard, 1884–1934* (New York: Routledge, 1992), 51–53 and 154–57, where fifteen engineers are mentioned. The mission report of engineer Yokoyama Kōzō, who mainly studied turbines as assistant naval inspector for *Kongō*, is mentioned on p. 53.

8. The Shipping Encouragement Law of the same year also contributed to the subsequent development.

Chapter 6

1. *Senkan Jun-yōsenkan, Battleships & Battle Cruisers* (Tokyo: Namiki Shobō, 2007), 211.

Chapter 7

1. Flow speed was 2.78 m/s, but two circulations were necessary to transform the exhaust steam into condensed water.

Chapter 8

1. In the mounts with fixed loading angle (5 degrees), the diameter could be decreased to 8.40 m.

2. London: Conway Maritime Press, 1981.

3. More data can also be found in various papers of the *Contributions to the History of Japanese Warships*, compiled by Hans Lengerer. Readers interested in additional literature may order them via email from Lars Ahlberg, lars.ake.ahlberg@telia.com, or by writing to hans.lengerer@gmx.de. A rather detailed and richly illustrated description (with drawings by Mizutani Kiyōtaka) of the superstructures of the Kongō class after the modernization conversions can be found in *Illustrated Record of the Transition of the Superstructures of BB Kongō Class: Introduction to CV Unryū Class* by Hans Lengerer (Katowice, Poland: Model Hobby, 2010), www.modelhobby.pl and (email) modelhobby@modelhobby.pl. See also *Warship 2012*, pp. 156–159, for more gunnery detail and illustrations.

Chapter 9

1. Owing to limited space, only the most important items of the reconstruction will be dealt with, focusing on the reinforcement of the horizontal and underwater protection in the first reconstruction and the improvement of the propulsion system in the second reconstruction. As for the modification, only those carried out before the first reconstruction are listed as examples. Further saving of space was intended with the combination of the three conditions (as built, first and second reconstruction) in the tables if all data were available. This is also advantageous in view of easy comparison, but the disadvantage may be the arrangement in other places than the description.

2. Japan admitted to possessing ten battleships (four Kongō class, two Fusō class, two Ise class, and two Nagato class), with a total weight of 315,000 tons. Fourteen unfinished and planned capital ships of the 8-8 Fleet were all to be canceled (however, two were converted into aircraft carriers). Other older semi-dreadnought- and pre-dreadnought-class battleships were all to be abolished. This made the IJN's battleship force 60 percent that of the USN's; namely, ten vs. eighteen ships. This forced Japan to fundamentally reconsider its strategy against the US.

3. In Part 3, Section I (Rules for Replacement), the signatory powers had agreed that no retained capital ship shall be reconstructed, except for the purpose of providing means of defense against air and submarine attacks and that, for this purpose, the existing ships may be equipped with bulges or blisters or anti-air-deck protection, provided that the increase of displacement does not exceed 3,000 tons (3,048 metric tons) for each ship. No alteration in side armor, in caliber, or in number of and general type of mounting of main armament shall be permitted. However, there were some exceptions for France and Italy, and one for Britain in case of the battle cruiser *Renown*.

4. According to *Kaigun Gunbi Enkaku* by Kaigun Daijin Kanbō (Tokyo: Gannandō Shoten, 1970, reprint), a conference between the vice chief of navy general staff, RAdm. Katō Hiroharu, and the vice navy minister, VAdm. Ide Kenji, took place on September 12, 1922. The principal goals were (1) to confirm the "out-range" principle in the decisive battle and (2) to complete the fighting power of the capital ships. In this conference the progressive modernization of the eight capital ships was completed before the post-Jutland battleships *Nagato* and *Mutsu* were decided. The main items were the increase of the firing range and the efficiency of the main guns in order to obtain similar results as the guns of the Nagato class. With these objects in view, Katō and Ide laid down the following: (1) an increase in the elevation of the main guns of the Fusō and Kongō classes to more than 30 degrees, (2) owing to the increased muzzle velocity of the main guns of the Ise class and both the increased elevation and muzzle velocity of the main guns of the Fusō and Kongō classes,

the firing range may be increased to about 30,000 meters, (3) the output of the engines of the main gun turrets has to be increased in order to secure undisturbed continuous firing of all guns, and (4) the elevation of the secondary guns of the Fusō and Kongō classes shall be increased to obtain a range of 15,000 meters.

However, there was some uncertainty about the interpretation of the respective articles (Part 3, Section I) of the Washington Treaty, and this caused a diplomatic problem (caused by the protests of the "big three"), but after a Japanese diplomatic "offensive" between March and August 1923, each country could execute an increase of elevation without any official mutual agreement.

Therefore, the authors doubt the execution in 1920 (*Hiei*) and 1921 (*Kirishima*), as stated in *Nihon Kaigun Kansai Heiki Daizukan* ("All about Japanese naval shipboard weapons"), by Yamamoto Yoshihide et al. (Tokyo: Kabushiki Kaisha Bestsellers, 2002).

5. It was planned to fill these spaces with some rows of watertight steel tubes (compare "bulges").

6. The results of the research undertaken by then RAdm. (constructor) Hiraga Yuzuru in Britain (and also in the US) in 1924 were significant for the conversion of the Japanese capital ships. Due to his very friendly relations with leading British naval architects, Hiraga could obtain confidential data about the Nelson class and particularly their horizontal and vertical protection systems. However, the IJN did not solely rely on information from abroad but made their own research, using the incomplete battleship *Tosa*. Therefore, most of the decisions were made after Hiraga's return from abroad and the evaluation of the results of the experiments.

7. For more on this, see the authors' *Capital Ships of the Imperial Japanese Navy, 1868–1945*, vol. 3 (Zagreb, Croatia: Despot Infinitus, 2019).

8. Steam pressure was 19.3 bar; steam temperature, 200°C. During trials on May 25, 1928, *Haruna* obtained 25.861 knots with 75,807 hp and at 33,825 tons of displacement.

9. *Nihon Zōsen Gakkai* (Tokyo: Hara Shobō, 1977).

10 This defect also existed in the old battleships (Fusō and Ise classes), which, like the Kongō class, also had too small immunity zones.

11. For example, the completion of the aircraft carrier *Hiryū* in sixteen months, the heavy cruiser *Chikuma* in fourteen months, and the submarine tender *Takasaki* in thirty-three months, etc. Lack of budget also prevented the construction of smaller (attrition type) vessels, but insufficient shipbuilding capacity also played an important role.

Chapter 10

1. The main source is *Senshi Sōsho*, vol. 83, pp. 208–15 (Bōeichō Bōeikenshūjo Senshibu [Tokyo: Asagumo Shimbunsha, 1975]). Samuel E. Morison describes the bombardment in vol. V, pp. 172–75, of *History of United States Naval Operations in World War II* (Boston: Little, Brown, 1949). The entries in VAdm. Ugaki Matome's diary, *Fading Victory* (Pittsburgh, PA: University of Pittsburgh Press, 1991), on October 14–15 are very interesting. For instance, he noted on the fourteenth that "hoping to put the airfield out of use is a hope against hope. We should not be optimistic."

2. An unsuccessful attack by the 6th Sentai (heavy cruisers *Aoba*, *Kinugasa*, and *Furutaka*) had been carried out on October 11–12.

3. This was part of an overall plan to wrest the airfield from the American forces and then, through massive coordinated attacks, to end the Southern Solomon Campaign, centered on Guadalcanal.

4. The 3rd Sentai demanded the fire to be as high as 27 meters in order for it to be seen from about 40,000 meters, and at least 30,000 meters for safe navigation, but the land forces could only, for various reasons (e.g., material, geographical conditions, manpower), manage a height of about 20 meters.

5. The main sources are *Senshi Sōsho*, vol. 83, pp. 383–97; Samuel Eliot Morison, *History of United States Naval Operations in World War II*, vol. 5, *The Struggle for Guadalcanal, August 1942–February 1943* (Edison, NJ: Castle Books, 2001); Hara Tameichi, *Japanese Destroyer Captain* (New York: Ballantine Books, 1965); James W. Grace, *The Naval Battle of Guadalcanal* (Annapolis, MD: Naval Institute Press, 1999); Shiraishi Hikaru, *History of Kongō Class Battleships*; and Tsutsumi Akio, "Hardware of Kongō Class," in *World's Vintage Warships*, vol. 5, *Kongō Class (Kessaku Gunkan Ākaibu 5: Senkan Kongō Gata)* (Tokyo: Kaijinsha, 2018).

6. *History of United States Naval Operations in World War II*, vol. V, p. 239.

7. Tsutsumi Akio, "Hardware of Kongō Class," 133.

8. Robert Lundgren, *The World Wonder'd: What Really Happened off Samar* (Ann Arbor, MI: Nimble Books, 2014), 255.

9. Shiraishi Hikaru, *History of Kongō Class Battleships*, 145.